THE CERTIFIED RELIABILITY ENGINEER HANDBOOK

Also available from ASQ Quality Press:

The Certified Supplier Quality Professional Handbook
Mark Allen Durivage, editor

Practical Process Validation
Mark Allen Durivage and Bhavan "Bob" Mehta

The Certified Pharmaceutical GMP Professional Handbook, Second Edition
Mark Allen Durivage, editor

Practical Design of Experiments (DOE): A Guide for Optimizing Designs and Processes
Mark Allen Durivage

Practical Attribute and Variable Measurement Systems Analysis (MSA): A Guide for Conducting Gage R&R Studies and Test Method Validations
Mark Allen Durivage

Practical Engineering, Process, and Reliability Statistics
Mark Allen Durivage

HALT, HASS, And HASA Explained: Accelerated Reliability Techniques, Revised Edition
Harry W. Mclean

Failure Mode and Effect Analysis: FMEA from Theory to Execution, Second Edition
D. H. Stamatis

The Certified Quality Engineer Handbook, Fourth Edition
Sarah E. Burke and Rachel T. Silvestrini

The Certified Six Sigma Green Belt Handbook, Second Edition
Roderick A. Munro, Govindarajan Ramu, Daniel J. Zrymiak

The Certified Six Sigma Yellow Belt Handbook
Govindarajan Ramu

Søren Bisgaard's Contributions To Quality Engineering
Ronald J.M.M. Does, Roger W. Hoerl, Murat Kulahci, G. Geoffrey Vining, Editors

To request a complimentary catalog of ASQ Quality Press publications, call 800-248-1946, or visit our website at http://www.asq.org/quality-press.

THE CERTIFIED RELIABILITY ENGINEER HANDBOOK

Third Edition

Mark Allen Durivage, Editor

ASQ Quality Press
Milwaukee, Wisconsin

First Impression, 2018
Indian edition published by Infotech Standards India Pvt. Ltd.
ISBN 978-81-748-9058-0

Original Edition entitled The Certified Reliability Engineer Handbook, 3rd Edition
by Mark Allen Durivage, editor.
American Society for Quality, Quality Press, Milwaukee 53203
© 2017 by ASQ, ISBN 978-0-87389-960-4

ASQ Mission: The American Society for Quality advances individual, organizational, and community excellence worldwide through learning, quality improvement, and knowledge exchange.

This edition is authorized for sale in India.

Quality Press
600 N. Plakinton Avenue,
Milwaukee, Wisconsin 53203
Call toll free 800-248-1946
Fax 414-272-1734
www.asq.org
http://qualitypress.asq.org
http:// standarsgroup.asq.org
E-mail: authors@asq.org

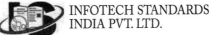

INFOTECH STANDARDS
INDIA PVT. LTD.
4760-61, 2nd Floor, "SAI SAROVAR"
23, Ansari Road, Daryaganj
New Delhi - 110002, INDIA
Ph. : 011-43586946, 23264946
Fax : 011-43586947
www.standardsmedia.com
E-mail : info@standardsmedia.com

Table of Contents

List of Figures and Tables

Preface

The chapters and sections are numbered by the same format used in the Body of Knowledge (BoK) for the Certified Reliability Engineer (CRE) examination. This format makes for some awkward placement and, in some cases, redundancy. However, it also facilitates access for readers who might be struggling with some particular point in the BoK, which more than balances the disadvantages.

The CRE Certification will provide valuable credentials to reliability and quality engineering professionals in the growing field of reliability engineering. The purpose of this handbook is to assist individuals preparing for the CRE examination and to provide a reference for the practitioner. Throughout this handbook, several "typical" examples are provided based on the collective experience and knowledge of the authors and editor. However, these "typical" examples are not explicitly specified in regulations, leaving decisions and the burden of justifying practices using sound scientific principles, which provide the context of the rationale, up to the company.

Acknowledgments

I would like to acknowledge the previous work of Donald W. Benbow and Hugh W. Broome for their previous versions of *The Certified Reliability Engineer Handbook*. Several sections of this book come directly from their previous work. Some changes have been made to clarify and augment some of their points and present the topics in a consistent manner.

Additionally, the Reliability and Risk Division leadership team should be acknowledged for supporting the update to this handbook. The division helped secure volunteer members who are CREs to contribute to the writing and editing processes.

The following individuals are to be recognized as contributing chapter authors for this handbook: David Auda, Jim Breneman, Dan Burrows, Mark Durivage, Tim Gaens, and Rong Pan. By using several individual subject matter experts, the overall quality and technical content of this handbook has been greatly enhanced.

I would like to thank those who have inspired, taught, and trained me throughout my academic and professional career. Additionally, I would like to thank ASQ Quality Press, especially Paul O'Mara, Managing Editor, for his expertise and technical competence, which made this project a reality. I also appreciate the fine copyediting and typesetting by Westchester Publishing Services. Lastly, I would like to acknowledge my wife Dawn and my sons Jack and Sam, whose patience allowed me time to organize, write, and edit this handbook.

Mark Allen Durivage, ASQ Fellow
Editor and Project Leader
Lambertville, Michigan

LIMIT OF LIABILITY/DISCLAIMER OF WARRANTY

The editor and authors have put forth their best effort in compiling the content of this book; however, no warranty with respect to the material's accuracy or completeness is made. Additionally, no warranty is made in regards to applying the recommendations made in this book to any business structure or environments. Businesses should consult regulatory, quality, and/or legal professionals prior to deciding on the appropriateness of advice and recommendations made within this book. The editor and authors shall not be held liable for loss of profit or other commercial damages resulting from the employment of recommendations made within this book including special, incidental, consequential, or other damages.

Part I
Reliability Fundamentals

Part I

Chapter 1
A. Leadership Foundations

The structure of this book is based on the Body of Knowledge (BoK) specified by ASQ for the Certified Reliability Engineer (CRE). Before the formal BoK is presented, a definition of reliability is needed. *Reliability* is defined as the probability that an item will perform a required function without failure under stated conditions for a specified period of time. A statement of reliability has four key components:

- *Probability*. For example, a timing chain might have a reliability goal of 0.9995. This would mean that at least 99.95% are functioning at the end of the stated time.

- *Required function*. This should be defined for every part, subassembly, and product. The statement of the required function should explicitly state or imply a failure definition. For example, a pump's required function might be moving at least 20 gallons per minute. The implied failure definition would be moving fewer than 20 gallons per minute.

- *Stated conditions*. These include environmental conditions, maintenance conditions, usage conditions, storage and moving conditions, and possibly others.

- *Specified period of time*. For example, a pump might be designed to function for 10,000 hours. Sometimes it is more appropriate to use some other measure of stress than time. A tire's reliability might be stated in terms of miles, and that of a laundry appliance in terms of cycles.

1. BENEFITS OF RELIABILITY ENGINEERING

> Describe the value that reliability has on achieving company goals and objectives, and how reliability engineering techniques and methods improve programs, processes, products, systems, and services. (Understand)
>
> Body of Knowledge I.A.1

The following are among the influences that have increased the importance of the study of reliability engineering:

- Customers expect products to not only meet the specified parameters upon delivery, but to function throughout what they perceive as a reasonable lifetime.

- As products become more complex, the reliability requirements of components increase. Suppose, for instance, that a system has 1000 independent components that must function in order for the system to function. Further suppose that each component has a reliability of 99.9%. The system would have a reliability of $0.999^{1000} = 0.37$, an obviously unacceptable value.

- An unreliable product often has safety and health hazards.

- Reliability values are used in marketing and warranty material.

- Competitive pressures require increased emphasis on reliability.

- An increasing number of contracts specify reliability requirements.

The study of reliability engineering responds to each of these influences by helping designers determine and increase the useful lifetime of products, processes, and services.

2. INTERRELATIONSHIP OF SAFETY, QUALITY, AND RELIABILITY

> Describe the relationship of and distinguish between reliability and quality, and describe the importance of safety in reliability engineering and how reliability impacts safety. (Understand)
>
> Body of Knowledge I.A.2

In most organizations the quality assurance function is designed to continually improve the ability to produce products and services that meet or exceed customer requirements. Narrowly construed, this means, in the manufacturing industries, producing parts with dimensions that are within tolerance. Quality engineering must expand this narrow construction to include reliability considerations, and all quality engineers should have a working knowledge of reliability engineering. What, then, is the distinction between these two fields?

- Once an item has been successfully manufactured, the traditional quality assurance function has done its job (although the search for ways to improve is continuous). The reliability function's principal focus is on what happens next. Answers are sought to questions such as:

  - Are components failing prematurely?

  - Was burn-in time sufficient?

– Is the failure rate acceptable?

– What changes in design, manufacturing, installation, operation, or maintenance would improve reliability?

• Another way to delineate the difference between quality and reliability is to note how data are collected. In the case of manufacturing, data for quality engineering are generally collected during the manufacturing process. Inputs such as voltages, pressures, temperatures, and raw material parameters are measured. Outputs such as dimensions, acidity, weight, and contamination levels are measured. The data for reliability engineering generally are collected after a component or product is manufactured. For example, a switch might be toggled repeatedly until it fails, and the number of successful cycles noted. A pump might be run until its output in gallons per minute falls below a defined value, and the number of hours recorded.

• Quality and reliability engineers provide different inputs into the design process. Quality engineers suggest changes that permit the item to be produced within tolerance at a reasonable cost. Reliability engineers make recommendations that permit the item to function correctly for a longer period of time.

The preceding paragraphs show that although the roles of quality and reliability are different, they do interrelate. For example, in the product design phase both quality and reliability functions have the goal of proposing cost-effective ways to satisfy and exceed customer expectations. This often mandates that the two functions work together to produce a design that both works correctly and performs for an acceptable period. When processes are designed and operated, the quality and reliability engineers work together to determine the process parameters that impact the performance and longevity of the product so that those parameters can be appropriately controlled. A similar interrelationship holds as specifications are developed for packaging, shipment, installation, operation, and maintenance.

Reliability will be impacted by product design and by the processes used in the product's manufacture. Therefore, the designers of products and processes must understand and use reliability data as design decisions are made. Generally, the earlier reliability data are considered in the design process, the more efficient and effective their impact will be.

Safety considerations pervade all aspects of both the quality engineering and reliability engineering fields. When a process/product change is proposed, the proposal should be accompanied by a thorough study of the impact the improvement will have on safety. Questions to investigate include:

• *Could this change make the production process less safe? How will this be mitigated?*

Example: Workers accustomed to doing things the old way may be more at risk with the proposed changes.

• *Could this change make the use of the product less safe? How will this be mitigated?*

Example: The new dishwasher latch, if not engaged properly, allows steam to escape into the electronic timer, causing a fire hazard.

- *With the failure of another component now more likely, are there new safety risks?*

  Example: Proposals for increasing the useful life of a component should be accompanied by a study on the effect the increased life will have on other components.

- *As the product reaches its wear-out phase, could this change introduce safety risks? How will this be mitigated?*

  Example: The new lighting system contains chemical compounds that are toxic when improperly disposed of.

When conducting a failure modes and effects analysis (FMEA) study, all failure modes should be investigated for possible safety risks. And once a reliable product is designed, quality engineering techniques are used to make sure that the processes produce that product.

3. RELIABILITY ENGINEER LEADERSHIP RESPONSIBILITIES

> Describe how to be a reliability champion by influencing program decisions and facilitating cross-functional communication. (Understand)
>
> Body of Knowledge I.A.3

John Quincy Adams said it best: "If your actions inspire others to dream more, learn more, do more, and become more, you are a *leader*."

This idea applies to a reliability leader as well, whether a senior reliability engineer, supervisor, manager, or reliability fellow. It is the reliability leader's primary job to:

- Instill a vision of "giving the most accurate answer with the data available"

- Influence the behavior of either an individual or a group, regardless of the reason, in an effort to achieve reliability goals in a given situation

- Understand the business ramifications of a reliability question or solution

- Explain in clear terms the reliability and safety risks involved in a management decision so that management can make an informed decision

- Remind people working on your team of their ethical responsibilities, in documentation and face-to-face communication

- Support the decision of the reliability position to management

Key "facets" of leadership[1] include:

- **Focus**—get the job done
- **Authenticity**—have "constancy of purpose" (Deming)
- **Courage**—stand up to criticism, support reliability decisions
- **Empathy**—understand all areas of a problem and people interaction
- **Timing**—know when to make a critical decision

4. RELIABILITY ENGINEER ROLE AND RESPONSIBILITIES IN THE PRODUCT LIFECYCLE

> Describe how the reliability engineer influences the product lifecycle, and describe a reliability engineer's role in the design review process in order to anticipate how reliability can impact risk and costs and ensure performance over time. (Understand)
>
> Body of Knowledge I.A.4

Producing a product that is safe must be a top priority for every organization. The responsibility of the reliability engineer in meeting this priority includes the following:

1. Collecting and analyzing data regarding failures and failure rates

2. Presenting those data and analyses in an understandable format

3. Making sure that the key decision makers have an understanding of the analyses

In discharging these responsibilities, the following are among the additional items that must be considered:

1. *Could the failure of the product cause some chain of events with safety/liability implications?* This analysis should be done in conjunction with the safety organization, since the safety organization is responsible for defining risk (human injury or death or accidents).

   Example: The product is installed as part of a system in which the failure of the product was not contemplated in system design.

2. *What aspects of the product could possibly cause safety/liability hazards even though the product hasn't failed?*

   Example: During normal maintenance, the product must be partially disassembled, which may expose energized electrical conductors.

3. *What misuse of the product might cause safety/liability issues?*

   Examples: The product, when stacked more than three high for shipping, can cause damage to nearby items. If the product is exposed to temperatures below –15°F, the seals will fail. If the product is not installed within one degree of level, it presents possible hazards. If the pH of the solvent used in the product is below 3.2, the product will develop hazardous leaks. When used on a windy day, the product functions correctly but endangers downwind organisms.

In any of these situations the reliability engineer must work with the safety organization to perform a safety hazard analysis.

4. *Can the final disposition of the product present safety/liability issues?*

   Example: The product, when crushed for recycling, releases gases that produce a reaction in some people.

5. *Can the malfunction of other parts of the system cause safety/liability issues for the product?*

   Example: When exposed to fluid pressures outside its operating range, the product will act unpredictably.

6. *What is the impact of government regulation, current or contemplated, on safety/liability issues?*

   Example: Several states are contemplating legislation that will declare some types of metallurgical content of a component hazardous.

7. *Does the product design compromise the reliability of components?*

   Example: An electronic component has an acceptable reliability based on a minimum level of air circulation, but its enclosure is not properly ventilated.

5. FUNCTION OF RELIABILITY IN ENGINEERING

> Describe how reliability techniques can be used to apply best practices in engineering (e.g., measuring reliability early), how industry standards can impact reliability, and how reliability can inform the decision analysis process. (Analyze)
>
> Body of Knowledge I.A.5

The study of reliability engineering is usually undertaken primarily to determine and improve the useful lifetime of products. Data are collected on the failure rates of components and products, including those produced by suppliers. Competitors' products may also be subjected to reliability testing and analysis.

Reliability techniques can also help other facets of an organization:

- Reliability analysis can be used to improve product design. Reliability predictions provide guidance as components are selected. Derating techniques aid in increasing a product's useful lifetime. Reliability improvements can be effected through component redundancy.

- Marketing and advertising can be enhanced as warranty and other documents that inform customer expectations are prepared. Warranties that are not supported by reliability data can cause extra costs and inflame customer ire.

- It is increasingly important to detect and prevent or mitigate product liability issues. Warnings and alarms should be incorporated into the design when hazards can't be eliminated. Products whose failure can introduce safety and health hazards need to be analyzed for reliability so that procedures can be put in place to reduce the probability that they will be used beyond their useful lifetime. Failure rates typically escalate in the final phase of a product's life. Components whose useful lifetime is shorter than the product's should be replaced on a schedule that can be determined through reliability engineering techniques.

- Manufacturing processes can use reliability tools in the following ways:

  - The impact of process parameters on product failure rates can be studied.

  - Alternative processes can be compared for their effect on reliability.

  - Reliability data for process equipment can be used to determine preventive maintenance schedules and spare parts inventories.

  - The use of parallel process streams to improve process reliability can be evaluated.

  - Safety can be enhanced through the understanding of equipment failure rates.

  - Vendors can be evaluated more effectively.

- Every facet of an organization, including purchasing, quality assurance, packaging, field service, logistics, and so on, can benefit from a knowledge of reliability engineering. An understanding of the lifecycles of the products and equipment they use and handle can improve the effectiveness and efficiency of their function.

6. ETHICS IN RELIABILITY ENGINEERING

> Identify appropriate ethical behaviors for a reliability engineer in various situations. (Evaluate)
>
> Body of Knowledge I.A.6

The ASQ Code of Ethics (Figure 1.1) provides useful guidelines. Some relevant illustrative examples are given below.

[I] will do whatever I can to promote the reliability and safety of all products that come within my jurisdiction. This indicates that the reliability engineer's responsibilities are not limited to crunching numbers and producing good analyses but include the promotion of product reliability and safety.

Fundamental Principles

ASQ requires its members and certification holders to conduct themselves ethically by:

1. Being honest and impartial in serving the public, their employers, customers, and clients.

2. Striving to increase the competence and prestige of the quality profession.

3. Using their knowledge and skill for the enhancement of human welfare.

Members and certification holders are required to observe the tenets set forth below:

Relations with the Public

Article 1—Hold paramount the safety, health, and welfare of the public in the performance of their professional duties.

Relations with Employers, Customers, and Clients

Article 2—Perform services only in their areas of competence.

Article 3—Continue their professional development throughout their careers and provide opportunities for the professional and ethical development of others.

Article 4—Act in a professional manner in dealings with ASQ staff and each employer, customer, or client.

Article 5—Act as faithful agents or trustees and avoid conflic of interest and the appearance of conflicts of interest.

Relations with Peers

Article 6—Build their professional reputation on the merit of their services and not compete unfairly with others.

Article 7—Assure that credit for the work of others is given to those to whom it is due.

Figure 1.1   ASQ Code of Ethics.

EXAMPLE 1.1

A design team has decided on a more hazardous configuration against the recommendation of the reliability engineer. What should the reliability engineer do? The engineer must answer the question, "Have I done whatever I can to promote the reliability and safety of all products?" If the answer is "no," then the code of ethics requires further action. If the design team decided on a more hazardous configuration against the recommendation of the reliability engineer, that decision should be brought to the attention of the reliability engineer's manager and director for their review.

[I] will be dignified and modest in explaining my work and merit. This phrase requires that all who subscribe to this code of ethics recognize that their efforts should be expended on objective analysis of facts and not on self-promotion.

[I] will preface any public statements that I may issue by clearly indicating on whose behalf they are made. Engineers are frequently called on to apply their expertise to issues not directly related to their employer. These opportunities vary from service on a committee in a professional organization to providing advice on public works projects. When it is necessary to issue a statement in this capacity, the code of ethics

requires a disclaimer separating one's views from those of the employer. On the other side of the coin, when the engineer is asked to speak for the employer, the statement should make that fact clear as well.

[I] will inform each client or employer of any business connections, interests, or affiliations which might influence my judgment or impair the equitable character of my services. Professionals of all types make value judgments as part of their responsibilities. This section of the code of ethics requires a conscious search to identify any connections that might bias conclusions. In some situations, especially public service, any connection that could even be perceived as a conflict of interest should be divulged.

[I] will indicate to my employer or client the adverse consequences to be expected if my professional judgment is overruled. The reliability engineer is required to present both good news and bad news scenarios when making recommendations. This equips the decision maker with options, complete with the likely outcomes of each. If hypothesis tests were used to reach conclusions, the significance level should be disclosed. For sampling reports, the confidence level and margin of error should be included.

[I] will not disclose information concerning the business affairs or technical processes of any present or former employer or client without his consent. This clause says that even in the absence of a confidentiality agreement, the individual is honor bound to act as if one is in place. As a practical matter, it may be advisable to have a signed statement from the former employer or client releasing the information.

[I] will take care that credit for the work of others is given to those whom it is due. This clause requires action on the part of the person preparing or presenting a report. Rather than leaving the report uncredited, which might imply that the credit is due the presenter, the "take care" phrase requires an acknowledgment of those involved. If a team is due credit, the team members should usually be named.

The entire ASQ Code of Ethics should be studied and used as a basis for action by all in this field.

7. SUPPLIER RELIABILITY ASSESSMENTS

> Explain how supplier reliability impacts the overall reliability program and describe key reliability concepts that should be included in supplier reliability assessments. (Analyze)
>
> Body of Knowledge I.A.7

In an ideal world, every supplier would have an excellent reliability engineering program with regular, dependable reports delivered to customers. While awaiting this state of affairs it is essential that the customer choose between three scenarios:

1. The customer assumes all responsibility for the reliability engineering function and requires supplier compliance with all specifications. With this arrangement the supplier must report any proposed changes in the process or product so that the potential impact on reliability can be studied. This option is more common in situations where the customer has full design responsibilities and outsources relatively minor components.

2. The supplier assumes responsibility for reliability engineering and reports its analysis and decision-making process to the customer for agreement. The customer is, of course, ultimately responsible to its customers, but the supplier may share financial responsibility for warranty claims and so on. This option is more common when the supplier has design control of the supplied component.

3. Some sort of shared responsibility for the reliability engineering analysis and interpretation exists, perhaps involving a third party. Third-party involvement is more common when the supply chain is long geographically.

With any of these options the arrangement must be clearly spelled out in the contractual agreement between the parties. The customer will want to conduct assessments customized to that agreement.

Examples:

- For suppliers with a long-term relationship based on mutual trust and understanding, the reliability functions conducted by the supplier can be verified at the time of a quality audit. At least one auditing team member should be familiar with reliability engineering functions. The supplier's collection and analysis of lifecycle cost data should be studied, and the mechanism for feedback of this information to the product/design functions should be confirmed.

- For suppliers without a strong favorable history with the components involved, the customer should consider performing actual testing and evaluation of the products. This could vary from a full-fledged reliability program to less elaborate programs, depending on the situation.

The full reliability program would begin with establishing goals and translating goals into product/process design requirements and continue through validating production output. Less elaborate programs could consist of monitoring the reliability engineering function at the supplier's location, training supplier personnel, and/or testing random samples from production to assure that reliability requirements are being met.

8. PERFORMANCE MONITORING

> Describe the importance of performance monitoring to ensure that product reliability or safety requirements continue to be met, and identify lifecycle points in which process and product reliability data are collected and evaluated. (Understand)
>
> Body of Knowledge I.A.8

Performance monitoring involves periodically measuring a project's progress toward explicit short- and long-term reliability, maintainability, and safety (RMS) objectives and giving feedback on the results to decision makers who can use the information in various ways to improve performance.

Uses of Performance Indicators

Strategic Planning

For any program, incorporating performance measurement forces greater consideration of the critical assumptions that underlie that program's relationships and the paths it is following. So, performance indicators help clarify the RMS objectives and logic in the program.

Performance Accounting

Performance indicators can help inform resource allocation decisions if they are used to direct RMS resources to the most successful activities and thereby promote the most efficient use of those resources.

Forecasting and Early Warning During Program Implementation

Measuring progress against indicators points toward future performance, providing feedback that can be used for planning, identifying areas needing RMS improvement, and suggesting what can be done.

Measuring Program Results

Good performance indicators measure what a program has achieved relative to its RMS objectives, not just what it has completed, thus promoting RMS accountability.

Program Marketing and Public Relations

Performance indicators can be used to demonstrate program RMS results to satisfy an external audience/customer. RMS performance data can be used to communicate the value of a program or project.

Benchmarking

Performance indicators can generate RMS data against which to measure other projects or programs. They also provide a way to identify good RMS applications, thus learning from success and from experience how to improve the RMS performance of other projects or programs.

Quality Management

Performance indicators can be used to measure customer satisfaction relative to customer requirements. Performance can be monitored through administering satisfaction surveys and reviewing complaints.

How Are RMS Performance Indicators Developed?

Performance indicators must be based on the unique objectives of individual projects and the customer's requirements. Identifying the RMS objectives—indeed all project objectives—can flow from the customer's requirements via a quality function deployment (QFD).

As the project's RMS objectives are developed, the best mix of outputs to achieve these objectives and components is derived. Tracking parameters for these outputs (e.g., mean time between failures, reject rates, number of defectives, aborts, material defects per item, etc.) can be set up for regular, timely reporting.

For example, looking at a typical product development cycle, the reliability (and indeed, closely related safety) tools and methods are used/modified/developed for the product (see Figure 1.2).

Some performance monitoring examples are shown in Figures 1.3 through 1.6.

NOTE

1. Paraphrased from Brian Ward, *Lead People, Manage Things* (Edmonton, AB: Affinity Consulting, 2009), 93–97.

Design and development	Test and evaluation	Production and operation
• FMEA/FMECA • Predictions • Allocations • Design reviews • Critical items list	• Qualification tests • Failure reporting, analysis, and corrective action system (FRACAS) • Failure review board • Growth models • Reliability trending	• Reliability metrics • Cost-effective analysis • Supportability model • Warranty projections • Logistics support • Proposal support • Usage studies

Figure 1.2   Reliability tasks occur throughout the life of the program.

Figure 1.3   Reliability allocations.

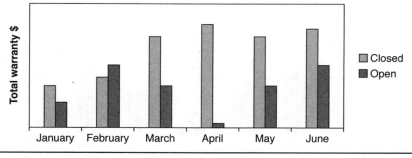

Figure 1.4   Warranty predictions (predicted vs. actual).

Figure 1.5 Reliability growth models.

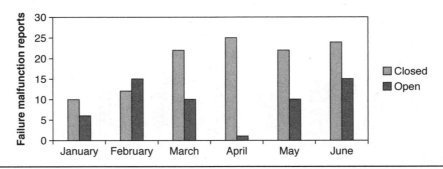

Figure 1.6 FRACAS.

Chapter 2
B. Reliability Foundations

1. BASIC RELIABILITY TERMINOLOGY

> Explain basic terms related to reliability and the associated metrics (e.g., MTTF, MTBF, MTTR, service interval, maintainability, availability, failure rate, reliability, and bathtub curve.). (Apply)
>
> Body of Knowledge I.B.1

Reliability is the probability that an item can perform its intended function for a specified interval under stated conditions. There are several measures of reliability, including *mean time to failure* (MTTF) and *mean time between failures* (MTBF).

The *mean life* of a product is the average time to failure of identical products operating under identical conditions. Mean life is also referred to as the expected time to failure. Mean life is denoted by MTTF for non-repairable products and MTBF for repairable products. The reliability engineer should exercise care in the use of the terms MTTF and MTBF. These terms are usually used when the underlying failure distribution is the exponential and the failure rate is constant. The relationships given in the remainder of this chapter are based on this assumption. MTTF and MTBF are often denoted with the Greek theta (θ). "Time" as used here refers to some measure of life units for the product. In the case of automotive products, the life units may be miles. In other equipment, life units may be cycles, rounds fired, and so forth. Some documents, for instance, replace MTBF with *mean cycles between failures* (MCBF). For a particular set of failure times, the mean life is obtained by averaging the failure times. This value serves as an estimate for θ. If n items are tested to failure, the general formula is

$$\text{MTTF} = \theta = \frac{\sum t_i}{n}$$

where

n = Number of items

t_i = Failure times

EXAMPLE 2.1

Ten randomly selected non-repairable products are tested to failure, and their failure times in hours are: 132, 140, 148, 150, 157, 158, 159, 163, 163, 168.

$$\text{MTTF} = \theta = \frac{132 + 140 + 148 + 150 + 157 + 158 + 159 + 163 + 163 + 168}{10} = 153.8 \text{ hours}$$

The general formula for the situation where a number of repairable items are tested for a given amount of time, with failed items being promptly replaced, is

$$\text{MTBF} = \frac{nm}{r}$$

where

n = Number of items

m = Number of hours in the test

r = Number of failures

Suppose 100 repairable items are tested for 1000 hours each, and failed items are promptly repaired and returned to the test. Suppose 25 failures occurred during the test. Then,

$$\text{MTBF} = \theta = \frac{100,000}{25} = 4000 \text{ hours}$$

Censored Data

There are four types of failure data:

1. *Exact failure times,* in which the exact failure time is known.

2. *Right-censored* data, in which it is known only that the failure happened or would have happened after a particular time. This occurs if an item is still functioning when the test is concluded.

3. *Left-censored* data, in which it is known only that the failure happened before a particular time. This occurs if the items are not checked prior to being tested but are periodically examined, and a failure is observed at the first examination.

4. *Interval-censored* data, in which it is known only that the failure happened between two times; for example, if the items are checked every five hours and an item was functioning at hour 145 but had failed sometime before hour 150.

Failure rate is the reciprocal of the mean life and is defined as the number of failures per unit of time. Failure rate is usually denoted by the letter f or the Greek letter lambda (λ). We will denote failure rate as λ or $\lambda(t)$. $\lambda(t)$ is also called the *hazard function*. So,

$$\lambda = \frac{1}{\text{MTBF}}$$

or

$$\lambda = \frac{1}{\text{MTTF}}$$

and, of course,

$$\text{MTBF} = \frac{1}{\lambda}$$

and

$$\text{MTTF} = \frac{1}{\lambda}$$

Availability can be defined as the probability that a product is operable and in a committable state when needed. In other words, it is the probability that an item has not failed or is not undergoing repair. This measure takes into account an item's reliability and its maintainability. Another way to express this is the proportion of time a system is in a functioning condition. This can be written as the fraction

$$A = \frac{\text{Total time a functional unit is capable of being used during a given interval}}{\text{The length of the interval}}$$

The *mean time to repair* (MTTR) is the average time to fix a repairable system. If the product is repairable and needs no preventive maintenance, and if repair can begin immediately when failure occurs, availability can be defined as

$$A = \frac{\text{MTBF}}{\text{MTBF} + \text{MTTR}}$$

A more general formula for availability can be written as the ratio of the average value of the uptime of a system to the sum of the average values of uptime and downtime:

$$\text{Availability} = \frac{\text{Average uptime}}{\text{Average uptime} + \text{Average downtime}}$$

Dependability is a very similar concept. It is defined as the probability that a product will function at a particular point in time during a mission.

Maintainability is the probability that a failed product will be repaired within a given amount of time once it has failed. Thus, maintainability is a function of time. If there is a 95% probability that a product will be operable within three hours, then $M(3) = 0.95$. In defining maintainability it is necessary to describe exactly what is included in the maintenance action. The following items are typical: diagnosis time, part procurement time, teardown time, rebuild time, and verification time.

Preventive maintenance (PM)—that is, the replacement, at scheduled intervals, of parts or components that have not failed rather than waiting for a failure—is frequently more cost-effective. Preventive maintenance reduces the diagnosis and part procurement times and thus may improve maintainability.

As component and product design decisions are made, the reliability engineer can aid in calculating the cost–benefit relationships by providing life expectancies for various design options.

MTTF is defined as the average time elapsed until the product is no longer performing its function. If the item is repairable, MTBF is the metric used. MTTF and MTBF are reciprocals of λ:

$$\text{MTTF} = \frac{1}{\lambda} \text{ or MTBF} = \frac{1}{\lambda}$$

EXAMPLE 2.2

If $\lambda = 0.00023$ failures per hour, MTBF ≈ 4348 hours.

Reliability R(*t*) is defined as

$$R(t) = \frac{\text{Number of units functioning at the end of the time period}}{\text{Number of units that were functioning at the start of the test}}$$

B*X* *life*, or B(*X*) *life*, is the amount of time that has elapsed when *X*% of the population has failed. For example B(10) = 367 hours means R(367) = 0.90.

Mean time between repairs (MTBR) provides another measure of the reliability of a product. MTBR data should include information about the type of repair and resources required. These data are helpful in determining spare parts inventories, planning for resources, and scheduling preventive maintenance.

Mean time between unplanned maintenance action (MTBUMA) indicates the level of confidence that can be placed in the machine when it is placed in a vital role. If MTBUMA is relatively short, redundant equipment may be needed.

Service interval refers to the recommended time between routine checks and replacements. Familiar examples include lubrication and filter change schedules.

EXAMPLE 2.3

A set of 283 non-repairable units are tested, and the number of failures during each 100 block of time is recorded. The test produced the following data:

Time interval (hrs)	# failures
0–99	0
100–199	2
200–299	10
300–399	30

Calculate $\lambda(t)$, MTBF, and R(*t*) for each time block.

Solution:

Using the formulas given in the definitions:

Time interval (hrs)	# failures	# surviving	$\lambda(t)$	MTBF (hrs)	R(t)
0–99	0	283	0.0000	Undefined	1.000
100–199	2	281	0.0001	10,000	0.993
200–299	10	271	0.356	28.1	0.958
300–399	30	241	0.1107	9.0	0.852

Relationship to Product Specifications

It is customary to specify dimensions, weights, carbon content, and so forth, for products. From the reliability engineering standpoint, it would often be more productive to specify one or more of the reliability metrics listed previously. This has proved especially useful when specifying purchased parts because suppliers often know more about the characteristics of their products than the customer. Although Example 2.4 is anecdotal and somewhat subjective, it illustrates this point.

EXAMPLE 2.4

An automotive company had specified black rubber door seals, giving content, hardness, profile dimensions, and other characteristics. Instead, they now specify reliability requirements such as resistance to ultraviolet (UV) exposure for specified amounts of time and passing rain tests for specified time periods. The customer has left other details up to the supplier and has found that its research requirements are reduced, the new seal does a better job, and the price is slightly reduced because the rubber supplier designed a product that is also easier to manufacture.

Maintainability

Maintainability is a metric usually specified as a probability that a particular maintenance activity can be accomplished in a stated period of time. It is made up of two components: serviceability and repairability. *Serviceability* refers to the level of difficulty encountered when performing the maintenance activity, and *repairability* refers to the level of difficulty when returning a failed item to usefulness. The ultimate goal is to develop a *reliability-centered maintenance* (RCM) program. Steps in that direction include:

1. Develop a functional hierarchy of the machines and their components

2. Make a complete list of failure modes for the machines

3. Perform an evaluation of each PM activity to determine whether it really aids in preventing failure modes

4. Reorganize PM activities to align with the information from steps 1–3

Product Lifecycle

Reliability engineers identify three stages in the lifecycle of a product:

1. The first stage is referred to variously as the *early failure* stage, the *infant mortality* stage, or the *decreasing failure rate* stage. The failures that occur during the early failure stage are usually associated with manufacturing rather than design. Examples of causes of failure include inadequate test or burn-in time, poor quality control, poor handling, weak materials or components, and human error in fabrication or assembly. Ideally, all these failures should occur in-house and be corrected before the customer takes possession.

2. The second stage is called the *constant failure rate* stage, the *random causes* stage, or the *useful life* stage. During the useful life stage the failure rate is approximately constant. Note that the failure rate is not necessarily zero. During this stage the failures have random causes and can't usually be assigned to production problems. Reducing the failure rate during this stage usually requires changes in product design.

3. The third stage is called the *wear-out* stage, *fatigue* stage, or the *increasing failure rate* stage. The wear-out stage is characterized by an increasing failure rate over time. These failures are caused by product or component fatigue.

A graph of the failure rate is shown as the *bathtub curve* in Figure 2.1. Note that although the useful life stage is sometimes referred to as the random causes stage, random causes are generally present during all three stages.

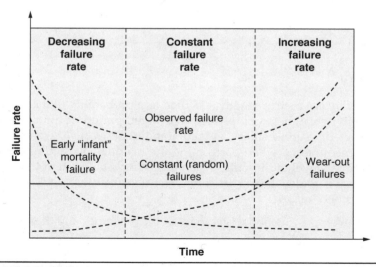

Figure 2.1   Reliability bathtub curve.

Source: Adapted from M. A. Durivage, *Practical Engineering, Process, and Reliability Statistics* (Milwaukee, WI: ASQ Quality Press, 2014).

2. DRIVERS OF RELIABILITY REQUIREMENTS AND TARGETS

> Describe how customer expectations and industry
> standards, safety, liability, and regulatory concerns
> drive reliability requirements. (Understand)
>
> Body of Knowledge I.B.2

Reliability analysis provides estimates of the probability of failure. The reliability engineer must go beyond these calculations and examine the consequences of failure. These consequences typically represent costs to the customer. The customer finds ways of sharing these costs with the producer through the warranty system, loss of business, decrease in reputation, or the civil litigation system. Therefore, an important reliability function is the anticipation of possible failures and the establishment of reliability acceptance goals that will limit their occurrence and consequent costs. The acceptance criteria associated with these goals generally fall into three categories:

- Functional requirements (such as 20 gallons per minute for a pump)

- Environmental requirements (such as temperature, radiation, pH)

- Time requirements (such as failure rate during useful life, time elapsed before wear-out phase begins)

Once component, product, and system reliability goals have been set, a testing protocol should be implemented to provide validation that these goals will impact the failure rates and the associated consequences as planned. These reliability goals typically impose specifications on the product. In anticipation of the start of production, reliability engineers provide further testing procedures to provide verification that these specifications are being met.

A reliability program should impact many functions in an enterprise, including research, purchasing, manufacturing, quality assurance, testing, shipping, and field service, among others. A reliability program should have the following elements:

1. *Established reliability goals and requirements.* The general goal of reliability efforts is to delight customers by increasing the reliability of products. The reliability program accomplishes this goal by establishing reliability goals and meeting them. Customer input and market analysis typically determine minimum reliability requirements. In general, consumers have rising expectations for reliability. The minimum reliability requirements are time dependent because reliability changes throughout the life of the product.

2. *Product design.* The reliability program must have a mechanism for translating the minimum reliability requirements into design requirements. Reliability requirements should be documented for each stage of a product's design and for all subsystems and components.

3. *Process design.* As the product design firms up, attention can shift toward the design of the processes that will produce it. Reliability requirements must be finalized for components, whether produced in-house or

purchased from suppliers. These requirements must be linked to manufacturing process parameters by determining what processes and what settings will produce components with the required reliability.

4. *Validation and verification.* As either prototypes or the first production pieces become available, the reliability program must facilitate tests that are conducted to validate that the reliability requirements do indeed produce the desired product reliability. When these requirements have been validated it is necessary to verify that the production processes can produce products that meet these requirements.

5. *Post-production evaluation.* The reliability program must make provisions for collecting and analyzing data from products during their useful life:

   a. Random samples from regular production should be collected and tested for reliability.

   b. Customer feedback should be actively solicited and analyzed.

   c. Field service and warranty records should be studied.

6. *Training and education.* Although listed last, this is certainly not the least important element of a reliability program. No reliability program can succeed without a basic understanding of its elementary concepts by people at all levels. Support from key managers is essential because their cooperation is needed for the testing and analysis process. Top-level management must see the importance of the program to the success of the enterprise. So, this element of the reliability program must sometimes be given first priority if the rest of the program is to succeed.

Design requirements originate from customer needs. These requirements, as determined by the marketplace, customer input, organizational objectives, and other sources, must often be prioritized. A classic example is the motto NASA adopted in the 1990s, "faster—better—cheaper," to which the engineers famously replied, "We can do any two."

Faster

Meeting reliability design requirements within time and resource constraints requires an efficient testing and documentation program. The tasks associated with the program must be accomplished in synchronization with other design, development, and manufacturing functions. These tasks must be given adequate priority at each stage of design if unpleasant late-term surprises are to be avoided.

The reliability engineer should provide the project manager with time/resource needs during the project planning phase. The project manager is typically responsible for assuring that these needs are fulfilled at the appropriate stages.

3. CORRECTIVE AND PREVENTIVE ACTION

> Identify corrective and preventive actions to take in specific situations and evaluate their measures of effectiveness. (Evaluate)
>
> Body of Knowledge I.B.3

The ultimate test of the effectiveness of a corrective and preventive action (CAPA) is the ability to turn the action on or off and observe the corresponding effect on the process. Data should be collected before and after the installation of the corrective/preventive action. This section lists some tools for determining whether these data provide evidence that the action has been successful.

The histogram is probably the simplest tool to use. Suppose the proposed corrective/preventive action was designed to raise the mean effective lifetime of the item. Random samples from the process before and after the action should show a difference in their centers. If the two histograms look like those in Figure 2.2, one could conclude that the action was effective. If, on the other hand, the two histograms looked like those shown in Figure 2.3, the results would be inconclusive. In this case it would be necessary to subject the data to the hypothesis test for means of two populations. In a similar manner, if the corrective/preventive action was designed to reduce the variation in characteristic x, the histograms might look like those in Figure 2.4, in which case it would be safe to conclude that the action was effective. Again, if the results from the histograms were ambiguous, it would be possible to reach a more definitive conclusion by using a hypothesis test, in this case the test for two population standard deviations.

There is a caveat regarding the use of hypothesis tests for proportions: Consider avoiding the aggregation of defect types. It is sometimes best to delineate categories' defect types and study them individually.

One of the frustrating aspects of CAPA problem solving is the tendency for the same problem to reoccur. This may be because the installed solution did not really

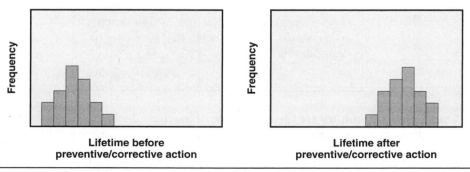

Figure 2.2 Histograms showing increase in mean lifetime.

Figure 2.3   Inconclusive histograms.

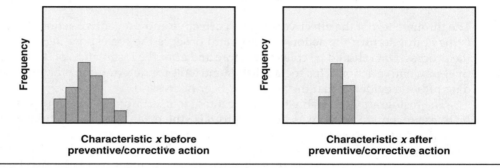

Figure 2.4   Histograms showing reduction of variation in characteristic *x*.

solve the problem, or it may be because the solution, although correcting the problem, was discontinued for some reason. Therefore, installing a system that monitors the process, to ensure that the problem doesn't reoccur, is a major CAPA activity.

In situations where the problem occurs very rarely it is often best to establish a control chart to determine whether the desired change has occurred. Documentation regarding problem-solving activity should be maintained and available to team members. Properly cross-referenced, this documentation can aid team members by providing a history of current or similar problems.

4. ROOT CAUSE ANALYSIS

> Describe root cause analysis, and use a root cause and failure analysis tool to determine the causes of degradation or failure. (Evaluate)
>
> Body of Knowledge I.B.4

Once defects or failures are identified, one of the most difficult and critical tasks in the entire enterprise begins—that of determining the root cause or causes.

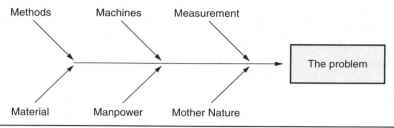

Figure 2.5   Traditional cause–and–effect diagram with the six Ms.

Cause-and-Effect Diagram

The *cause-and-effect diagram*, also called the *fishbone* or *Ishikawa diagram*, helps a team identify, explore, and communicate all the possible causes of the problem. It does this by dividing possible causes into broad categories that help stimulate inquiry as successive steps delve deeper. The general structure of the diagram, shown in Figure 2.5, illustrates why it is also called the fishbone diagram. The choice of categories or names of the main "bones" depends on the situation. Some alternatives might include policies, technology, tradition, legislation, and so on.

A team may use a cause-and-effect diagram to generate a number of potential causes in each category by going around the room and asking each person to suggest one cause and its associated category. As each cause is identified, it is shown as a subtopic of the main category by attaching a smaller line to the main "bone" for that category. The activity continues until the team is satisfied that all possible causes have been listed. Individual team members can then be assigned to collect data on various branches or sub-branches for presentation at a future meeting. Ideally, the data should be derived by changing the nature of the cause being investigated and observing the result. For example, if voltage variation is a suspected cause, put in a voltage regulator and see if the number of defects changes. One advantage of this approach is that it forces the team to work on the causes and not focus on symptoms, personal feelings, history, and various other baggage. An alternative to the meeting format is to have an online fishbone diagram to which team members may post possible causes over a set period of time.

Five Whys

The *five whys* is another technique that helps dig deeper into a problem (see Example 2.5). This tool consists of repeating the question "Why does this happen?" as each answer surfaces.

EXAMPLE 2.5

Why is this part defective? Because the hole is too large.

Why is the hole too large? Because the bit "walked" during the drill operation.

Why did the bit walk? Because the holding fixture had some play in it.

Why did the fixture have play? Because the pneumatic clamps didn't apply enough pressure.

Why don't the clamps apply sufficient pressure? Because of variation in the air pressure to the shop floor.

Needless to say, the number five is arbitrary, and in this case additional inquiry into air pressure variation would be appropriate.

A flowchart of the process will often aid in identifying root causes (see Figure 2.6). Enhancements should include data on quality levels and possible causes at each step of the process. This tool can be especially helpful if the process is large or complex.

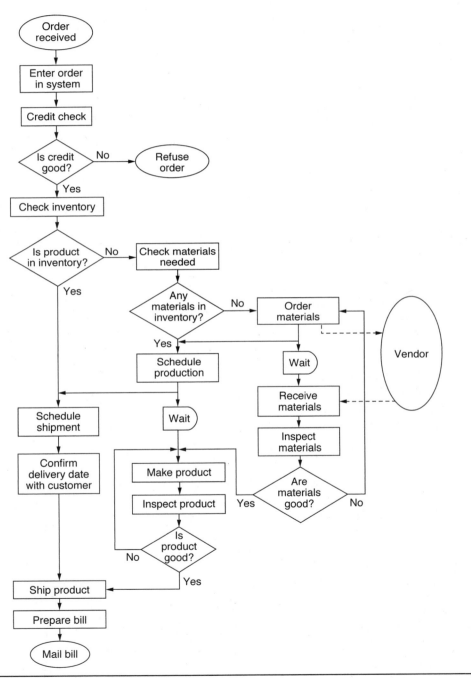

Figure 2.6 Enhanced process flowchart.

Scatter Diagrams

When several causes for a problem have been proposed, it may be necessary to collect data to help determine which is a potential root cause. One way to analyze such data is with a *scatter diagram* (see Figure 2.7). In this technique, measurements are taken for various levels of the variables suspected of being a cause. Then each variable is plotted against the measured value of the problem to get a rough idea of correlation or association.

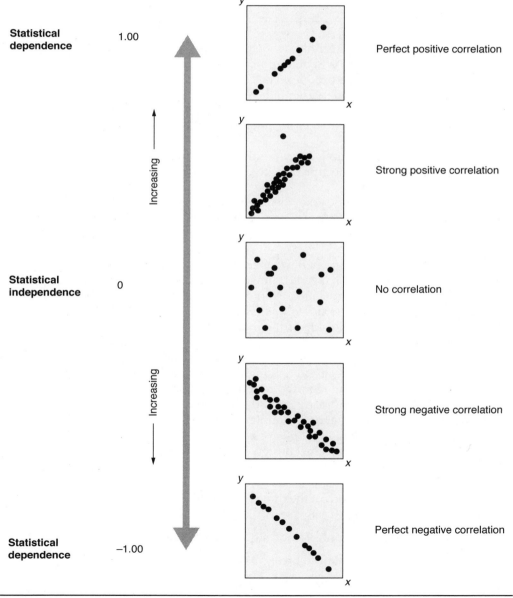

Figure 2.7   Relative degrees of correlation.

Source: Adapted from M. A. Durivage, *Practical Engineering, Process, and Reliability Statistics* (Milwaukee, WI: ASQ Quality Press 2014).

5. PRODUCT LIFECYCLE ENGINEERING STAGES

> Describe the impact various lifecycle stages (concept/design, development/test, introduction, growth, maturity, decline) have on reliability, and the cost issues (product maintenance, life expectation, software defect phase containment, etc.) associated with those stages. (Understand)
>
> Body of Knowledge I.B.5

Reliability engineering techniques help quantify the "pay me now or pay me later" concept. The goal is to determine the reliability level that will minimize the total lifecycle cost of the product. The lifecycle cost of a product includes the cost to purchase, operate, and maintain the product during its useful lifetime. In some cases, such as automotive products, where the customer seldom keeps the product for its entire useful lifetime, costs associated with depreciation may be factored into lifecycle costs.

The real cost of failures is frequently underestimated. If a 90-cent natural gas valve component fails to function, the cost may far exceed the 90-cent replacement cost.

Reliability engineers take the long-term view and develop cost-effective ways to reduce lifecycle costs. These may range from design techniques such as redundancy and derating to specification of manufacturing parameters such as burn-in time.

Increased reliability sometimes means increased manufacturing cost and selling price. Properly implemented, however, the result will be a decrease in lifecycle cost. Consider, for instance, a national truck line that discovered that its most frequent cause of vehicle downtime was loss of a headlight bulb. This entailed stopping the truck at the side of the road and summoning a repair vehicle from the nearest company depot. The resultant delay caused late deliveries and dissatisfied customers. The trucking company determined that a much more reliable bulb reduced lifecycle costs even though the new bulb had a considerably higher initial purchase price and required retrofitting a step-up transformer to obtain the required voltage. The company now specifies the more reliable bulb for new truck purchases. In this case the truck manufacturer can be faulted for producing a product that didn't have the lowest lifecycle cost.

As component and product design decisions are made, the reliability engineer can aid in calculating the cost–benefit relationships by providing life expectancies for various design options.

Knowing the locations of the three stages of the bathtub curve can help answer important questions such as:

- Is the quality control system doing a good job?
- What is the optimum break-in/burn-in time?
- What is the optimum warranty period?
- What are the optimum replacement times for various components?

- What are the spare parts requirements?
- Is the preventive maintenance schedule optimized?
- Is the failure rate during the useful life stage low enough to meet customer expectations?

Each of these items relates to costs in some way, so insight gained from the bathtub curve can have a direct impact on financial performance.

Data are used to determine the shape of the bathtub curve, including locating the boundaries between the stages. Reliability engineers try to change the curve by improving the product. They typically do one or more of the following:

1. Improve the early failure stage by shortening its length and giving it a flatter slope. This is usually accomplished by studying the processes used by the company and/or its suppliers to see where tighter control of process parameters is needed. Shortening the length of the early failure phase reduces costs by decreasing burn-in time and reducing the risk of early failure after installation.

2. Improve the useful life stage by decreasing the constant failure rate. Failure data are studied to determine the most frequent failure types. Reliability engineers work with product/process engineers to find changes that will decrease the failure rate. These activities reduce cost per unit of useful time by increasing life expectancy.

3. Improve the wear-out stage by delaying its onset and flattening the curve. The timing and steepness of the failure rate curve is generally a function of design. However, the wear-out phase can often be postponed somewhat and its slope reduced by more aggressive preventive maintenance and component replacement schedules. Delaying wear-out increases useful life and reduces cost per unit of useful time.

During the useful life (constant failure rate stage) of the product, the formula for product reliability is

$$R(t) = e^{-\lambda}t$$

where t is the time elapsed and λ is the constant failure rate.

EXAMPLE 2.6

A batch of 364 light bulbs has a constant failure rate of 0.000058 failures per hour. Find the reliability after 1500 hours of service. About how many bulbs have burned out at the end of the 1500-hour period?

Solution:

$$R(1500) = e^{-(0.000058)(1500)} \approx 0.917$$

This indicates that about 91.7% of the bulbs are still functioning, and 8.3% have burned out. 364(0.083) ≈ 30 of the bulbs have burned out.

6. ECONOMICS OF PRODUCT MAINTAINABILITY AND AVAILABILITY

> Describe the cost tradeoffs associated with product maintainability strategies and availability. (Understand)
>
> Body of Knowledge I.B.6

System availability is determined by reliability (the probability of the system not failing) and maintainability (the ability to restore the system to service). Availability is the measure of the time the system is in an operating state compared to the total time. There are several commonly used measures of availability. The various availabilities depend on the downtimes that are included in the total time. In the following equations, the failure rate of the system is assumed to be constant.

Inherent availability excludes preventive maintenance and any logistic downtime. Included in the total time is downtime due to corrective maintenance.

$$A = \frac{MTBF}{MTBF + MTTR}$$

MTTR is the mean time to repair and includes the time for corrective maintenance actions along with the probability of the occurrence of the failure.

Achieved availability includes the downtime due to corrective and preventive maintenance actions. Only the active time is included. Not included is any delay time in acquiring supplies and administrative downtime. The *mean time between maintenance actions* (MTBMA) includes both scheduled and unscheduled maintenance actions.

MTBMA is a function of the failure rate (λ) and the preventive maintenance rate (μ). If the preventive maintenance rate is constant,

$$MTBMA = \frac{1}{\lambda + \mu}$$

The *mean active maintenance time* (MAMT) includes the average (mean) corrective maintenance time and the average time to perform preventive maintenance. Included in the calculation is the frequency at which the actions will occur. The achieved availability can be calculated as

$$A = \frac{MTBMA}{MTBMA + MAMT}$$

Operational availability includes all downtime. The *mean downtime* (MDT) includes logistic time, time waiting for replacement parts, and administrative downtime. Operational availability is calculated as

$$A = \frac{MTBMA}{MTBMA + MDT}$$

The effort during design should be to ensure a high probability that the equipment is ready to be used when the customer demands its use. This requires that both reliability and the ability to maintain the equipment be specified characteristics of the design.

7. COST OF POOR RELIABILITY

> Describe how poor reliability affects costs over the lifecycle. (Understand)
>
> Body of Knowledge I.B.7

The goal is to determine the reliability level that will minimize the total lifecycle cost of the product. The *lifecycle cost* of a product includes the cost to purchase, operate, and maintain the product during its useful lifetime. In some cases, such as automotive products, where the customer seldom keeps the product for its entire useful lifetime, costs associated with depreciation may be factored into lifecycle costs.

The real cost of failures is frequently underestimated. If a 90-cent natural gas valve component fails to function, the cost may far exceed the 90-cent replacement cost.

Reliability engineers take the long-term view and develop cost-effective ways to reduce lifecycle costs. These may range from design techniques such as redundancy and derating to specification of manufacturing parameters such as burn-in time.

Increased reliability sometimes means increased manufacturing cost and selling price. Properly implemented, however, the result will be a decrease in lifecycle cost. Consider, for instance, a national truck line that discovered that its most frequent cause of vehicle downtime was loss of a headlight bulb. This entailed stopping the truck at the side of the road and summoning a repair vehicle from the nearest company depot. The resultant delay caused late deliveries and dissatisfied customers. The trucking company determined that a much more reliable bulb reduced lifecycle costs even though the new bulb had a considerably higher initial purchase price and required retrofitting a step-up transformer to obtain the required voltage. The company now specifies the more reliable bulb for new truck purchases. In this case the truck manufacturer can be faulted for producing a product that didn't have the lowest lifecycle cost.

As component and product design decisions are made, the reliability engineer can aid in calculating the cost–benefit relationships by providing life expectancies for various design options.

Knowing the locations of the three stages of the bathtub curve (see Figure 2.1) can help answer important questions such as:

- Is the quality control system doing a good job?

- What is the optimum break-in/burn-in time?

- What is the optimum warranty period?

- What are the optimum replacement times for various components?

- What are the spare parts requirements?

- Is the preventive maintenance schedule optimized?

- Is the failure rate during the useful life stage low enough to meet customer expectations?

Each of these items relates to costs in some way, so insight gained from the bathtub curve can have a direct impact on financial performance.

Data are used to determine the shape of the bathtub curve, including locating the boundaries between the stages. Reliability engineers try to change the curve by improving the product. They typically do one or more of the following:

1. Improve the early failure stage by shortening its length and giving it a flatter slope. This is usually accomplished by studying the processes used by the company and/or its suppliers to see where tighter control of process parameters is needed. Shortening the length of the early failure phase reduces costs by decreasing burn-in time and reducing the risk of early failure after installation.

2. Improve the useful life stage by decreasing the constant failure rate. Failure data are studied to determine the most frequent failure types. Reliability engineers work with product/process engineers to find changes that will decrease the failure rate. These activities reduce cost per unit of useful time by increasing life expectancy.

3. Improve the wear-out stage by delaying its onset and flattening the curve. The timing and steepness of the failure rate curve is generally a function of design. However, the wear-out phase can often be postponed somewhat and its slope reduced by more aggressive preventive maintenance and component replacement schedules. Delaying wear-out increases useful life and reduces cost per unit of useful time.

During the useful life (constant failure rate stage) of the product, the formula for product reliability is

$$R(t) = e^{-\lambda}t$$

where t is the time elapsed, λ is the constant failure rate, and e is the base of natural logarithms 2.718281828. . . .

EXAMPLE 2.7

A batch of 364 light bulbs has a constant failure rate of 0.000058 failures per hour. Find the reliability after 1500 hours of service. About how many bulbs have burned out at the end of the 1500-hour period?

Solution:

$$R(1500) = e^{-(0.000058)(1500)} \approx .917$$

This indicates that about 91.7% of the bulbs are still functioning, and 8.3% have burned out. 364(0.083) ≈ 30 of the bulbs have burned out.

Reliability Engineering for Software Products

The reliability effort for software products consists of three general phases:

- Error prevention

- Fault detection and removal

- Fault containment through redundancy

The software package is written, then tested against predetermined criteria. Typically, a relatively large number of faults are identified in the early stages of testing, and as this phase continues, the number of faults decreases. At some point the product is released to customers, at which point faults continue to crop up, sometimes at a higher rate than before release. The software package may continue to be used until other considerations force its obsolescence. The typical reliability curve for a software product is shown in Figure 2.8. Software reliability engineering attempts to improve the reliability curve in Figure 2.8 by:

- Reducing the time and effort involved in the test phase (defect containment phase)

- Lowering the failure rate during the useful life of the product

- Employing redundant techniques to automatically detect and contain faults

Techniques that have been used include:

- Use of alternate formulas to calculate a value, and comparing results

- Use of dual processors, and comparing results

- Establishing known limits on a result and flagging values outside the limits

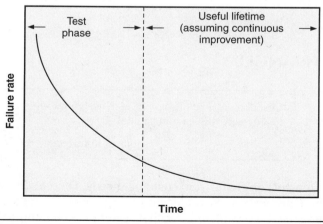

Figure 2.8   Reliability curve for a typical software product.

Obviously, it is better to prevent errors than to detect faults. Many errors can be prevented by designing thorough requirements prior to code development. The requirements should be stated in terms of imperatives—statements that command that something must occur. Weak phrases that can be interpreted in more than one way should be eliminated from a requirements document. There should be no incomplete requirements of the "to be determined" (TBD) or "to be supplied" (TBS) type. In addition, the requirements should be structured much like a good modular quality program. Developing a high-quality requirements document is worth the effort.

A software team that begins with a good set of requirements can still introduce errors, of course. General rules for software code include:

- Make it modular.

- Keep it simple—excess complexity is difficult to debug and maintain. (Sometimes referred to as the Shirley Temple rule: "Don't be too cute.")

- Provide copious documentation and comments.

The testing protocol must test every requirement at least once. Adequate resources must be provided to allow for complete testing.

In addition to a product's service lifecycle, every product has a market lifecycle with these stages: concept/design, introduction, growth, maturity, decline. The reliability engineer can make useful contributions at each of these stages. The principal way that reliability engineers can influence the service lifecycle is to provide data during the *concept/design* stage to help assure that components and assemblies will perform throughout their designed life. These data may be obtained through testing proposed designs, from standard tables, or by using components whose lifecycle information is available.

During the *introduction* and *growth* stages the reliability engineer will begin to rely more on warranty data from the field. In the product *maturity* and *decline* stages the reliability engineer may be called on to study the use of the product in different environments or applications in an effort to extend its market life.

8. QUALITY TRIANGLE

> Describe the relationship between cost, time, and quality with respect to reliability. (Understand)
>
> Body of Knowledge I.B.8

Design requirements originate from customer needs. These requirements, as determined by the marketplace, customer input, organizational objectives, and other sources, must often be prioritized. A classic example is the motto NASA adopted in the 1990s, "faster—better—cheaper," to which the engineers famously replied, "We can do any two."

Meeting reliability design requirements within time and resource constraints requires an efficient testing and documentation program. The tasks associated with the program must be accomplished in synchronization with other design, development, and manufacturing functions. These tasks must be given adequate priority at each stage of design if unpleasant late-term surprises are to be avoided.

The reliability engineer should provide the project manager with time/resource needs during the project planning phase. The project manager is typically responsible for assuring that these needs are fulfilled at the appropriate stages.

9. SIX SIGMA METHODOLOGIES

> Describe how six sigma principles support reliability engineering. (Understand)
>
> Body of Knowledge I.B.9

Some implementations of reliability engineering have consisted of testing products at the end of the manufacturing phase to determine their lifecycle parameters. At this point it is, of course, too late to have much impact on those parameters. Reliability engineering tools help the design engineer work more efficiently and effectively in various ways:

- MTBF values for existing products can be determined and reasonable goals established

- MTBF values for components and purchased parts can be determined

- Failure types and times of occurrence can be anticipated

- Optimal break-in/burn-in times can be determined

- Recommendations for warranty times can be established

- The impact of age and operating conditions on the life of the product can be studied

- The effects of parallel or redundant design features can be determined

- Accelerated life testing can be used to provide failure data

- Field failure data can be analyzed to help evaluate product performance

- Concurrent engineering can improve the efficiency and effectiveness of product development by scheduling design tasks in parallel rather than sequentially

- Reliability engineering can provide information to individual teams about failure rates of their proposed components

- Cost accounting estimates can be improved through the use of lifecycle cost analysis using reliability data

- When management employs failure modes and effects analysis (FMEA)/failure modes, effects, and criticality analysis (FMECA) techniques, reliability engineering provides essential input

Lean manufacturing, with its emphasis on workplace organization and standardized work procedures, can reduce product variation. This in turn makes a more predictable lifecycle and helps the reliability engineer provide more useful data to the design function. The term "lean thinking" refers to the use of ideas originally employed in lean manufacturing to improve functions in all departments of an enterprise. The National Institute of Standards and Technology (NIST), through its Manufacturing Extension Partnership, defines *lean* as:

> A systematic approach to identifying and eliminating waste (non-value-added activities) through continuous improvement by flowing the product at the pull of the customer in pursuit of perfection.

ASQ defines *non-value-added* as:

> A term that describes a process step or function that is not required for the direct achievement of process output. This step or function is identified and examined for potential elimination.

This represents a shift in focus for manufacturing engineering, which has traditionally studied ways to improve value-added functions and activities (for example, how can this process run faster and more precisely?). Lean thinking doesn't ignore the value-added activities, but it does shine the spotlight on waste. Lean manufacturing seeks to eliminate or reduce waste by use of the following:

- Teamwork with well-informed, cross-trained employees who participate in the decisions that impact their function

- Clean, organized, and well-marked work spaces

- Flow systems instead of batch and queue (that is, reduce batch size toward its ultimate ideal—one)

- Pull systems instead of push systems (that is, replenish what the customer has consumed)

- Reduced lead times through more efficient processing, setups, and scheduling

The history of lean thinking may be traced to Eli Whitney, who is credited with spreading the concept of part interchangeability. Henry Ford, who went to great lengths to reduce cycle times, furthered the ideas of lean thinking. And later, the

Toyota Production System (TPS) packaged most of the tools and concepts now known as lean manufacturing.

Six Sigma strategies support extensive data collection and analysis. This can aid the reliability engineering function by increasing emphasis on designed experiments and lifecycle testing programs. A wide range of companies have found that when the Six Sigma philosophy is fully embraced, the enterprise thrives. What is this Six Sigma philosophy? Several definitions have been proposed, with the following common threads:

- Use of teams that are assigned well-defined projects that have direct impact on the organization's bottom line

- Training in statistical thinking at all levels and providing key people (designated "Black Belts") with extensive training in advanced statistics and project management

- Emphasis on the DMAIC (define, measure, analyze, improve, and control) approach to problem solving

- A management environment that supports these initiatives as a business strategy

Opinions on the definition of Six Sigma differ:

- *Philosophy.* The philosophical perspective views all work as processes that can be defined, measured, analyzed, improved, and controlled (DMAIC). Processes require inputs and produce outputs. If inputs are controlled, the outputs will be controlled. This is generally expressed as the $y = f(x)$ concept.

- *Set of tools.* Six Sigma as a set of tools includes all the qualitative and quantitative techniques used by the Six Sigma expert to drive process improvement. A few such tools include statistical process control (SPC), control charts, FMEA, and process mapping. Six Sigma professionals do not completely agree as to exactly which tools constitute the set.

- *Methodology.* The methodological view of Six Sigma recognizes the underlying and rigorous DMAIC approach. DMAIC defines the steps a Six Sigma practitioner is expected to follow, starting with identifying the problem and ending with implementing long-lasting solutions. While DMAIC is not the only Six Sigma methodology in use, it is certainly the most widely adopted and recognized.

- *Metrics.* In simple terms, Six Sigma quality performance means 3.4 defects per million opportunities (accounting for a 1.5-sigma shift in the mean).

Lean and Six Sigma have the same general purpose of providing the customer with the best possible quality, cost, delivery, and a newer attribute—nimbleness. The two initiatives approach their common purpose from slightly different angles:

- Lean focuses on waste reduction, whereas Six Sigma emphasizes variation reduction

- Lean achieves its goals by using less technical tools such as kaizen, workplace organization, and visual controls, whereas Six Sigma tends to use statistical data analysis, design of experiments, and hypothesis tests

10. SYSTEMS ENGINEERING AND INTEGRATION

> Describe the role of reliability engineering within systems engineering, including the integration of components and their interfaces/interactions within the system. (Understand)
>
> Body of Knowledge I.B.10

Systems engineering may be defined as a branch of engineering that integrates the activities of other disciplines to produce a product or service. It is generally recognized as having six steps:

1. *State the problem.* Begins with an investigation of customer needs. This is different from customer requirements because there may be needs that are not understood or articulated by customers. Was there a huge outcry for iPads before they were produced? The problem should include a list of mandatory features and a list of "nice but not mandatory" features. Design requirements take shape during this phase.

   Some prioritization of these requirements may be possible also. For example, "operates at 60 hertz" might be a higher-priority requirement than "switchable between 50 hertz and 60 hertz." The design team studies the customer needs in the market niche for which the product is intended as these requirements are formed and prioritized. The next two steps often uncover additional features that can be included in these requirements.

2. *Study alternatives.* Sometimes called *divergent* thinking, this step opens the box to innovative and creative options, which are then studied for feasibility. One or more of the alternatives is selected to proceed to step 3. Steps 2 and 3 often are in a continuous loop as alternatives are studied and modeled. During these phases it is necessary to solidify the design requirements and to prioritize them. Care must be exercised to avoid "mission creep"—the tendency to add too many new features.

3. *Model or simulate the system.* Using physical or software approaches, the system is operated in an often primitive way, sometimes at a slower speed, in an effort to identify problems and opportunities.

4. *Integrate the various elements.* Interface the various elements of the system so the entire entity operates as one.

5. *Run the system.* Study the outputs to verify that they meet all the mandatory output requirements stated in step 1.

6. *Study performance.* Evaluate the entire system, measuring its performance against alternatives and the requirements stated in step 1.

Each of these steps is subject to constant reevaluation, so the series of steps is more like a series of interlocking and repeating loops. The objective is to build a system that not only has useful and productive elements but also blends these elements into a smoothly operating unit.

Part II

Risk Management

Part II

Chapter 3
A. Identification

1. RISK MANAGEMENT TECHNIQUES

> Use risk management tools and processes to iden-
> tify, document, and track concerns. Identify and
> prioritize safety, economic, performance, and cus-
> tomer satisfaction concerns utilizing an appropriate
> risk management framework. (Analyze)
>
> Body of Knowledge II.A.1

A typical risk management program has three fundamental elements:

1. *Identification of potentially undesirable effects.* The reliability engineer working with other disciplines across the organization will strive to ensure a robust product/service is developed.

   A variety of approaches are employed in discovering all possible ways in which the product/service can fail to perform its intended function. Systems are growing in complexity and along with the historical discrete failures that dominated mechanical systems of the past, the challenge has grown to include combinations of failures that include hardware, software, and human cognition. Complex systems can also fail functionally without any component, software, or human failure, simply due to complexity in design. It is important to note that highly complex systems do not allow complete coverage of all possible failure scenarios, and innovative approaches may need to be applied in an attempt to uncover subtle issues that can lead to functional failure.

   Warranty data and other forms of customer feedback should be analyzed. Product testing reports should include safety issues that may have emerged. All available product data should be searched for occurrence of any emergent potential safety hazards. In addition, if databases for similar products are available, these should also be studied. Out of an abundance of caution, retrograde analysis, which assumes functional failure scenarios without component/software failure, is employed as an investigative method.

2. *Risk analysis.* The standard analysis techniques are failure modes and effects analysis (FMEA); failure modes, effects, and criticality

analysis (FMECA); production reliability acceptance test (PRAT); fault tree analysis (FTA); success tree analysis (STA); and failure reporting, analysis, and corrective action system (FRACAS). Additional approaches such a preliminary hazards analysis (PHA), failure modes, effects, and diagnostic analysis (FMEDA), and systems theoretic process analysis (STPA) are used to assist the facilitator in the investigation of potential failures.

The risk matrix is another approach to cataloging potential risk. These techniques can be used to probabilistically estimate the risk associated with various events. Based on these results, a prioritized list should be developed that will provide guidance about where initial in-depth preventive actions are focused.

3. *Improvement through prevention, intervention, assist, and/or rescue.* In the case of safety hazards, there is the additional urgency to avoid harm to personnel. In cases in which flaws in products or processes permit hazardous conditions to occur, an engineering change request (ECR) should be initiated. It is always necessary to consider human cognition error. From one perspective, human error occurs because systems to prevent all possible human errors may not be achievable. In other words, the onus is on the product/process/software design community to prevent them when possible and, if not preventable, then to detect them on condition when possible so that appropriate actions can be taken to avoid abrupt failure, Finally, if human errors are not preventable and not conditionally detectable, then the consequences of the failure must be mitigated. Procedures for preventing/mitigating human error are variously called *mistake-proofing, poka-yoke,* and *zero quality control* (ZQC).

Human error has tended to fall into the following categories: misunderstanding, misidentification, inexperience, inattention, and lack of standards. With highly complex systems that integrate user-automated assist features, human behavioral conditioning becomes an issue. Operators have relaxed attention, depending on the system to inform them of when human intervention is required. This demands developing intuitive mental models for the human and system sensing/actuation in an appropriate timeframe to allow the operator to effectively respond. The traditional way to deal with human mistakes is to incorporate design elements that will prevent them from occurring or prevent their occurrence from causing defects. Principal types of mistake-proofing techniques include:

— *Physical barriers to errors.* (The round shaft won't fit through the square hole.)

— *Visual reminders.* (A photograph of correct and incorrect results is better than a note written on a print or a paragraph of text.)

— *Use of automated equipment.* (The conveyor will stop if the microswitch detects an error.)

— *Standardizing.* (The operator takes the same action on a family of parts.)

Often, the best way to prevent reoccurrence of human error is to approach a person who has made the error with the question, "How can we design a system that will make that error impossible to occur?"

Activity must be continuous in the three elements of the risk management program. As the higher-priority hazards are satisfactorily dispositioned, action can focus on the lower-priority items.

2. TYPES OF RISK

> Identify the various types of risks, including technical, scheduling, safety, and financial, and describe their relationship to reliability. (Analyze)
>
> Body of Knowledge II.A.2

Reliability engineering is primarily focused on testing and evaluation of technical properties of products. However, the reliability program must be cognizant of a broader view to include the various systems that bring the product to the customer.

The best lifecycle analysis may be made irrelevant if these systems fail. Examples of these issues follow:

- *Scheduling.* Are advance planning and provision for contingencies adequate? Will conflicts with schedules of other products impact delivery?

- *Safety.* Will various phases of the lifecycle cause health and safety hazards to the user or others? Will proposed changes in processes, installers, or others impact safety?

- *Financial.* How will changes in exchange rates for international transactions impact the organization? Is the information regarding creditworthiness of customers adequate?

- *Regulatory.* Will domestic/international political trends impact the organization? What expenses or delays will occur to meet proposed regulations?

- *Suppliers.* How would change of status (for example, a buyout) of a supplier impact the delivery schedule? Will changes in the transportation infrastructure impact supplies? Can the supplier make changes that are not reportable under the form, fit, or function categories, but can result in the introduction of issues in the customer domain?

- *Materials.* How will changes in cost/availability of key materials impact the product? What effect will supply/demand and international relations have on the product?

ISO Guide 73:2009 defines *risk* as the effect of uncertainty on objectives. Risk assessment/risk management uses qualitative and quantitative data to provide estimates of the impact of various adverse events. The purpose is to identify and prioritize vulnerabilities so that corrective action can be initiated. One approach is to form a matrix listing product and/or services in a vertical column, with an estimate of the importance of each in another vertical column. Across the top of the matrix a list of risk types can be listed. A matrix typically provides for multiplying an estimated importance score of an adverse event by an estimate of the probability that the event will occur.

Reliability engineering data can improve the risk assessment process by providing more accurate values for probability of product failure at given points in the product's lifecycle. Changes in reliability obviously impact the resulting risk assessment scores.

Chapter 4
B. Analysis

Risk analysis techniques such as fault tree analysis (FTA), success tree analysis (STA), risk matrix, hazard analysis, failure modes and effects analysis (FMEA), failure modes, effects, and criticality analysis (FMECA), common mode failure analysis, and system safety are used to quantify and manage risk. These techniques can be used to estimate the risk associated with various events. It then becomes possible to establish a prioritized list that will provide guidance as the root causes are addressed and mitigated or eliminated.

Risk analysis and risk management are becoming increasingly emphasized as product and processes become more complex. For example, ISO 9001:2015 *Quality Management Systems* includes the integration of risk-based thinking as part of the quality management system and decision-making processes.

1. FAULT TREE ANALYSIS (FTA)

> Use fault tree analysis (FTA) techniques to evaluate product or process failure. (Analyze)
>
> Body of Knowledge II.B.1

Fault tree analysis is a "top down" approach that is used to identify the cause, causes, or combinations of causes of failures. FTA utilizes symbols from the electronic and logic fields.

FTA can be performed without regard to the likelihood of occurrence of the event or cause, known as a *qualitative fault tree analysis*. FTA can be combined with probability techniques, failure rate analyses, and other relevant quantitative reliability data to better estimate the probability of failure and to prioritize actions, known as a *quantitative fault tree analysis*.

FTA can be used to analyze complex systems including electronic, mechanical, and software elements and the interaction and interface of subsystems.

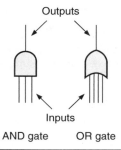

Figure 4.1 AND and OR gate symbols.

AND and OR Gates

The primary symbols used in FTA are the AND gate and the OR gate. Each of these has at least two inputs and a single output (see Figure 4.1).

The output for the AND gate occurs if and only if all inputs occur. The output for the OR gate occurs if and only if at least one input occurs.

Rectangles are typically used for labeling inputs and outputs. The failure mode being studied is sometimes referred to as the "top" or "head" event. An FTA helps the user to consider underlying causes for a failure mode and to study relationships between various failures.

Voting OR Gates

In a voting OR gate, the output occurs if and only if k or more of the input events occur, where k is specified, usually on the gate symbol (see Figure 4.2).

FTA is very useful in the early stages of design, especially in situations where the product being designed is complex and/or has interdependencies with other components. FTA provides a diagram of the complexities and helps users visualize possible corrective/preventive actions. In typical use, the analysis begins with a fault or failure that has been singled out for further study and asks, "What condition(s) could cause this failure?"

Reference Example 4.1 for the agitator function of a mixing tank.

Figure 4.2 Voting OR gate.

EXAMPLE 4.1

The failure mode being studied is the stoppage of agitation in a tank before mixing is complete. This becomes the top event. Further team study indicates that this stoppage will occur if any of the following occurs:

- Power loss
- Timer shuts off too soon
- Agitator motor failure
- Agitator power train failure

Power loss will occur if the external power source fails and the backup generator fails. The timer shuts off too soon if it is set incorrectly or has a mechanical failure. The agitator motor fails if overheated, or a fuse or capacitor fails. The agitator power train fails if both belts A and B break, or if a clutch or transmission fails. This is symbolized by the FTA diagram shown in Figure 4.3.

Figure 4.3   Fault tree analysis diagram of agitation failure.

Further analysis and assignment of probabilities can be done using metrological records and insulator testing results. At this point the design team could determine whether the wire strength, insulator design, amount of sag, and so on, are appropriate.

Reference Example 4.2 for the loss of continuity of a power transmission line.

EXAMPLE 4.2

The failure to be studied is specified as a loss of continuity between points A and B on a power transmission line. Suppose the team has determined three events, any one of which would cause the outage:

1. Wind more than 130 miles per hour (mph)

2. Wind more than 70 mph with more than one inch of ice buildup on the line

3. Insulator failure

The fault tree could be drawn as shown in Figure 4.4.

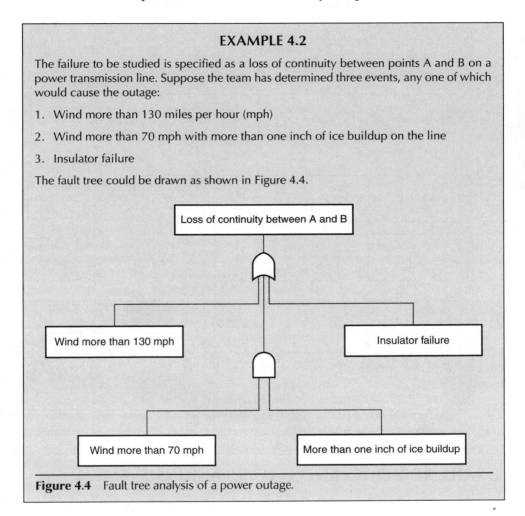

Figure 4.4 Fault tree analysis of a power outage.

Success Tree Analysis (STA)

Success tree analysis approaches a system more positively, asking "What must occur for the system to function successfully?" Reference Example 4.3 for an STA for the previous agitator function (Example 4.1).

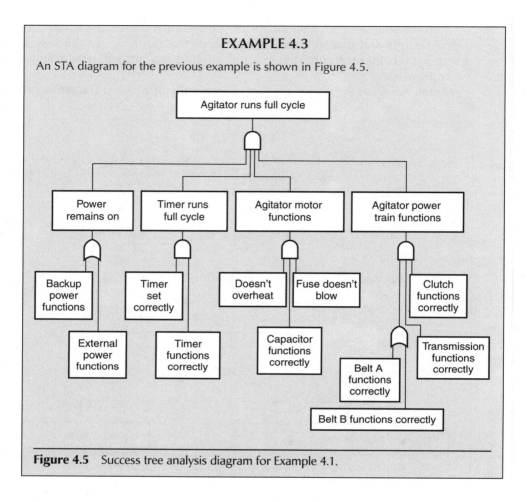

EXAMPLE 4.3

An STA diagram for the previous example is shown in Figure 4.5.

Figure 4.5   Success tree analysis diagram for Example 4.1.

Reference IEC 61025 Fault Tree Analysis for additional information on fault tree analysis.

2. FAILURE MODES AND EFFECTS ANALYSIS (FMEA)

Define and distinguish between failure mode and effects analysis (FMEA) and failure mode, effects, and criticality analysis (FMECA) and apply these techniques to systems, products, processes, and designs. (Evaluate)

Body of Knowledge II.B.2

FMEA

Failure modes and effects analysis is an engineering technique used to drive product and process reliability improvement. It is a structured analysis of a system or

Item	Potential failure mode	Effects	Sev	Causes	Occ	Current controls	Det	RPN	Recom'ed actions	Responsible and date	Action Actions taken	Results Sev	Occ	Det	RPN
A29	Pin bends	V16 sags	6	Low carbon	1	Hardness check	8	48	Change spec. to supplier	Jim Hzn. 8/21/17	Spec. chgd.	6	1	2	12

Figure 4.6   An example of the heading for an FMEA table.

Part II.B.2

subsystem to identify potential failures, the causes of these failures, and the effect these failures will have on the operation of the product or process. *Modes* are technical events that occur, whereas *effects* refers to the impact of those events.

An example of the heading for an FMEA table is shown in Figure 4.6.

The purpose of FMEA is the anticipation and mitigation of the negative effects of possible failures prior to the time they occur. It is best implemented by a broad-based team with representation from all functions that can be impacted by the results. This typically includes design, production, purchasing, quality, sales, and others as appropriate. Although customers are not always represented on the team, it behooves all team members to think as customers during FMEA activities. FMEA should be used at every stage, from product and process design through service delivery activities.

The steps of FMEA are:

1. Prior to the first team meeting, determine the product or process to be analyzed and gather associated data.

2. List all possible failure modes. It is very important that this step be given time and resources. If one or more failure modes are overlooked, the remainder of the FMEA becomes less valuable. For each failure mode ask how, where, when, and why the failure would occur and what impact the failure would have.

3. Calculate a risk priority number (RPN) for each failure mode. Do this by assigning a value. Some organizations and industries use values of 1 to 10 (see Tables 4.1 and 4.2) and some use 1 to 5 (see Tables 4.3 and 4.4) for FMEA for each of these categories:

   S = Severity: the impact this failure would have

   O = Occurrence: the probability that this failure will occur

   D = Detection: the probability that the failure would be avoided or detected

   The RPN is the product of the three numbers: RPN = S × O × D

4. Develop an action plan for the risks the team and management personnel deem most significant.

5. Document and report the results.

Table 4.1   Example of a 1–10 point FMEA rating scheme.

	Criticality/Severity
10	Dangerously high. Failure could injure the customer or an employee.
9	Extremely high. Failure would create noncompliance with federal regulations.
8	Very high. Failure renders the unit inoperable or unfit for use.
7	High. Failure causes a high degree of customer dissatisfaction.
6	Moderate. Failure results in a subsystem or partial malfunction of the product.
5	Low. Failure creates enough of a performance loss to cause the customer to complain.
4	Very low. Failure can be overcome with modifications to the customer's process or product, but there is minor performance loss.
3	Minor. Failure would create a minor nuisance to the customer, but the customer can overcome it without performance loss.
2	Very minor. Failure may not be clear to the customer, but would have minor effects on the customer's process or product.
1	None. Failure would not be noticeable to the customer and would not affect the customer's process or product.

	Occurrence
10	Very high. Failure is almost inevitable. More than one occurrence per day or a probability of more than three occurrences in 10 events ($C_{pk} < 0.33$).
9	High. Failures occur almost as often as not. One occurrence every three to four days or a probability of three occurrences in 10 events ($C_{pk} \approx 0.33$).
8	High. Repeated failures. One occurrence per week or a probability of five occurrences in 100 events ($C_{pk} \approx 0.67$).
7	High. Failures occur often. One occurrence every month or one occurrence in 100 events ($C_{pk} \approx 0.83$).
6	Moderately high. Frequent failures. One occurrence every three months or three occurrences in 1000 events ($C_{pk} \approx 1.00$).
5	Moderate. Occasional failures. One occurrence every six months to one year or five occurrences in 10,000 events ($C_{pk} \approx 1.17$).
4	Moderately low. Infrequent failures. One occurrence per year or six occurrences in 100,000 events ($C_{pk} \approx 1.33$).
3	Low. Relatively few failures. One occurrence every one to three years or six occurrences in 10 million events ($C_{pk} \approx 1.67$).
2	Low. Failures are few and far between. One occurrence every three to five years or two occurrences in one billion events ($C_{pk} \approx 2.00$).
1	Remote. Failure is unlikely. One occurrence in greater than five years or less than two occurrences in one billion events ($C_{pk} > 2.00$).

Table 4.1   Example of a 1–10 point FMEA rating scheme. (Continued)

Detection

10	Absolute uncertainty. The product is not inspected or the defect caused by failure is not detectable.
9	Very remote. Product is sampled, inspected, and released based on acceptable quality level (AQL) sampling plans.
8	Remote. Product is accepted based on no defectives in a sample.
7	Very low. Product is 100% manually inspected in the process.
6	Low. Product is 100% manually inspected using go/no-go or other mistake-proofing gauges.
5	Moderate. Some statistical process control (SPC) is used in process and product is final inspected off-line.
4	Moderately high. SPC is used and there is immediate reaction to out-of-control conditions.
3	High. An effective SPC program is in place with process capabilities (C_{pk}) greater than 1.33.
2	Very high. All product is 100% automatically inspected.
1	Almost certain. The defect is obvious or there is 100% automatic inspection with regular calibration and preventive maintenance of the inspection equipment.

Table 4.2   Example of RPN action requirements for 1–10 ranking scheme.

RPN	Risk acceptability	Action
1 to 25	Low	Although low risk, continue mitigation process as far as possible.
26 to 75	Tolerable	This risk should only be revisited in future design review if corrective action enhances the reliability or product appeal.
76 to 125	Undesirable	Risk is acceptable only if it cannot be further mitigated by organizational or technological solutions that do not reduce the clinical/functional utility of the product.
Above 125	Intolerable	Risk should be eliminated or reduced by protective measures. Justification required for risk that is accepted.

Part II.B.2

Table 4.3 Example of a 1–5 ranking scheme.

	Criticality/Severity
5	Catastrophic. Failure affects safety and/or involves noncompliance with government regulations.
4	Critical. Customer dissatisfaction due to the nature of the failure, such as unusable product. May cause disruption to future processes. Process changes to be examined.
3	Serious. Customer is made uncomfortable or is bothered by failure. May require change in controls.
2	Minor. Customer may notice a slight deterioration of the product.
1	Negligible. Customer will probably not notice the failure.

	Occurrence
5	Certain to fail (less than 1 in 100)
4	High number of failures likely (1 in 100+)
3	Occasional failure likely (1 in 1000+)
2	Few failures likely (1 in 10,000+)
1	Failure unlikely (greater than 1 in 10,000)

	Detection
5	Undetectable. Controls very likely will NOT detect the existence of a failure. Very high risk that the product will be shipped with this defect.
4	Poor. Controls likely will NOT detect the existence of a failure. Likely that the product will be shipped with the defect.
3	Moderate. Controls may detect the existence of a failure. Moderate risk that the product will be shipped with this defect.
2	Good. Controls have a good chance of detecting the existence of a failure. Low risk that the product will be shipped with this defect.
1	Excellent. Controls almost certainly will detect the existence of a failure. Remote risk that the product will be shipped with this defect.

Each of these steps requires a great deal of serious effort and time. Some guidelines for assigning the numbers required in step 3 follow (note that some standards and industries have specific guidelines for assigning values for FMEA).

Another consideration is evaluating the criticality and probability of occurrence. Table 4.5 and Table 4.6 provide example criticality and occurrence action requirements.

Once the RPN has been calculated for each failure mode, step 4 is to determine which ones should have corrective or preventive actions. If several of the RPN values are clearly grouped at the upper end, these will typically be the place to begin. When two failure modes have very similar RPN values, it is necessary to look a little deeper to determine which to work on first. One approach to prioritizing in

Table 4.4 Example of RPN action requirements for 1–5 ranking scheme.

RPN	Risk acceptability	Action
1 to 14	Low	Although low risk, continue mitigation process as far as possible.
15 to 29	Tolerable	This risk should only be revisited in future design review if corrective action enhances the reliability or product appeal.
30 to 49	Undesirable	Risk is acceptable only if it cannot be further mitigated by organizational or technological solutions that do not reduce the clinical/functional utility of the product.
Above 49	Intolerable	Risk should be eliminated or reduced by protective measures. Justification required for risk that is accepted.

Table 4.5 Example of criticality/severity and occurrence action requirements for 1–10 ranking scheme.

Occurrence		Criticality/Severity				
		Catastrophic	Critical	Serious	Minor	Negligible
		10–9	8–7	6–5	4–3	2–1
Certain	10–9	Unacceptable	Unacceptable	Unacceptable	Unacceptable	ALARP
High	8–7	Unacceptable	Unacceptable	Unacceptable	ALARP	ALARP
Occasional	6–5	Unacceptable	Unacceptable	ALARP	ALARP	ALARP
Few	4–3	Unacceptable	ALARP	ALARP	ALARP	Acceptable
Unlikely	2–1	ALARP	ALARP	ALARP	Acceptable	Acceptable

*ALARP = as low as reasonably practicable.

Table 4.6 Example of criticality/severity and occurrence action requirements for 1–5 ranking scheme.

Occurrence		Criticality/Severity				
		Catastrophic	Critical	Serious	Minor	Negligible
		5	4	3	2	1
Certain	5	Unacceptable	Unacceptable	Unacceptable	Unacceptable	ALARP
High	4	Unacceptable	Unacceptable	Unacceptable	ALARP	ALARP
Occasional	3	Unacceptable	Unacceptable	ALARP	ALARP	ALARP
Few	2	Unacceptable	ALARP	ALARP	ALARP	Acceptable
Unlikely	1	ALARP	ALARP	ALARP	Acceptable	Acceptable

*ALARP = as low as reasonably practicable.

this situation is to focus on failure modes with higher severity and then higher occurrence. Example 4.4 shows how to calculate the RPN reduction percentage.

EXAMPLE 4.4

The percentage of RPN reduction is calculated by:

$$\%RPN \text{ reduction} = \frac{RPN_i - RPN_r}{RPN_i}$$

Where:

RPN_i = Initial RPN

RPN_r = Revised RPN

The initial RPN was 36; the FMEA team was able to reduce the RPN to 24. What is the percentage of RPN reduction?

FMECA

Failure modes, effects, and criticality analysis bases the prioritization scheme of addressing failure modes on severity of the failure modes and probability of occurrence. These two variables can be used to construct a two-dimensional graph displaying each failure mode as a point. Severity can be plotted on the horizontal axis and occurrence on the vertical axis. More severe failure modes will plot farther to the right, and more probable ones farther up from the horizontal axis. If a set of failure modes is grouped in the upper right corner, those should be addressed with highest priority.

In Example 4.5, failure modes 8, 5, and 3 appear to be the place to start. The probability of occurrence and the severity scales are typically the same as those defined in the previous section.

Other tools for assessing criticality include flowcharts and block diagrams. These graphical tools display the relationships and dependencies of various subsystems and components. They are especially useful for complex systems. Users of FMECA have the option of including additional concerns such as safety, downtime, preventive maintenance, and stocks of spare parts.

FMEA and FMECA in Design

Reliability improvement will occur when design changes are incorporated into the system to eliminate a failure, reduce the probability the failure will occur, or reduce the effect the failure has on the operation of the system. A most important factor for the success of the technique is that the FMEA/FMECA is performed in time to economically make changes to the design using the results of the FMEA/FMECA effort. The FMEA/FMECA is meant to be a before-the-fact action, not an after-the-fact exercise.

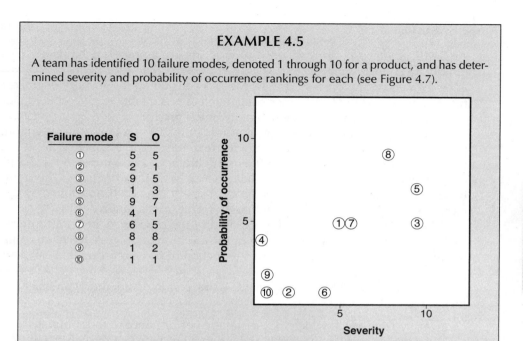

Figure 4.7 Severity and probability of occurrence rankings for 10 failure modes.

The FMEA/FMECA is changed from a qualitative analysis to a quantitative analysis by assigning values to the probability of the failure occurring, to the severity of the effect of the failure on the operation of the system, and to the probability that the system controls will detect and eliminate the failure before the design is complete.

The FMEA team should represent a broad cross-section of technical and non-technical expertise. The team should include, but not be limited to, representatives from product design, product service, manufacturing engineering, quality engineering, reliability engineering, purchasing (to represent suppliers), and marketing (to represent the customer), as well as experts in materials, thermodynamics, dynamics, and other specializations. This breadth and depth of experience for the design FMEA team is critical.

Addressing critical failure modes at the earliest possible stage of design is most cost-effective, as seen in Example 4.6.

EXAMPLE 4.6

A group is charged with producing a design for an operator cab for an existing agricultural tractor. The FMECA team identifies ultraviolet (UV) deterioration of the seal where the steering column intersects the cab wall as one of the critical failure modes. Possible preventive actions include:

- Protection of the seal from UV exposure
- Using UV-resistant seal material
- Designing the steering linkage so the seal isn't needed

It is likely that none of these solutions would be available once the design has been finalized.

Types of FMEA

An FMEA can be performed on a product or on a process. The *design FMEA* (DFMEA) is performed on the design or product. The *process FMEA* (PFMEA) is performed on the process. The DFMEA is considered a reliability engineering function while the PFMEA is often considered to be a quality engineering function. Both activities will improve the reliability of the product.

The DFMEA will document weaknesses in the design that can cause failures to occur during product use. A change made to the design because of the DFMEA will reduce the failure rate during the useful life period and increase the duration of the useful life by eliminating or delaying early wear-out failures. The result is improved reliability of the product. Product safety can also be improved by elimination of any unsafe conditions that might result from a failure.

The PFMEA will uncover the potential of the process to add nonconformity to the product. Process improvement or the addition of process detection controls because of the PFMEA will result in a reduction of process errors that can lead to product early life failures.

Other types of FMEA and FMECA are coming into more prevalent use, including:

- *System FMEA*, which focuses on the performance of the complete system and the interfaces and interactions between the subsystems and elements that make up the system

- *Machinery and equipment FMEA*, which focuses on the machinery and equipment used in the production system and impacts production, productivity, and overall equipment effectiveness

- *Software FMEA*, which focuses on the software, modules, and subroutines themselves as well as the interface between software and hardware and the interface between software and user

Several FMEA and FMECA models exist for various organizations and industries; therefore, using a FMEA/FMECA, its format, and its scoring for a particular effort should be determined before making any design changes or before any new process begins.

3. COMMON MODE FAILURE ANALYSIS

> Describe common mode failure (also known as common cause failure) and how it affects risk. (Understand)
>
> Body of Knowledge II.B.3

To avoid confusion it is necessary to distinguish common cause failure from common cause variation as applied to control charts. A *common cause failure* (CCF) occurs when two or more components fail as a result of a shared cause.

Recognizing and mitigating common cause failure is a vital part of designing for reliability since eliminating or mitigating the causes of failure is a primary aim of reliability efforts. Whether performing FTA, hazard analysis, FMEA, or a risk matrix, consider if there exist common causes that could result in multiple faults, hazards, or failures and place special emphasis on eliminating these common causes, since their elimination will often produce the greatest improvement in reliability for the effort.

Fault tree analysis is especially susceptible to missing the total impact of a common cause since FTA is often performed with a very narrow focus. For example, if the fault being studied is a sudden rise in engine compartment temperature, a fault tree analysis that only considers the impact of this event on the braking system would be too narrow. Other functions could be impaired by the common cause, including the engine control computer, electronic controls, wiring, power steering system, and so on. So, a single cause might generate multiple faults and failures.

Another caution in considering common mode failures is with redundant systems, whereby one cause can lead to the failure of otherwise redundant elements, leading to system failure. For example, a sudden rise in engine compartment temperature could cause the failure of redundant circuits and components in the engine control computer. Or a bent or damaged conduit could cause the failure of redundant wiring that is routed through the same conduit.

Part II.B.4

4. HAZARD ANALYSIS

> Describe how hazard analysis informs the development process, and how information obtained as a result of the hazard analysis is used by the reliability engineer. (Understand)
>
> Body of Knowledge II.B.4

A *hazard* is a condition, event, or circumstance that could lead to or contribute to an unplanned or undesirable event. The risk of the hazard is often classified as high risk, moderate risk, or low risk.

Hazard analysis is a method to assess risk based on the severity of the risk and the likelihood of occurrence of the risk. Hazard analysis is often used early in development to begin to assess risk.

Three fundamental questions are asked in a hazard analysis:

1. What might go wrong? The risk.

2. What is the probability that it will go wrong? The likelihood.

3. What are the consequences? The severity.

The hazard is then the combination of the likelihood and severity of the risk. Figure 4.8 shows a typical hazard analysis risk matrix, with risk scoring and color coding.

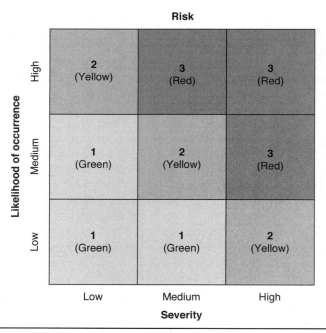

Figure 4.8   Hazard analysis risk matrix.

Reference Example 4.7 for a hazard analysis of a fuel pumping mechanism.

EXAMPLE 4.7				
Risk event	**Severity**	**Likelihood**	**Risk**	**Risk control**
Fuel tank overfill with no spillage	Low: Pump lever disengaged before overfill	Low: Low occurrence of pump lever disengagement failure	1 (Green)	Pump venturi mechanism disengages pump lever
Fuel tank overfill with minor spillage	Medium: Pump lever disengaged after overfill with minor fuel spillage	Low: Low occurrence of pump lever disengagement failure	1 (Green)	Pump venturi mechanism disengages pump lever
Fuel tank overfill with major spillage	High: Pump lever not disengaged causing major fuel spillage	Low: Low occurrence of pump lever disengagement failure	2 (Yellow)	Pump venturi mechanism disengages pump lever Monthly inspection and cleaning of pump venturi mechanism Master pump shutoff device

Note that hazard analysis is similar to FMEA except that hazard analysis typically does not include detection in the analysis. Hazard analysis may be used as an input to the FMEA.

Several hazard analysis models exist for various organizations and industries; therefore, using a hazard analysis, its format, and its scoring for a particular effort should be determined beforehand. A notable application of hazard analysis is the Food and Drug Administration (FDA) 21 CFR Part 120 Hazard Analysis and Critical Control Point (HACCP) System.

5. RISK MATRIX

Describe how risk matrices are used in the assessment of risk in regard to likelihood and severity. (Understand)

Body of Knowledge II.B.5

The risk matrix approach is common in reliability engineering and other efforts that involve the identification, classification, and prioritization of risk. Several reliability-specific techniques such as hazard analysis, FMEA, and FMECA are customized techniques in the use of a risk matrix.

A common risk matrix approach is to list potential risks and evaluate their severity and their likelihood to then determine the risk. Section 4 provides more detail on this approach.

Another common risk matrix approach is to create a matrix listing product and/or services in a vertical column, with an estimate of the importance of each in another vertical column. Across the top of the matrix a list of risk types can be listed. A matrix such as that, shown in Figure 4.9, typically provides for

	Importance	Risk types																			
		Technical			Scheduling				Safety	Financial		Regulatory				Supplier			Materials			Etc.
		A	B	C	A	B	C	D	A	B	A	B	C	A	B	C	D	A	B	C	A	B	C	
Product 1																								
Product 2																								
Product 3																								
Service 1																								
Service 2																								

Figure 4.9   Example of risk assessment matrix.

multiplying an estimated importance score of an adverse event by an estimate of the probability that the event will occur.

Reliability data can improve the risk assessment process by providing more accurate values for probability of failure at given points in the lifecycle. Changes in reliability obviously impact the resulting risk assessment scores. The risk matrix helps to prioritize risk vulnerabilities.

Many risk matrix models exist for various organizations and industries; therefore, using a risk matrix, its format, and its scoring for a particular effort should be determined beforehand.

6. SYSTEM SAFETY

> Identify safety-related issues by analyzing customer feedback, design data, field data, and other information. Prioritize safety concerns, and identify steps that will minimize the improper use of equipment, products, or processes. (Evaluate)
>
> Body of Knowledge II.B.6

A typical system safety program (see Figure 4.10) has eight elements and three key functions:

1. *Identification of safety hazards.* The reliability engineer, working with the safety organization to achieve a safe product, must be innovative and diligent in the discovery of all possible ways that any failure, combination of failures, or other combination of circumstances would present a safety hazard to personnel. Hazard analysis can be used to achieve this objective. Warranty data and other forms of customer feedback should also be analyzed. Product testing reports should include safety issues that may have emerged. All available product data should be searched for occurrence of safety hazards. In addition, if databases for similar products are available, these should also be studied.

2. *Risk analysis.* The standard analysis techniques such as risk matrix, FTA, hazard analysis, and FMEA/FMECA can be employed in risk analysis for system safety. These techniques can be used to estimate the risk associated with various events. It then becomes possible to establish a prioritized list that will provide guidance as the root causes are attacked and resolved.

3. *Corrective and preventive action* should be employed for any risk analysis technique in general. In the case of safety hazards, there is the additional urgency to avoid harm to personnel. In cases in which flaws in products or processes permit hazardous conditions to occur, design and process changes should be initiated.

Figure 4.10 Typical system safety program.

As Low As Reasonably Practicable (ALARP)

As low as reasonably practicable (ALARP) is a principle used in system safety whereby risk is reduced as far as reasonably practicable. For a risk to be determined to be ALARP, it must be demonstrated that the cost involved in reducing the risk further would be grossly disproportionate to the benefit gained.

Human Error and Mistake-Proofing

It is always necessary to consider human error. From one perspective, human error occurs because no system is in place to prevent it. In other words, the onus is on the product/process design community to reduce or eliminate errors. Procedures for preventing/mitigating human error are variously called mistake-proofing, poka-yoke, and zero quality control (ZQC). Human error tends to fall into the following categories: misunderstanding, misidentification, inexperience, inattention, and lack of standards. The ideal way to deal with human mistakes is to incorporate design elements that will prevent them from occurring or prevent their occurrence from causing defects.

Often, the best way to prevent reoccurrence of human error is to ask the person who made the error, "How can we design a system that will make that error impossible to occur?"

Principal types of mistake-proofing techniques include:

- *Physical barriers to errors.* (The round shaft won't fit through the square hole.)

- *Visual reminders.* (A photograph of correct and incorrect results is better than a note written on a print or a paragraph of text.)

- *Use of automated equipment.* (The conveyor will stop if the microswitch detects an error.)

- *Standardizing.* (The operator takes the same action on a family of parts.)

Continuous Effort

Activity must be continuous in the elements of the system safety program. As the higher-priority hazards are corrected/prevented, action can focus on lower-priority items.

Several system safety approaches exist for various organizations and industries; therefore, the approach used for system safety for a particular effort should be determined beforehand.

Chapter 5
C. Mitigation

Identify appropriate risk mitigation (treatment) plans
to include controls that will minimize risk and
subsequent impact in terms of safety, liability, and
regulatory compliance. (Evaluate)

Body of Knowledge II.C

Reliability analysis provides estimates of the probability of failure. The reliability engineer must go beyond these calculations and examine the consequences of failure, including safety. These consequences typically represent costs to the customer. The customer finds ways of sharing these costs with the producer through the warranty system, loss of business, decrease in reputation, or the civil litigation system. Therefore, an important reliability function is the anticipation of possible failures and the establishment of reliability acceptance goals that will limit their occurrence and consequent costs.

The acceptance criteria associated with these goals generally fall into three categories:

- *Functional requirements* (such as 20 gallons per minute for a pump)

- *Environmental requirements* (such as temperature, radiation, pH)

- *Time requirements* (such as failure rate during useful life, time elapsed before wear-out phase begins)

Once component, product, and system reliability goals have been set, a testing protocol should be implemented to provide validation that these goals will impact the failure rates and the associated consequences as planned. These reliability goals typically impose specifications on the product. In anticipation of the start of production, reliability engineers use further testing procedures to provide *verification* that these specifications are being met.

STRATEGIES TO MINIMIZE RISK

Once reliability goals have been set and the risks identified, the reliability engineer must consider the risk–benefit analysis and determine the best strategies to minimize the associated risks. Manuele (2003) provides a "Safety Decision Hierarchy" that is readily applied to ensure safety, liability, and regulatory compliance. Manuele suggests using the following activities in the order presented:

1. Eliminate hazards and risks through system design and redesign

2. Reduce risks by substituting less hazardous methods or materials

3. Incorporate safety devices (fixed guards, interlocks)

4. Provide warning systems (lights, buzzers, labels)

5. Apply administrative controls (work methods, training, etc.)

6. Provide personal protective equipment

A graphic representation of the risk reduction activities is presented in Figure 5.1.

PRODUCT IMPROVEMENT

Product improvement often means redesigning components. The integration of new components requires an orderly procedure if genuine improvement is to occur. The relatively short product lifetimes in areas such as electronics and software has caused increased emphasis on obsolescence management. The following paragraphs identify ways to reduce the risks associated with obsolescence and redesigned components.

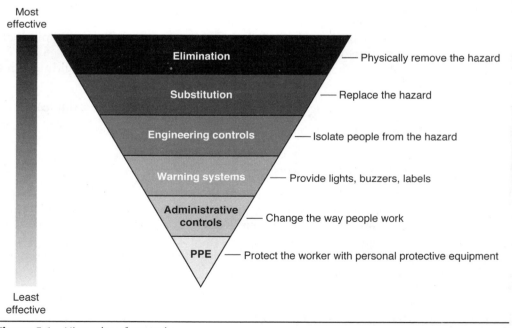

Figure 5.1   Hierarchy of controls.

Source: Adapted from https://www.cdc.gov/niosh/topics/noise/images/HOC.png.

END OF LIFE CONSIDERATIONS

It is inevitable that components or entire systems will eventually become obsolete due to the unavailability of replacement parts or changes in technology. Components and systems should document end of life considerations during the design and development phase to ensure there is a documented plan to address these considerations.

Obsolescence from the Producer's Viewpoint

When any component of a system is changed, the result is a new system, which must be tested to verify that it performs as specified. In many cases, qualifying the component independently from the system will miss undesirable interactions with other components. Judgment is required, of course, in deciding how much of the new system must be requalified. Redesign of a pivot pin in a vehicle door latch linkage does not require requalification of an entire vehicle, for example. It is necessary, however, that the new latch system be tested not only on a lab bench but also on vehicles in their designed environment.

Once the decision has been made to make the change, the disposition of obsolete parts must be managed. In some cases the change occurs when the supply of obsolete parts has been exhausted. If not, the inventory of obsolete parts must be segregated to prevent its use in the production process.

The repair and maintenance of parts in the field is another consideration. Will the new design be installed, or are the obsolete parts to be used?

Obsolescence from the Customer's Viewpoint

What strategies can a customer use when an environment of continuous improvement means component changes? The warranty documents the responsibility that the supplier has to the customer. Some provisions that are useful include:

- Commitment to support the product with replacement parts for a stated period of time.

- Lifetime buy, which is the practice of providing the buyer with enough replacement parts to cover the needs for the lifetime of the system. This option requires a careful forecasting methodology.

- Backwards compatibility, guaranteeing that new or redesigned components will function within the existing system.

Part II.C

Part III

Probability and Statistics for Reliability

Part III

Chapter 6
A. Basic Concepts

1. BASIC STATISTICS

> Define various basic statistical terms (e.g., population, parameter, statistic, sample, the central limit theorem, parametric and non-parametric), and compute and interpret their values. (Analyze)
>
> Body of Knowledge III.A.1

The *probability* that a particular event occurs is a number between 0 and 1 inclusive. For example, if a lot consisting of 100 parts has four defectives, we would say that the probability of randomly drawing a defective is 0.04, or 4%.

The word *random* implies that each part has an equal chance of being selected. If the lot had no defectives, the probability would be zero or 0%. If the lot had 100 defectives, the probability would be 1 or 100%.

Statisticians use the word *mean* in place of the word average. In the case of discrete values, the mean is also called the expected value or expectation. For the set of values $x_1, x_2, \ldots x_n$ the formula for the mean is

$$\frac{\sum x_i}{n}$$

The mean is called a *measure of central tendency*. The symbol most often used for the mean is $\bar{x}$ pronounced "x-bar." The median and mode are other measures of central tendency. The *median* is the middle number when the numbers are sorted by size. For example, the median of a sorted set of 11 values is the sixth from the end. If there is an even number of values, the median is the mean of the two middle values. The *mode* is the number in the list that appears most frequently.

There are three frequently used *measures of dispersion*. The *range* of a set of numbers is obtained by subtracting the smallest value from the largest value. One of the disadvantages of using the range as a measure of dispersion is that it uses only two of the values in the data set, the largest and the smallest. If the data set is large, the range does not make use of much of the information contained in the data. For this and other reasons, the *standard deviation* is frequently used to measure dispersion. The standard deviation can be found by entering the values of the data set into a calculator that has a standard deviation key. See the calculator manual for the appropriate steps.

Statistics texts sometimes refer to the *sample variance*, which has the rather ugly formula

$$\text{Sample variance} = \frac{\Sigma(x - \bar{x})^2}{n - 1}$$

One disadvantage of the variance is that, as the formula indicates, it is measured in units that are the square of the units of the original data set. That is, if the *x*-values are in inches, the variance is in square inches. If the *x*-values are in degrees Celsius, the variance is in square degrees Celsius, whatever that may be. For many applications it is useful to use a measure of dispersion that is in the same units as the original data. For this reason, the preferred measure of dispersion is the square root of the variance, which is called the *sample standard deviation*. Its formula is

$$\text{Sample standard deviation} = s = \sqrt{\frac{\Sigma(x - \bar{x})^2}{n - 1}}$$

The sample standard deviation is used to estimate the standard deviation of the data set by using a sample from that data set. In some situations it may be possible to use the entire data set rather than a sample. Statisticians refer to the entire data set as a *population*, and its standard deviation is called the *population standard deviation*, symbolized by the lowercase Greek sigma, σ. It is common to use capital N to refer to the number of values in the population. The only difference in the formula is that the divisor in the fraction is N rather than $n - 1$:

$$\text{Population standard deviation} = \sigma = \sqrt{\frac{\Sigma(x - \mu)^2}{N}}$$

where μ = population mean.

When using the standard deviation function on a calculator, care should be taken to use the appropriate key. Unfortunately, there is not universal labeling among calculator manufacturers. Some label the sample standard deviation key s_{n-1} and the population standard deviation key s_n, while others use S_x and s_x. Try entering the values 2, 7, 9, and 2 in a calculator and verify that the sample standard deviation rounds to 3.6 and the population standard deviation rounds to 3.1. One of the uses of the standard deviation is to compare the amount of dispersion for two data sets. It also has applications in statistical inference.

To review the notation, in a statistical study the *population* is defined as the collection of all individuals, items, or data under consideration. The part of the population from which information is collected is called the *sample*. A *random sample* is chosen by selecting units for a sample in such a manner that all combinations of units under consideration have an equal or ascertainable chance of being selected as the sample. For example, if 1500 citizens are randomly selected from the United States and their heights are measured, the *population* would be all US citizens, and the *sample*, in this case, a *random sample*, would be the 1500 who were selected. If the mean of those 1500 heights is 64.29, the conclusion is that the *sample mean* is 64.29.

The value 64.29 is called a *statistic*, which is defined as a descriptive measure of a sample. The next step is to infer the mean height of the population, which is

Part III.A.1

likely to be around 64.29. The actual population mean is called a *parameter*, which is defined as a descriptive measure of a population. So, it can be said that a statistic is an estimated value of a parameter.

Different symbols are used to denote parameters and statistics. Parameters are usually denoted by Greek letters, and statistics are usually denoted by Latin letters. For instance, the Greek letter mu (μ) is used for the population mean and the Latin letter x with a bar above it ($\bar{x}$), pronounced "x-bar," is used for the sample mean.

The Central Limit Theorem

A frequent question is the validity of $\bar{x}$ control charts when the population is not normal. The control chart operates under the assumption that the region bounded by ± 3 contains 99.7% of the points from a stable process. This assumes that the distribution of the points is normal. An important statistical principle called the *central limit theorem* comes to the rescue. It states that:

> The distribution of sample averages is approximately normal even if the population from which the sample is drawn is not normally distributed. The approximation improves as the sample size increases.

Because the $\bar{x}$ chart plots averages, the central limit theorem says that normality is (approximately) guaranteed. This theorem should be kept in mind when selecting the sample size for $\bar{x}$ charts. However, a sample size of less than five is appropriate only if the population is normal.

The central limit theorem supports three-sigma control limits for $\bar{x}$ charts, but the principal reason for plotting averages rather than individual values is that the average is more sensitive to process shifts than the individual value. In other words, given a shift in the process average, the $\bar{x}$ chart is more likely to detect it than the individuals chart.

Parametric vs. Non-Parametric Statistics

Parametric statistics assume that sample data come from a population that follows a known probability distribution. Non-parametric statistics sample data come from an unknown population.

Parametric statistics provide more information about the population than non-parametric statistics. When the assumptions (about the distribution) are correct, parametric methods will produce more accurate and precise estimates than non-parametric methods.

Hypotheses Testing

The *hypothesis test*, another tool used in inferential statistics, is closely related to confidence intervals. When testing hypotheses, we usually work with small samples from large populations. Because of the uncertainties of dealing with sample statistics, decision errors are possible.

There are two types of errors: type I errors and type II errors. A *type I error* occurs when the null hypothesis is rejected when it is, in fact, true. In most tests of hypotheses, the risk of committing a type I error (known as the alpha [α] risk) is stated in advance along with the sample size to be used (see Table 6.1). A *type II error*

Table 6.1 Hypothesis truth table.

Decision on null hypothesis	Null hypothesis is true	Null hypothesis is false
Accept (fail to reject)	Correct decision probability = $1 - \alpha$	Type II error probability = β
Moderate	Type I error probability = α	Correct decision probability = $1 - \beta$

occurs when the null hypothesis is accepted when it is false. If the means of two processes are, in fact, different, and we accept the hypothesis that they are equal, we have committed a type II error. The risk associated with type II errors is referred to as the beta (β) risk. This risk is different for every alternative hypothesis and is usually unknown except for specific values of the alternative hypothesis (see Table 6.1).

An α risk of 0.10 means that, in the long run, the null hypothesis will be rejected when it is true (type I error) 10 times out of a hundred; an α risk of 0.05 means that, in the long run, the null hypothesis will be rejected when it is true (type I error) five times out of a hundred; and an α risk of 0.01 means that, in the long run, the null hypothesis will be rejected when it is true (type I error) one time out of a hundred, and so on.

Type I and type II errors cannot occur at the same time. Type I error can happen only if H_0 is true, and type II error can happen only when H_0 is false. If the probability of type I error is high, then the probability of type II error is low.

The statistical power of a test is another consideration when conducting tests of hypotheses. The power of a test is $1 - \beta$, and is expressed as a probability ranging from 0 to 1. The higher the power, the more sensitive the test is in detecting differences where differences exist between the hypothesized parameter and its true value. Increasing the sample size, reducing the variance, increasing the effect size index, or decreasing the α level will increase the statistical power.

Tests of hypotheses and the apportionment of the risk usually fall into two categories: *one-tailed tests*, where all of the risk is in a single tail of the distribution, and *two-tailed tests*, where the risk is evenly split between the two tails of the distribution. When we conduct tests of hypotheses, we must calculate a value and compare it to a critical value from a reference table. It is possible we can fail to reject the the upper-tailed test (Figure 6.1), lower-tailed test (Figure 6.2), and double-tailed test (Figure 6.3) null hypotheses.

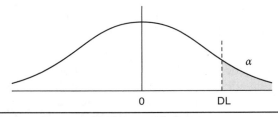

Figure 6.1 Representation of a one–tailed (upper–tailed) test.

Source: M. A. Durivage, *Practical Engineering, Process, and Reliability Statistics* (Milwaukee, WI: ASQ Quality Press, 2014). Used with permission.

Part III.A.1

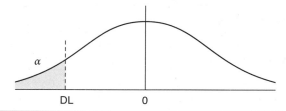

Figure 6.2 Representation of a one–tailed (lower–tailed) test.

Source: M. A. Durivage, *Practical Engineering, Process, and Reliability Statistics* (Milwaukee, WI: ASQ Quality Press, 2014). Used with permission.

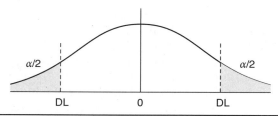

Figure 6.3 Representation of a two–tailed test.

Source: M. A. Durivage, *Practical Engineering, Process, and Reliability Statistics* (Milwaukee, WI: ASQ Quality Press, 2014). Used with permission.

Steps in Hypothesis Testing

Textbooks tend to treat hypothesis tests as somewhat more formal procedures. Many list seven or eight steps to be followed for each type of test. Although not all books agree on the steps themselves, this list is fairly generic:

1. Determine that the conditions or assumptions required for the test are met.

2. State the null and alternative hypotheses (H_0 and H_a) and determine whether it is a one-tailed or two-tailed test.

3. Determine the α value. This is similar to the use of α in confidence intervals. In hypothesis testing jargon, the value of α is referred to as the *significance level*.

4. Determine the critical values. These are typically found in a table such as the Z, t, or χ^2 tables. Use these values to define the reject region.

5. Calculate the test statistic. Each hypothesis test type has a formula for the test statistic. Some of the inputs to the formulas come from the sample data.

6. Determine whether the null hypothesis should be rejected. If the value of the test statistic is in the reject region, then the null hypothesis is rejected and the alternative hypothesis is accepted. If the value of the test statistic does not fall in the reject region, the null hypothesis is not rejected.

7. State the conclusion in terms of the original problem.

Hypothesis Tests for Means

The hypothesis test usually studied first is the one-sample z-test for population mean. Its steps are:

1. Conditions:

    a. Normal population or large sample ($n \geq 30$)

    b. σ known

2. $H_0: \mu = \mu_0$ and $H_a: \mu \neq \mu_0$ or $\mu < \mu_0$ or $\mu > \mu_0$

    This is a two-tailed test when H_a has the $\neq$ sign. It is a left-tailed test when H_a has the $<$ sign, and a right-tailed test when H_a has the $>$ sign.

3. Determine the α value.

4. Determine the critical values:

    a. For a two-tailed test, use a Z-table to find the value that has an area of $\alpha/2$ to its right. This value and its negative are the two critical values. The reject region is the area to the right of the positive value and the area to the left of the negative value.

    b. For a left-tailed test, use a Z-table to find the value that has an area of α to its right. The negative of this value is the critical value. The reject region is the area to the left of the negative value.

    c. For a right-tailed test, use a Z-table to find the value that has an area of α to its right. This value is the critical value. The reject region is the area to the right of the positive value.

5. Calculate the test statistic:

$$z = (\bar{x} - \mu_0)\frac{\sqrt{n}}{\sigma}$$

6. If the test statistic is in the reject region, reject H_0. Otherwise, do not reject H_0.

7. State the conclusion in terms of the problem.

In many applications, the population standard deviation is not known. As with the confidence interval, the appropriate distribution is found in the t-table. The procedure is the same as the previous seven steps, except for steps 1, 4, and 5, which will now read:

1. Condition: population is normally distributed or $n \geq 30$.

4. The critical values are obtained from the t-table using degrees of freedom of $n - 1$.

5. The formula for the test statistic is

$$t = (\bar{x} - \mu_0)\frac{\sqrt{n}}{s}$$

where s is the sample standard deviation.

This hypothesis test is referred to as the *t*-test for one population mean. It is important to note here that the fact that the null hypothesis is not rejected does not mean it is true. The conclusion is that the probability that it is true is less than 90%.

EXAMPLE 6.1

A vendor claims that the average weight of a shipment of parts is 1.84. The customer randomly chooses 64 parts and finds that the sample has an average weight of 1.88. Suppose that the standard deviation of the population is known to be 0.03. Should the customer reject the lot? Assume the customer wants to be 95% confident that the supplier's claim is incorrect before he rejects.

1. Conditions (a) and (b) are met.

2. H_0: $\mu = 1.84$ and H_a: $\mu \neq 1.84$. This is a two-tailed test.

3. From the problem, $\alpha = 0.05$.

4. Critical values are the *z*-value that has 0.025 to its right and the negative of this value. These values are 1.96 and –1.96. The reject region consists of the area to the right of 1.96 and the area to the left of –1.96.

5. $z = (1.88 - 1.84)\dfrac{\sqrt{64}}{0.03} \approx 10.7$

6. Since 10.7 is in the reject region, H_0 is rejected.

7. At the 0.05 significance level, the data suggest that the vendor's assertion that the average weight is 1.84 is false.

EXAMPLE 6.2

A vendor claims that the average weight of a shipment of parts is 1.84. The customer randomly chooses 64 parts and finds that the sample has an average of 1.88 and standard deviation of 0.03. Should the customer reject the lot? Assume the customer wants to be 95% confident that the supplier's claim is incorrect before he rejects. (This is the same as the last example, except that 0.03 is the sample standard deviation rather than the population standard deviation.)

1. Condition is met.

2. H_0: $\mu = 1.84$ and H_a: $\mu \neq 1.84$. This is a two-tailed test.

3. From the problem, $\alpha = 0.05$.

4. The positive critical value would be in row 63 of the 0.025 column of the *t*-table. Since the table has no row 63, it is appropriate to use the more conservative row 60. This value is 2.000. The other critical value is –2.000. The reject region consists of the area to the right of 2.000 and the area to the left of –2.000.

5. $t = (1.88 - 1.84)\dfrac{\sqrt{64}}{0.03} \approx 10.7$

6. Since 10.7 is in the reject region, H_0 is rejected.

7. At the 0.05 significance level, the data suggest that the vendor's assertion that the average weight is 1.84 is false.

EXAMPLE 6.3

A cut-off saw has been producing parts with a mean length of 4.125. A new blade is installed, and we want to know whether the mean has decreased. We select a random sample of 20, measure the length of each part, and find that the average length is 4.123 and the sample standard deviation is 0.008. Assume that the population is normally distributed. Use a significance level of 0.10 to determine whether the mean length has decreased.

Since the population standard deviation is unknown, the t-test will be used.

1. Condition is met.

2. $H_0: \mu = 4.125$ and $H_a: \mu < 4.125$. This is a left-tailed test.

3. From the problem, $\alpha = 0.10$.

4. The positive critical value is in the 19th row of the 0.10 column of the t-table. This value is 1.328. The critical value is –1.328. The reject region consists of the area to the left of –1.328.

5. $t = (4.123 - 4.125)\dfrac{\sqrt{20}}{0.008} \approx -1.1$

6. Since –1.1 is not in the reject region, H_0 is not rejected.

7. At the 0.10 significance level, the data indicate that the average wall thickness of the product from vendor 1 is larger than the average wall thickness of the product from vendor 2.

Hypothesis Tests for Means of Two Populations

The next two hypothesis tests are for means of two populations. The procedure for the non-pooled t-test for two population means is:

1. Conditions:

   a. Normal populations or large samples ($n \geq 30$)

   b. Independent samples (that is, each of the pairs of sets of samples is equally likely to be selected)

2. $H_0: \mu_1 = \mu_2$ and $H_a: \mu_1 \neq \mu_2$ or $\mu_1 < \mu_2$ or $\mu_1 > \mu_2$

   This is a two-tailed test when H_a has the $\neq$ sign. It is a left-tailed test when H_a has the $<$ sign and a right-tailed test when H_a has the $>$ sign.

3. Determine the α value.

4. Determine the critical values.

   a. For a two-tailed test, use a t-table to find the value that has an area of $\alpha/2$ to its right. This value and its negative are the two critical values. The reject region is the area to the right of the positive value and the area to the left of the negative value.

   b. For a left-tailed test, use a t-table to find the value that has an area of α to its right. The negative of this value is the critical value. The reject region is the area to the left of the negative value.

Part III.A.1

c. For a right-tailed test, use a t-table to find the value that has an area of α to its right. This value is the critical value. The reject region is the area to the right of the positive value. The bad news here is that the degrees of freedom, instead of being $n - 1$, is obtained from the formulas

$$a_1 = \frac{s_1^2}{n_1} \qquad a_2 = \frac{s_2^2}{n_2}$$

where s_1 is the standard deviation of the sample from population 1, n_1 is the number of elements in the sample from population 1, and s_2 and n_2 are those from population 2, and

$$\text{Degrees of freedom} = \frac{\left(a_1 + a_2\right)^2}{\left[\dfrac{a_1^2}{n_1 - 1} + \dfrac{a_2^2}{n_2 - 1}\right]}$$

rounded down to the nearest whole number.

5. Calculate the test statistic:

$$t = \left(\overline{x}_1 - \overline{x}_2\right) / \sqrt{a_1 + a_2}$$

6. If the test statistic is in the reject region, reject H_0. Otherwise, do not reject H_0.

7. State the conclusion in terms of the problem.

EXAMPLE 6.4

Two vendors of a valve diaphragm present significantly different cost quotations. The wall thickness is the critical quality characteristic. Use the following data to determine whether the average thickness of the products from vendor 1 is greater than that from vendor 2. Test at the 0.10 significance level. Assume the populations are normally distributed and that the samples are independent.

Wall thickness measurements are:

Vendor 1:	86	82	91	88	89	85	88	90	84	87	88	83	84	89
Vendor 2:	79	78	82	85	77	86	84	78	80	82	79	76		

Solution:

Analysis of the data on a scientific calculator shows that

$$\overline{x}_1 = 86.7, \overline{x}_2 = 80.5, s_1 = 2.76, s_2 = 3.26, n_1 = 14, \text{ and } n_2 = 12.$$

1. Conditions are met.

2. $H_0: \mu_1 = \mu_2$ and $H_a: \mu_1 > \mu_2$. This is a right-tailed test.

3. $\alpha = 0.10$.

$$a_1 = \frac{2.76^2}{14} = 0.54 \quad a_2 = \frac{3.26^2}{12} = 0.89$$

$$df \approx \frac{(0.54 + 0.89)^2}{\left(\frac{0.54^2}{13} + \frac{0.89^2}{11}\right)} = \frac{2.04}{0.09} \approx 22 \text{ (when rounded down)}$$

4. The critical value is found in the 22nd row of the $t_{0.10}$ column of the t-table. This value is 1.321. The reject region is the area to the right of 1.321.

5. $t = \frac{(86.7 - 80.5)}{\sqrt{0.54 + 0.89}} = 5.2$

6. Reject H_0 since the value of the test statistic is in the reject region.

7. At the 0.10 significance level, the data indicate that the average wall thickness of the product from vendor 1 is larger than the average wall thickness of the product from vendor 2.

You may be wondering why step 7 is phrased ". . . the data indicate . . ." rather than something like "the data prove." The 0.10 significance level means that there is a 10% chance that a rejected null hypothesis is actually true. Rejecting a true null hypothesis is referred to as a *type I error*, denoted by α, and is sometimes called the *producer's risk* because in lot sampling plans it is the probability that the plan will reject a good lot. Failing to reject a false hypothesis is called a *type II error* and is sometimes referred to as the *consumer's risk*. The probability of type II error is denoted β.

Paired-Comparison Tests

The next hypothesis test is called the *paired t-test for two population means*. Each pair in a paired sample consists of a member of one population and that member's corresponding member in the other population. Suppose, for instance, that we want to determine if a gasoline additive increases average mileage in the population consisting of several hundred company cars of various types and vintage.

One approach would be to randomly select 10 vehicles and record mileages using gasoline without the additive, and randomly select another 10 vehicles and record mileages using gasoline with the additive. These two samples could be tested using the previous hypothesis test (assuming the populations are normally distributed). If the additive causes a large increase in average mileage, this procedure would likely reject the null hypothesis that the averages are equal. If the additive causes a small increase in average mileage, the test might not detect it because of the large variation between cars. Thus, the test might fail to reject the null hypothesis even though it is false. Statisticians would say the test lacks *sensitivity*.

An alternate approach has probably already occurred to you: choose 10 cars at random, record their mileages using gas without the additive, then use gas with the additive in those same 10 cars. This arrangement reduces the sampling variation encountered when two samples of 10 are used. The approach is called the *paired sample* method and provides a very powerful test when it can be used. Sometimes it is impractical to use. Suppose we need to know whether the average effect of a particular drug is different for people with type A blood than for people with type B. One possible approach would be to select 10 type A people and measure the effects of the drug on them, then drain their blood and refill them with type B and again measure the effects of the drug. One might conclude that the drug was fatal for the population having type B blood.

The procedure for the paired *t*-test for two population means is:

1. Conditions:

   a. Paired sample

   b. Large sample or differences are normally distributed

2. $H_0: \mu_1 = \mu_2$ and $H_a: \mu_1 \neq \mu_2$ or $\mu_1 < \mu_2$ or $\mu_1 > \mu_2$

   This is a two-tailed test when H_a has the $\neq$ sign, a left-tailed test when H_a has the $<$ sign, and a right-tailed test when H_a has the $>$ sign.

3. Determine α.

4. Find the critical value(s) from the *t*-table using degrees of freedom = $n - 1$.

5. Calculate the test statistic:

   a. Let d_1 be the difference within the first element of the sample.

   b. Let d_2 be the difference within the second element of the sample, and so on.

   c. Find the average $\bar{d}$ and standard deviation s_d of these d values.

   d. The test statistic is

$$t = \bar{d}\,\frac{\sqrt{n}}{s_d}$$

6. If the test statistic is in the reject region, reject H_0. Otherwise, do not reject H_0.

7. State the conclusion in terms of the problem.

EXAMPLE 6.5

For the gasoline additive problem discussed previously, suppose the data are:

Vehicle #:	1	2	3	4	5	6	7	8	9	10
mpg with additive:	21	23	20	20	27	18	22	19	36	25
mpg without additive:	20	20	21	18	24	17	22	18	37	20

Do the data indicate that the additive increases average gas mileage at the 0.05 significance level? Assume that the differences are normally distributed.

1. Conditions are met.

2. $H_0: \mu_1 = \mu_2$ and $H_a: \mu_1 > \mu_2$. This is a right-tailed test.

3. $\alpha = 0.05$.

4. Since df $= 10 - 1$, the critical value is in the ninth row of the 0.05 column of the t-table. This value is 1.833.

5. Use the following table to get the data for the test statistic formula:

Vehicle #:	1	2	3	4	5	6	7	8	9	10
mpg with additive:	21	23	20	20	27	18	22	19	36	25
mpg without additive:	20	20	21	18	24	17	22	18	37	20
Difference d:	1	3	−1	2	3	1	0	1	−1	5

Using a scientific calculator, $\bar{d} = 1.4$ and $s_d = 1.90$.

The test statistic is $t = \dfrac{1.4\sqrt{10}}{1.90} \approx 2.33$

6. Since 2.33 is in the reject region, reject H_0.

7. At the 0.05 significance level, the data indicate that the average miles per gallon (mpg) is increased by using the additive.

Hypothesis Test for Two Population Standard Deviations

Many process improvement efforts are designed to reduce variation. This test is used to determine whether the standard deviations of two populations are different:

1. Conditions: the two populations are normally distributed and the samples are independent.

2. H_0: $\sigma_1 = \sigma_2$

   H_a: $\sigma_1 \neq \sigma_2$ (two-tailed), $\sigma_1 < \sigma_2$ (left-tailed), $\sigma_1 > \sigma_2$ (right-tailed)

3. Determine the significance level α.

4. The critical values are obtained from the F-table (Appendixes F, G, and H). They are $F_{1-\alpha/2}$ and $F_{\alpha/2}$ for the two-tailed test, $F_{1-\alpha}$ for the left-tailed test, and F_α for the right-tailed test. Use numerator df $= n_1 - 1$ and denominator df $= n_2 - 1$ where n_1, n_2 are sample sizes.

5. The test statistic is

$$F = \frac{s_1^2}{s_2^2}$$

where s_1 and s_2 are the sample standard deviations.

6. If the test statistic is in the reject region, reject H_0. Otherwise, do not reject H_0.

7. State the conclusion in terms of the problem.

Part III.A.1

EXAMPLE 6.6

Data from two competing machines include the following statistics:

$$\text{Machine 1: } n_1 = 21 \quad s_1 = 0.0032$$

$$\text{Machine 2: } n_2 = 25 \quad s_2 = 0.0028$$

Do these data suggest that the standard deviations of the machines are different at the 0.10 significance level? The populations are normal, and the samples have been drawn independently.

1. The conditions are met.

2. $H_0: \sigma_1 = \sigma_2 \; H_a: \sigma_1 \neq \sigma_2$

3. $\alpha = 0.10$.

4. This is a two-tailed test. The critical values are

$$F_{\alpha/2}\begin{bmatrix} 20 \\ 24 \end{bmatrix} = F_{0.05}\begin{bmatrix} 20 \\ 24 \end{bmatrix} = \frac{1}{F_{0.95}\begin{bmatrix} 24 \\ 20 \end{bmatrix}} = \frac{1}{2.08} \approx 0.48$$

$$F_{1-\alpha/2}\begin{bmatrix} 20 \\ 24 \end{bmatrix} = F_{0.95}\begin{bmatrix} 20 \\ 24 \end{bmatrix} = 2.03$$

   The reject region is the area to the left of 0.48 and the area to the right of 2.03.

5. The test statistic is

$$F = \frac{s_1^2}{s_2^2} = \frac{0.0032^2}{0.0028^2} \approx 1.31$$

6. Since the test statistic does not lie in the reject region, do not reject the null hypothesis.

7. At the 0.10 significance level, the data do not support the conclusion that the standard deviations of the two machines are different.

THE LEFT TAIL OF THE *F*-DISTRIBUTION

Note that the *F*-tables in the appendixes are limited to $F_{0.90}$, $F_{0.95}$, and $F_{0.99}$. This appears to restrict the user to right-tailed tests. A special property of the *F* distribution is used to find the left tail: let F_α with numerator df = n and denominator df = d be denoted by

$$F_\alpha\begin{bmatrix} n \\ d \end{bmatrix}$$

Then the special property may be stated

$$F_\alpha\begin{bmatrix} n \\ d \end{bmatrix} = \frac{1}{F_{1-\alpha}\begin{bmatrix} d \\ n \end{bmatrix}}$$

Example: Find $F_{0.05}$ with numerator df = 10 and denominator df = 20.

$$F_{0.05}\begin{bmatrix} 10 \\ 20 \end{bmatrix} = \frac{1}{F_{0.95}\begin{bmatrix} 20 \\ 10 \end{bmatrix}} = \frac{1}{2.77} \approx 0.036$$

Goodness-of-Fit Tests

Chi-square and other goodness-of-fit tests help determine whether a discrete sample has been drawn from a known population. Example 6.7 will illustrate this concept.

EXAMPLE 6.7

Suppose that all rejected products have exactly one of four types of defectives and that historically they have been distributed as follows:

Paint run	16%
Paint blister	28%
Decal crooked	42%
Door cracked	14%
Total	100%

Data on rejected parts for a randomly selected week in the current year:

Paint run	27
Paint blister	65
Decal crooked	95
Door cracked	21

The question: "Is the distribution of defective types for the selected week different from the historical distribution?" The test that answers this question is rather awkwardly called the χ^2 *goodness-of-fit test*. To get a feel for this test, construct a table that displays the number of defectives that would be expected in each category if the sample exactly followed the historical percentages:

Defective type	Probability	Observed frequency	Expected frequency
Paint run	0.16	27	33.28
Paint blister	0.28	65	58.24
Decal crooked	0.42	95	87.36
Door cracked	0.14	21	29.12
Total		208	

The expected frequency for "paint run" is found by calculating 16% of 208; for "paint blister" use 28% of 208, and so on. The question to be decided is whether the difference between the expected frequencies and observed frequencies is sufficiently large to conclude that the sample comes from a population that has a different distribution. Test this at the 0.05 significance level.

Continued

The test statistic is obtained by calculating the value of

$$\frac{(\text{Observed} - \text{Expected})^2}{\text{Expected}}$$

for each defective type:

Defective type	Probability	Observed frequency	Expected frequency	O – E	(O – E)²/E
Paint run	0.16	27	33.28	–6.28	1.19
Paint blister	0.28	65	58.24	6.76	0.78
Decal crooked	0.42	95	87.36	7.64	0.67
Door cracked	0.14	21	29.12	–8.12	2.26
Total		208			

The null hypothesis is that the distribution hasn't changed. This hypothesis will be rejected if the total of the last column is too large.

The procedure:

1. Conditions:

   a. All expected frequencies are at least 1.

   b. At most, 20% of the expected frequencies are less than 5.

2. H_0: The distribution has not changed.

   H_a: The distribution has changed.

3. Determine α, the significance level.

4. Find the critical value in row $k - 1$ in the χ^2_α column of the χ^2 table, where k = number of categories in the distribution. This is always a right-tailed test, so the reject region is the area to the right of this critical value.

5. Calculate the test statistic using the formula

$$\chi^2 = \sum \frac{(O - E)^2}{E}$$

   (the sum of the last column in the table).

6. Reject H_0 if the test statistic is in the reject region. Otherwise do not reject H_0.

7. State the conclusion.

Using the data and calculations of Example 6.7, follow the seven steps of the procedure to arrive at a reject or not reject decision as shown in Example 6.8.

EXAMPLE 6.8

1. The conditions are met.

2. H_0: The distribution of defective types has not changed.

   H_a: The distribution of defective types has changed.

3. $\alpha = 0.05$.

4. From row 3 of the $\chi^2_{0.05}$ column, the critical value is 7.815. The reject region is the area to the right of 7.815.

5. $\chi^2 = \dfrac{(O-E)^2}{E} \approx 4.9$

6. Since the test statistic does not fall in the reject region, do not reject H_0.

7. At the 0.05 significance level, the data do not indicate that the distribution has changed.

Hypothesis Tests for Proportions

The next hypothesis test is for *one population proportion.* To set the stage for this test, consider the problem posed in Example 6.9. To solve this problem, the following symbolism and steps will be used:

p = Population proportion

n = Sample size

x = Number of items in the sample with the defined attribute

p' = Sample proportion = x/n

p_0 = The hypothesized proportion

The problem posed in Example 6.9 is solved in Example 6.10. The hypothesis test steps:

1. Conditions: $np_0 \geq 5$ and $n(1 - p_0) \geq 5$.

2. H_0: $p = p_0$

   H_a: $p \neq p_0$ or $p < p_0$ or $p > p_0$ (two-tailed, left-tailed, and right-tailed, respectively)

3. Decide on α, the significance level.

4. Find the critical values in a standard normal table: $\pm z_{\alpha/2}$, $-z_\alpha$, z_α (two-tailed, left-tailed, and right-tailed, respectively)

5. Calculate the test statistic using the formula

$$z = \frac{p' - p_0}{\sqrt{p_0(1 - p_0)/n}}$$

6. If the test statistic is in the reject region, reject H_0. Otherwise, do not reject H_0.

7. State the conclusion in terms of the problem.

The next hypothesis test is for *two population proportions*. The symbolism to be used is:

p_1 & p_2 = Proportions of populations 1 and 2 with the defined attribute

n_1 & n_2 = Sample sizes

x_1 & x_2 = Number of items in the sample with the defined attribute

p_1' & p_2' = Sample proportions = x_1/n_1 and x_2/n_2, respectively

---

EXAMPLE 6.9

A vendor claims that at most 2% of a shipment of parts is defective. Receiving inspection chooses a random sample of 500 and finds 15 defectives. At the 0.05 significance level, do these data indicate that the vendor is wrong?

The hypothesis test steps:

1. Conditions: Samples are independent.

$$x_1 \geq 5,\ n_1 - x_1 \geq 5,\ x_2 \geq 5,\ n_2 - x_2 \geq 5$$

2. H_0: $p_1 = p_2$

    H_a: $p_1 \geq p_2$ or $p_1 < p_2$ or $p_1 > p_2$ (two-tailed, left-tailed, and right-tailed, respectively)

3. Decide on α, the significance level.

4. Find the critical values in a standard normal table: $\pm z_{\alpha/2}$, $-z_\alpha$, z_α (two-tailed, left-tailed, and right-tailed respectively).

5. Calculate the test statistic using the formula

$$z = \frac{p_1' - p_2'}{\sqrt{p_p'(1 - p_p')}\sqrt{(1/n_1) + (1/n_2)}} \quad \text{where } p_p' = \frac{x_1 + x_2}{n_1 + n_2}$$

6. If the test statistic is in the reject region, reject H_0. Otherwise, do not reject H_0.

7. State the conclusion in terms of the problem.

Although not usually on a standard list of hypothesis tests, *Tukey's quick compact two-sample test* can be useful in comparing failure rates of two populations.

EXAMPLE 6.10

$$N = 500 \quad x = 15 \quad p' = 15 \div 500 = 0.03 \quad p_0 = 0.02$$

1. $np_0 = 500 \times 0.02 = 10$ and $n(1 - p_0) = 500 \times 0.98 = 490$.

   Both values are ≥ 5, so conditions are met.

2. H_0: $p = 0.02$ H_a: $p > 0.02$ (right-tailed test).

3. $\alpha = 0.05$.

4. Critical value $= 1.645$ from a normal table.

5. $z = \dfrac{0.03 - 0.02}{\sqrt{0.02 \times 0.98 \div 500}} \approx 1.597$

6. Do not reject H_0.

7. At the 0.05 significance level, the data do not support a conclusion that the vendor is incorrect in asserting that at most 2% of the shipment is defective.

EXAMPLE 6.11

Two machines produce the same parts. A random sample of 1500 parts from machine 1 has 36 defectives, and a random sample of 1680 parts from machine 2 has 39 defectives. Does machine 2 have a lower defective rate? Test at 0.01 significance level.

$$n_1 = 1500 \quad n_2 = 1680$$

$$x_1 = 36 \quad x_2 = 39$$

$$p_1' = 36/1500 = 0.024 \quad p_2' = 39/1680 \approx 0.0232$$

1. Conditions are satisfied.

2. H_0: $p_1 = p_2$

   H_a: $p_1 > p_2$ (right-tailed test)

3. $\alpha = 0.01$.

4. From a standard normal table the z-value with 0.01 to its right is 2.33.

5. $p_p' = (x_1 + x_2)/(n_1 + n_2) = (36 + 39)/(1500 + 1680) = 0.0236$

$$z = \frac{0.0240 - 0.0232}{\sqrt{0.0236(0.9764)} \ \sqrt{0.0006667 + 0.0005952}} \approx 0.148$$

6. Do not reject H_0.

7. At the 0.01 significance level, the data do not support the conclusion that machine 2 has a lower defective rate.

EXAMPLE 6.12

Ten items are randomly selected from population A and 10 from population B. The 20 items are tested to failure with the following results:

Time to Failure	948	942	939	930	926	918	917	910	897	895	886	880	870	865	862	850	835	830	821
Population In	B	B	B	B	A	B	B	A	B	B	A	A	B	A	A	B	A	A	A

$\longleftrightarrow$ Lead count = 4   Lag count = 3 $\longleftrightarrow$

In this case, lead count = 4 and lag count = 3, so end count $h = 3 + 4 = 7$ and

$$\alpha \leq \frac{h}{2^h} = \frac{7}{2^7} \approx 0.055$$

So, the conclusion is that the items in population B are more reliable than the items in population A at the 0.055 significance level.

Random samples of size $n \geq 8$ from each population are tested to failure, and the times to failure are sorted from highest to lowest. Define *lead count* as the number of consecutive items of one type at the top of the sorted list. Define *lag count* as the number of consecutive items at the bottom of the list from the other population. Define *end count* (h) as h = lead count + lag count.

The test shows that the population represented by the lead count is more reliable than the other population, with a significance level of

$$\alpha \leq \frac{h}{2^h}$$

Statistical vs. Practical Significance

In some situations it may be possible to detect a statistically significant difference between two populations when there is no practical difference. For example, suppose that a test is devised to determine whether there is a significant difference in the surface finish when a lathe is operated at 400 revolutions per minute (rpm) and 700 rpm. If large sample sizes are used, it may be possible to determine that the 400 rpm population has a tiny but statistically significant surface improvement. However, if both speeds produce surface finishes that are capable of meeting the specifications, the best decision might be to go with the faster speed because of its associated increase in throughput. Thus, the difference between two populations, although statistically significant, must be weighed against other economic and engineering considerations.

Significance Level, Power, Type I and Type II Errors

Since every hypothesis test infers properties of a population based on analysis of a sample, there is some chance that although the analysis is flawless, the conclusion may be incorrect. These *sampling errors* are not errors in the usual sense because they can't be corrected (without using 100% sampling with no measurement errors). The two possible types of errors have been named type I and type II.

A *type I error* occurs when a true null hypothesis is rejected. The probability of type I error is denoted α. This is the same α that is used in the formulas for confidence intervals and critical values. Hence, when a hypothesis test is conducted at the 0.05 significance level, there is a probability of 0.05 that the hypothesis will be rejected when it shouldn't have been. When using α in the construction of a confidence interval for the mean of a population, the probability that the population mean is not in the interval is α.

A *type II error* occurs when a false null hypothesis is not rejected. The probability of type II error is denoted β.

It is helpful to think of a sampling example. Suppose a lot of 1200 is to be inspected to an acceptable quality level (AQL) of 2.5% and that the appropriate sampling plan calls for a sample size of 80 with a reject number of six—that is, 80 parts are randomly selected and inspected and if six or more are defective, the entire lot is rejected. One of the myths of sampling theory is that any lot rejected by the sampling procedure fails to meet the 2.5% AQL requirement. But assume that the lot of 1200 has only 25 defectives, well below the 2.5% level.

Is it possible that the sample of 80 could include at least six of those 25 defectives? Of course. In fact, the probability that this occurs is α. The null hypothesis here is that the lot is good. The null hypothesis is true, but the sampling plan causes us to reject it erroneously. This type I error is due to sampling error. If we took many samples of size 80, at most only α percent of them should have six or more defectives.

It is easy to see why α is sometimes called the *producer's risk* because it is the probability that the lot, although meeting the AQL, will be rejected via sampling error.

Another myth of sampling theory is that a lot passed by the sampling procedure must meet the AQL. Assume that the lot of 1200 has 60 defectives, twice the defective level allowed by the AQL. It is possible that a sample of 80 could have fewer than six defectives. The probability that this will occur is β, which is also referred to as the *consumer's risk* because it is the probability that a lot that fails to meet the AQL will nevertheless be accepted through sampling error. The more powerful sampling plans keep the β value low. Thus the *power* of a sampling plan is defined as $1 - \beta$. The smaller the β, the larger the power.

For a given sample size and lot quality, the values of α and β depend on the accept and reject numbers of the sampling plan. If these numbers are adjusted to reduce α, then β will be increased and vice versa. To reduce both α and β it would be necessary to increase the sample size. Both could be reduced to zero if the sampling plan called for 100% sampling and no inspection errors occurred. But then it wouldn't be a sampling plan.

2. BASIC PROBABILITY CONCEPTS

> Use basic probability concepts (e.g., independence, mutually exclusive, conditional probability), and compute and interpret the expected values. (Analyze)
>
> Body of Knowledge III.A.2

Part III.A.2

Complementation Rule

The probability that an event A will not occur is given by the formula

$$1 - \text{(the probability that A does occur)}.$$

Stated symbolically, $P(\text{not } A) = 1 - P(A)$. Some texts use other symbols for "not A," including $-A$, $\sim A$, and sometimes $\overline{A}$.

Special Addition Rule

Suppose a card is randomly selected from a standard 52-card deck. What is the probability that the card is a club? Since there are 13 clubs, $P(\clubsuit) = 13/52 = 0.25$. What is the probability that the card is either a club or a spade? Since there are 26 cards that are either clubs or spades, $P(\clubsuit \text{ or } \spadesuit) = 26/52 = .5$. Therefore, it appears that $P(\clubsuit \text{ or } \spadesuit) = P(\clubsuit) + P(\spadesuit)$, which, generalized, becomes the special addition rule:

$$P(A \text{ or } B) = P(A) + P(B)$$

Caveat: Use only if events A and B cannot occur simultaneously. The general addition rule described next is safer to use because it is always valid.

General Addition Rule

What is the probability of selecting either a king or a club? Using the special addition rule:

$$P(K \text{ or } \clubsuit) = P(K) + P(\clubsuit) = \frac{4}{52} + \frac{13}{52} = \frac{17}{52}$$

This is incorrect, because there are only 16 cards that are either kings or clubs (the 13 clubs plus $K\spadesuit$, $K\diamondsuit$, and $K\heartsuit$). The reason that the special addition rule doesn't work here is that the two events (drawing a king and drawing a club) can occur simultaneously. We'll denote the probability that events A and B both occur as $P(A \& B)$. This leads to the general addition rule:

$$P(A \text{ or } B) = P(A) + P(B) - P(A \& B)$$

The special addition rule has the advantage of being somewhat simpler, but its disadvantage is that it is not valid when A and B can occur simultaneously. The general addition rule, although more complex, is always valid. For the above example,

$$P(K \& \clubsuit) = \frac{1}{52}$$

since only one card is both a K and a club. To complete the example:

$$P(K \text{ or } \clubsuit) = P(K) + P(\clubsuit) - P(K \& \clubsuit) = \frac{4}{52} + \frac{13}{52} - \frac{1}{52} = \frac{16}{52}$$

Two events that can't occur simultaneously are called *mutually exclusive* or *disjoint*. So, the caveat for the special addition rule is sometimes stated, "Use only if events A and B are mutually exclusive" or "Use only if events A and B are disjoint."

Contingency Tables

Suppose each part in a lot is one of four colors (red, yellow, green, blue) and one of three sizes (small, medium, large). A tool that displays these attributes is the contingency table:

	Red	Yellow	Green	Blue
Small	16	21	14	19
Medium	12	11	19	15
Large	18	12	21	14

Each part belongs in exactly one column, and each part belongs in exactly one row. So, each part belongs in exactly one of the 12 cells. When columns and rows are totaled, the table becomes:

	Red	Yellow	Green	Blue	Totals
Small	16	21	14	19	70
Medium	12	11	19	15	57
Large	18	12	21	14	65
Totals	46	44	54	48	192

Note that 192 can be computed in two ways. If one of the 192 parts is randomly selected, find the probability that the part is red.
    Solution:

$$P(\text{red}) = \frac{46}{192} \approx 0.240$$

Find the probability that the part is small.
    Solution:

$$P(\text{small}) = \frac{70}{192} \approx 0.365$$

Find the probability that the part is red and small.
    Solution: Since there are 16 parts that are both red and small,

$$P(\text{red \& small}) = \frac{16}{192} \approx 0.083$$

Part III.A.2

Find the probability that the part is red or small.

Solution: Since it is possible for a part to be both red and small simultaneously, the general addition rule must be used:

$$P(\text{red or small}) = P(\text{red}) + P(\text{small}) - P(\text{red \& small}) = \frac{46}{192} + \frac{70}{192} - \frac{16}{192} \approx 0.521$$

Find the probability that the part is red or yellow.

Solution: Since no part can be both red and yellow simultaneously, the special addition rule can be used:

$$P(\text{red or yellow}) = P(\text{red}) + P(\text{yellow}) = \frac{46}{192} + \frac{44}{192} \approx 0.469$$

Notice that the general addition rule could have been used:

$$P(\text{red or yellow}) = P(\text{red}) + P(\text{yellow}) - P(\text{red \& yellow}) = \frac{46}{192} + \frac{44}{192} - 0 \approx 0.469$$

Conditional Probability

Continuing with the contingency table, suppose the selected part is known to be green. With this knowledge, what is the probability that the part is large?

Solution: Since the part is located in the green column of the table, it is one of the 54 green parts. So, the denominator in the probability fraction is 54. Since 21 of those 54 parts are large,

$$P(\text{large, given that it is green}) = \frac{21}{54} \approx 0.389$$

This is referred to as *conditional probability*. It is denoted $P(\text{large}|\text{green})$ and pronounced "the probability that the part is large given that it is green." It is useful to remember that the category to the right of the | in the conditional probability symbol points to the denominator in the probability fraction. Find the following probabilities:

$$P(\text{small} | \text{red}) \quad \text{Solution: } P(\text{small} | \text{red}) = \frac{16}{46} \approx 0.348$$

$$P(\text{red} | \text{small}) \quad \text{Solution: } P(\text{red} | \text{small}) = \frac{16}{70} \approx 0.229$$

$$P(\text{red} | \text{green}) \quad \text{Solution: } P(\text{red} | \text{green}) = \frac{0}{54} = 0$$

A formal definition for conditional probability is

$$P(B|A) = \frac{P(A \ \& \ B)}{P(A)}$$

Verifying that this formula is valid in each of the previous examples will aid in understanding this concept.

General Multiplication Rule

Multiplying both sides of the conditional probability formula by P(A),

$$P(A \& B) = P(A) \times P(B|A)$$

This is called the *general multiplication rule*. It is useful to verify that this formula is valid using examples from the contingency table.

Independence and the Special Multiplication Rule

Consider the contingency table:

	X	Y	Z	Totals
F	17	18	14	49
G	18	11	16	45
H	25	13	18	56
Totals	60	42	48	150

$$P(G|X) = \frac{18}{60} = 0.300$$

and

$$P(G) = \frac{45}{150} = 0.300$$

so

$$P(G|X) = P(G)$$

The events G and X are called *statistically independent* or just *independent*. Knowing that a part is of type X does not affect the probability that it is of type G. Intuitively, two events are called independent if the occurrence of one does not affect the probability that the other occurs. The formal definition of independence of events A and B is

$$P(B|A) = P(B)$$

Making this substitution in the general multiplication rule produces the special multiplication rule:

$$P(A \& B) = P(A) \times P(B)$$

Caveat: Use only if A and B are independent.

Part III.A.2

EXAMPLE 6.13

A box holds 129 parts, of which six are defective. A part is randomly drawn from the box and placed in a fixture. A second part is then drawn from the box. What is the probability that the second part is defective? This is referred to as *drawing without replacement*. In other words, the probabilities associated with successive draws depend on the outcome of previous draws. Use the symbol D_1 to denote the event that the first part is defective and G_1 to denote the event that the first part is good, and so on. There are two mutually exclusive events that can result in a defective part on the second draw: good on first draw and defective on second, or else defective on first and defective on second. Symbolically, these two events are (G_1 and D_2) or else (D_1 and D_2). The first step is to find the probability for each of these events. So, if we wish to know the probability of the first part drawn being good *and* the second part drawn being defective, by the general multiplication rule

$$P\left(G_1 \& D_1\right) = P\left(G_1\right) \times P\left(D_2 | G_1\right) = \frac{123}{129} \times \frac{6}{128} \approx 0.045$$

Also, by the general multiplication rule

$$P\left(D_1 \& D_2\right) = P\left(D_1\right) \times P\left(D_2 | D_1\right) = \frac{6}{129} \times \frac{5}{128} \approx 0.002$$

Since the two events (G_1 & D_2) and (D_1 & D_2) are mutually exclusive, it is appropriate to use the special addition rule:

$$P(D_2) \approx 0.045 + 0.002 = 0.047$$

When drawing two parts, what is the probability that one will be good and one defective? Drawing one good and one defective can occur in two mutually exclusive ways:

P(one good and one defective) = P(G_1 & D_2 or G_2 & D_1) = P(G_1 & D_2) + P(G_2 & D_1)

$$P\left(G_1 \& D_2\right) = P\left(G_1\right) \times P\left(D_2 | G_1\right) = \frac{123}{129} \times \frac{6}{128} \approx 0.045$$

$$P\left(G_2 \& D_1\right) = P\left(D_1\right) \times P\left(G_2 | D_1\right) = \frac{6}{129} \times \frac{123}{128} \approx 0.045$$

So,

$$\text{P(one good and one defective)} \approx 0.045 + 0.045 = 0.090$$

SUMMARY OF KEY PROBABILITY RULES

For events A and B:

Special addition rule: P(A or B) = P(A) + P(B)   [Use only if A and B are mutually exclusive]

General addition rule: P(A or B) = P(A) + P(B) − P(A & B)   [Always true]

Special multiplication rule: P(A & B) = P(A) × P(B)   [Use only if A and B are independent]

General multiplication rule: P(A & B) = P(A) × P(B|A)   [Always true]

Conditional probability: P(B|A) = P(A & B) ÷ P(A)

Mutually exclusive (or disjoint):

1. A and B are mutually exclusive if they can't occur simultaneously.

2. A and B are mutually exclusive if P(A & B) = 0.

3. A and B are mutually exclusive if P(A or B) = P(A) + P(B).

Independence:

1. A and B are independent events if the occurrence of one does not change the probability that the other occurs.

2. A and B are independent events if P(B|A) = P(B).

3. A and B are independent events if P(A & B) = P(A) × P(B).

EXAMPLE 6.14

A box of 20 parts has two defectives. The quality technician inspects the box by randomly selecting two parts. What is the probability that both parts selected are defective? The general formula for this type of problem is:

$$P = \frac{\text{Number of ways an event can occur}}{\text{Number of possible outcomes}}$$

The "event" in this case is selecting two defectives, so "number of ways an event can occur" refers to the number of ways two defective parts could be selected. There is only one way to do this because there are only two defective parts; therefore, the numerator in the fraction is 1. The denominator in the fraction is the number of possible outcomes. This refers to the number of different ways of selecting two parts from the box.

This is also called the *number of combinations* of two objects from a collection of 20 objects. The formula is:

Number of combinations of r objects from a collection of n objects = $_nC_r$ where

$$_nC_r = \frac{n!}{r!(n-r)!}$$

Note: Another symbol for number of combinations is $\binom{n}{r}$

In this formula the exclamation mark is pronounced "factorial," so $n!$ is pronounced "n factorial." The value of 6! is $6 \times 5 \times 4 \times 3 \times 2 \times 1 = 720$. The value of $n!$ is the result of multiplying the first n positive whole numbers. Most scientific calculators have a factorial key, typically labeled x! To calculate 6! by using this key, press 6 followed by the x! key. Returning to the previous example, the denominator in the fraction is the number of possible combinations of two objects from a collection of 20 objects. Substituting into this formula:

$$_{20}C_2 = \frac{20!}{2!(20-2)!} = \frac{20!}{2!18!} = 190$$

Returning to the example, the probability is 1/190 ≈ 0.005.

EXAMPLE 6.15

A box of 20 parts has three defectives. The quality technician inspects the box by randomly selecting two parts. What is the probability that both parts selected are defective?

The bottom term of the fraction remains the same as in the previous example. The top term is the number of combinations of two objects from a collection of three objects:

$$\binom{n}{r} = \frac{n!}{n!(n-r)!} = \binom{3}{2} = \frac{3!}{2!(3-2)!} = \frac{6}{2!1!} = \frac{6}{2} = 3$$

To see that this makes sense, name the three defectives A, B, and C. The number of different two-letter combinations of these three letters is AB, AC, BC. Note that AB is not a different combination than BA, because it has the same two letters. If two defectives are selected, the order in which they are selected is not significant. The answer to the probability problem has a 3 as its top term:

$$P = \frac{3}{190} \approx 0.016$$

An important thing to remember: combinations are used when order is not significant.

Combinations

Note: Calculators have an upper limit to the value that can use the x! key. If a problem requires a higher factorial, use the statistical function in a spreadsheet program such as Microsoft Excel.

Permutations

With combinations, the order of the objects doesn't matter. Permutations are very similar except that the order does matter.

EXAMPLE 6.16

A box has 20 parts labeled A through T. Two parts are randomly selected. What is the probability that the two parts are A and T in that order? Note that selecting A and then T is different from selecting T and then A. The general formula applies:

$$P = \frac{\text{Number of ways an event can occur}}{\text{Number of possible outcomes}}$$

The bottom term of the fraction is the number of orderings or *permutations* of two objects from a collection of 20 objects. The general formula is:

$$\text{Number of permutations of } r \text{ objects from a collection of } n \text{ objects} = {}_nP_r = \frac{n!}{(n-r)!}$$

In this example

$$_{20}P_2 = \frac{20!}{(20-2)!} = 380$$

Of these 380 possible permutations, only one is AT, so the top term in the fraction is 1. The answer to the probability problem is

$$P = \frac{1}{380} \approx 0.003$$

EXAMPLE 6.17

A team with seven members wants to select a task force of three people to collect data for the next team meeting. How many different three-person task forces could be formed? This is not a permutations problem, because the order in which people are selected doesn't matter. In other words, the task force consisting of Barb, Bill, and Bob is the same task force as the one consisting of Bill, Barb, and Bob. Therefore, the combinations formula will be used to calculate the number of possible combinations of three objects from a collection of seven objects:

$$_7C_3 = \frac{7!}{(7-3)!3!} = 35$$

Thirty-five different task forces could be formed.

EXAMPLE 6.18

A team with seven members wants to select a cabinet consisting of a chairman, a facilitator, and a scribe. How many ways can the three-person cabinet be formed? Here, the order is important because the cabinet consisting of Barb, Bill, and Bob will have Barb as chairman, Bill as facilitator, and Bob as scribe, while the cabinet consisting of Bill, Barb, and Bob has Bill as chairman, Barb as facilitator, and Bob as scribe. The appropriate formula is the one for permutations of three objects from a collection of seven objects:

$$_7P_3 = \frac{7!}{(7-3)!} = 210$$

3. PROBABILITY DISTRIBUTIONS

Compare and contrast various distributions (e.g., binomial, Poisson, exponential, Weibull, normal, and log-normal), and recognize their associated probability plots. (Analyze)

Body of Knowledge III.A.3

Distributions based on random variables that can take on only integer values, or isolated and distinct values, are called *discrete distributions*. Distributions based on random variables that can take on an infinite number of values in a finite interval are called *continuous distributions*. Example 6.19 introduces the basic concepts of probability distributions.

EXAMPLE 6.19

A piece from a wood finishing process has the following specification: no bubbles with diameter larger than 0.5 millimeters (mm), and a maximum of 10 bubbles with diameter between 0.05 and 0.5 mm inclusive.

A batch of 50 pieces is inspected for number of bubbles with diameters between 0.05 and 0.5 mm with the following results:

Number of bubbles $0.05 \leq f \leq 0.5$ mm x	0	1	2	3	4	≥ 5
Frequency f	11	15	16	6	2	0
Relative frequency p	0.22	0.30	0.32	0.12	0.04	0.0

That is, there were 11 pieces with no bubbles with the stated diameters, and there were 15 pieces with one bubble with the stated diameter, and so forth. There were no pieces with five or more bubbles. Relative frequency is labeled p because if a piece is selected at random from the batch, this is the probability that it will have the stated number of bubbles. For example, the probability that the piece will have three bubbles is 0.12. The number of bubbles is a *variable*, and the number of bubbles on a randomly selected piece is called a *random variable*. The first and third rows of this table constitute what is called a *probability distribution*, and a histogram of these data, as shown in Figure 6.4, is called a *probability histogram*.

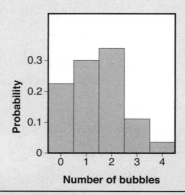

Figure 6.4 Example of a probability histogram.

---

4. PROBABILITY FUNCTIONS

> Compare and contrast various probability functions (e.g., cumulative distribution functions [CDFs], probability density functions [PDFs], and hazard functions), and recognize their application in various situations. (Apply)
>
> Body of Knowledge III.A.4

Discrete Distributions

Binomial Distribution

The *binomial distribution* is a discrete distribution whose random variable can take on one of only two possible values. In reliability applications, the two categories might be *operable* and *failed*. The binomial distribution consists of the set of possible *x*-values and their associated probabilities.

The function that defines the distribution is called the *binomial formula*:

$$P(X = x) = \frac{n!}{(n-x)!x!} p^x (1-p)^{n-x}$$

where:

n = Sample size

x = Number of failures

p = Proportion of the population that has failed

P(X = x) = The probability that the sample has *x* failures (for example, 5! = 5 × 4 × 3 × 2 × 1)

EXAMPLE 6.20

Suppose 25% of a very large population of parts has failed. If six parts are selected at random, find the probability that none of the six has failed.

Solution:

In this case, n = 6, p = 0.25, x = 0. Substituting into the binomial formula,

$$P(X = 0) = \frac{6!}{6!0!}(0.25)^0(0.75)^6 \approx 0.18$$

EXAMPLE 6.21

Find the binomial distribution for $p = 0.25$ and $n = 6$, and draw the associated histogram. As shown in the previous example, $P(X = 0) \approx 0.18$.

$$P(X = 1) = \frac{6!}{5!\,1!}\,0.25^1 0.75^5 \approx 0.36$$

$$P(X = 2) = \frac{6!}{4!\,2!}\,0.25^2 0.75^4 \approx 0.30$$

$$P(X = 3) = \frac{6!}{3!\,3!}\,0.25^3 0.75^3 \approx 0.13$$

$$P(X = 4) = \frac{6!}{2!\,4!}\,0.25^4 0.75^2 \approx 0.03$$

$$P(X = 5) = \frac{6!}{1!\,5!}\,0.25^5 0.75^1 \approx 0.004$$

$$P(X = 6) = \frac{6!}{6!\,0!}\,0.25^6 0.75^0 \approx 0.0002$$

Figure 6.5 shows the complete distribution using $x = 0, 1, \ldots, 6$.

Figure 6.5   Binomial probability distribution and histogram for $p = 0.25$ and $n = 6$.

The binomial distribution consists of the set of possible x-values and their associated probabilities.

The *probability density function* (PDF) is the expression that generates the distribution. In this case it is

$$P(X = x) = \frac{6!}{(6 - x)!\,x!}\,0.25^x 0.75^{(6-x)}$$

The *cumulative distribution function* (CDF) $F(x)$ is defined as the sum of the probabilities up to and including the x-value. More precisely, the CDF is defined as

$$F(x) = P(X \le x) = \sum_{t \le x} P(X = t)$$

In Example 6.21, the CDF could be used to answer the question "What is the probability that the sample includes two or fewer failed items?" as follows:

$$F(2) = \sum_{t \leq 2} f(t) = P(X = 0) + P(X = 1) + P(X = 2) \approx 0.18 + 0.36 + 0.30 \approx 0.84$$

The mean and standard deviation of a binomial distribution are given by the formulas

$$\mu = np$$

$$\sigma = \sqrt{np(1-p)}$$

In Example 6.21,

$$\mu = 6(0.25) = 1.5$$

and

$$\sigma = \sqrt{1.5(1-0.25)} \approx 1.06$$

Poisson Distribution

The *Poisson distribution* is a discrete probability distribution that may be used to find the probability that an event will occur a specified number of times. Since the random variable can take on any whole number, the probability distribution technically extends indefinitely.

The PDF formula is

$$P(X = x) = e^{-\lambda} \frac{\lambda^x}{x!}$$

where x = a whole number and λ = a real number.

Since the random variable can take on any whole number, the probability distribution technically extends indefinitely. From Example 6.22 a partial list:

$P(X = 0) \approx 0.005$, $P(X = 1) \approx 0.024$, $P(X = 2) \approx 0.066$, $P(X = 3) \approx 0.119$, $P(X = 4) \approx 0.16$, $P(X = 5) \approx 0.173$, $P(X = 6) \approx 0.16$, $P(X = 7) \approx 0.120$, $P(X = 8) \approx 0.081$, $P(X = 9) \approx 0.049$

EXAMPLE 6.22

Records indicate that the number of customers that arrive at a bank drive-up window between 1:00 p.m. and 2:00 p.m. has a Poisson distribution with $\lambda = 5.4$. Find the probability that exactly six people arrive.

Solution:

$$P(X = 6) = e^{-5.4}\frac{5.4^6}{6!} \approx 0.16$$

The CDF for the Poisson distribution is given by

$$\sum_{t \le x} P(X = t) = \sum_{t \le x} e^{-\lambda}\frac{\lambda^t}{t!}$$

In the previous example the CDF could be used to calculate the probability that at most four people arrive at the drive-up window:

$$\sum_{t \le 4} P(X \le t) = P(X = 0) + P(X = 1) + P(X = 2) + P(X = 3) + P(X = 4)$$

$$\approx 0.005 + 0.024 + 0.066 + 0.119 + 0.160 \approx 0.374$$

The mean and standard deviation of the Poisson distribution are

$$\mu = \lambda$$
$$\sigma = \sqrt{\lambda}$$

In Example 6.22, $\mu = 5.4$ and $\sigma \approx 2.32$.

Continuous Distributions

Exponential Distribution

The *exponential distribution* is a continuous distribution that is frequently used to model time to failure for products when the failure rate is constant.

The PDF is

$$f(t) = \lambda e^{-\lambda t}$$

where

λ = Constant failure rate

t = Time (or some other measure of product use, such as cycles, miles, rounds fired, and so on)

A PDF graph is shown in Example 6.23.

The CDF for the exponential distribution is

$$P(x \leq a) = F(a) = \int_0^a \lambda e^{-\lambda t} dt = 1 - e^{-\lambda t}$$

The CDF can be used to determine the probability of failure during the first t hours. The probability that a unit is still operating at t hours is P(operating at time t) = (1 − probability it has failed by time t) = $e^{-\lambda}t$.

P(operating at time t) is called *reliability at time t*, or R(t), so when the failure rate is constant,

$$R(t) = e^{-\lambda}t$$

EXAMPLE 6.23

Find the value of the PDF at 1000 hours given that the failure rate is 0.00053 failures per hour.

$$f(1000) = 0.00053e^{-0.00053 \times 1000} \approx 0.00031$$

This says that the probability of failure at 1000 hours is about 0.00031.

A sketch of the PDF in this example is shown in Figure 6.6. The mean and standard deviation of the PDF are $\mu = 1/\lambda$ and $\sigma = 1/\lambda$.

Figure 6.6 Probability density function for Example 6.23.

EXAMPLE 6.24

Find reliability at 1000 hours if $\lambda = 0.00053$ failures/hour.

Solution:

$$R(1000) = e^{-0.00053 \times 1000} \approx 0.59,$$

which indicates that approximately 59% of the units are still operating after 1000 hours, or the probability that a particular unit is still operating after 1000 hours is 0.59.

By definition, the mean time to failure (MTTF) is $1/\lambda$. Therefore, the reliability at MTTF is

$$R(MTTF) = R(1/\lambda) = e^{-\lambda \times 1/\lambda} = e^{-1} \approx 0.368$$

This shows that at MTTF, only about 37% of the products are operating, or the probability that a particular unit is still operating after MTTF is about 0.37. For repairable items, MTTF can be replaced by mean time between failures (MTBF) in the discussion in this paragraph.

Weibull Distribution

The *Weibull distribution* has a relatively simple distributional form. However, the shape parameter allows the Weibull to assume a wide variety of shapes. The Weibull distribution is widely used in reliability applications.

The PDF for the Weibull distribution is defined as

$$f(t) = \frac{\beta}{\eta} \left(\frac{t}{\eta} \right)^{\beta - 1} e^{-\left(\frac{t}{\eta} \right)^{\beta}}$$

where $t \geq 0$, shape parameter $\beta \geq 0$, scale parameter ≥ 0.

Various shapes are possible by selection of different values for β. If $\beta = 1$, the Weibull reduces to the exponential, and if $\beta \approx 3.44$, the curve approximates the normal distribution. See Figure 6.7.

The hazard function is given by

$$h(t) = \frac{\beta}{\eta^{\beta}} (t)^{\beta - 1}$$

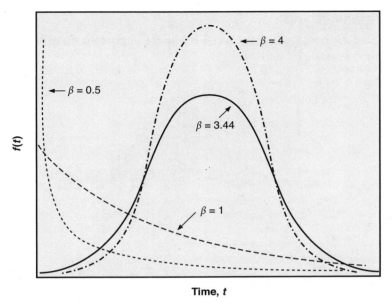

Figure 6.7 Plot of various members of the Weibull distribution.

The CDF for the Weibull is

$$F(t) = 1 - e^{-\left(\frac{t}{\eta}\right)^{\beta}}$$

Again,

$$R(t) = 1 - F(t) = e^{-\left(\frac{t}{\eta}\right)^{\beta}}$$

The two curved portions of the bathtub curve (Figure 2.1) are sometimes modeled by using the Weibull with appropriate shape parameters.

EXAMPLE 6.25

A product's time to failure has a Weibull distribution with $\beta = 0.72$ and $\eta = 10,000$. Find reliability at 200 hours.

Solution:

$$R(200) = e^{-\left(\frac{200}{10,000}\right)^{0.72}} \approx 0.94$$

indicating that about 94% of the products are operating after 200 hours.

Normal Distribution

The *normal distribution* is considered the most important distribution in both the theory and practice of statistics.

Its PDF is

$$f(x) = \frac{e^{\frac{-(x-\mu)^2}{2\sigma^2}}}{\sigma\sqrt{2\pi}}$$

where μ and σ are the mean and standard deviation, respectively.

In reliability applications, μ is the mean. Changes in this value cause the center of the distribution to be moved left or right along the x-axis. As the standard deviation decreases, the distribution becomes narrower, centered around the mean.

EXAMPLE 6.26

Assuming the following times to failure are sampled from a population that is normally distributed, find the PDF for the distribution.

42.3   45.6   49.5   53.6   54.8

Solution:

The population mean and standard deviation are estimated from the sample mean and sample deviation

$$\hat{\mu} = 49.16$$

and

$$\hat{\sigma} = 5.28$$

Substituting into the generic PDF formula:

$$f(x) = \frac{e^{\frac{-(x-49.16)^2}{55.76}}}{13.23}$$

When units have an increasing failure rate, such as during the wear-out phase, the times to failure are sometimes normally distributed, although it is more common to see a Weibull distribution here.

The standard normal curve has $\mu = 0$ and $\sigma = 1$, so its PDF is

$$f(x) = \frac{e^{-\frac{x^2}{2}}}{\sqrt{2\pi}} \approx 0.3989 e^{-\frac{x^2}{2}}$$

Applications requiring cumulative calculations are handled by finding the area under this curve. This is typically accomplished using statistical functions embedded in spreadsheet software (for example, NORMDIST in Excel) or using a standard normal table such as that found in Appendix E. For example, the area under the standard normal curve, to the right of $z = 1.28$ standard deviations, is found in the row labeled 1.2 and the column labeled 0.08. So, the area to the right of $z = 1.28$ is 0.1003, and since the total area under the standard normal curve is 1, it can be said that 10.03% of the area under the curve lies to the right of 1.28.

The standard normal table can be used to find specific areas under a nonstandard normal curve if the mean and standard deviation are known, as the following examples show.

EXAMPLE 6.27

The diameters of a batch of turned shafts are normally distributed with $\mu = 2.015$ and $\sigma = 0.0053$.

a. What percent of the batch has a diameter greater than the upper specification of 2.025?

b. What percent of the batch has a diameter smaller than the lower specification of 2.000?

Solution:

a. Find z, the number of standard deviations from the upper specification to the mean. The formula:

$$z = \frac{x - \mu}{\sigma} = \frac{2.025 - 2.015}{0.0053} \approx 1.89$$

From the standard normal table in the row labeled 1.8 and the column labeled 0.09, the value is 0.0294, which indicates that 2.94% of the batch exceeds the upper specification.

b. For the lower specification:

$$z = \frac{x - \mu}{\sigma} = \frac{2.000 - 2.015}{0.0053} \approx -2.83$$

The area to the left of −2.83 is the same as the area to the right of +2.83 because of the symmetry of the normal curve. From the standard normal table, 0.23% of the batch violates the lower specification.

EXAMPLE 6.28

The time to failure for a product is normally distributed with $\mu = 200$ hours and $\sigma = 1.84$. Find the probability of failure between $t = 201$ hours and $t = 202$ hours. That is, find

$$P(201 \leq x \leq 202)$$

Solution:

For 202 hours: $z = \dfrac{202 - 200}{1.84} \approx 1.09$

For 201 hours: $z = \dfrac{201 - 200}{1.84} \approx 0.54$

The area to the left of 1.09 from the standard normal table is 0.8621.

The area to the left of 0.54 from the standard normal table is 0.7054.

To find the area between these two values, subtract:

$$P(x \leq 1.09) = 0.8621$$
$$P(x \leq 0.54) = \underline{0.7054}$$
$$P(201 \leq x \leq 202) = 0.1567$$

15.67% of the units will fail between 201 and 202 hours.

Log-normal Distribution

If the natural logarithm (ln) of a random variable is normally distributed, the variable follows the *log-normal distribution*.

The PDF is

$$f(x) = \frac{e^{-0.5\left(\frac{x' - \mu_{x'}}{\sigma_{x'}}\right)^2}}{x\sigma_{x'}\sqrt{2\pi}}$$

where

$x' = \ln x$

$\mu_{x'} =$ Mean of the x' values

$\sigma_{x'} =$ Standard deviation of the x' values

The log-normal distribution has been found to be a good mathematical model for times to failure for some electronic and mechanical products, including transistors, bearings, and electrical insulation. It is sometimes a good model for times to repair a unit after a failure.

The mean and standard deviation of the log-normal distribution are given by

$$\mu = e^{\mu_{x'} + 0.5\sigma_{x'}^2}$$

$$\sigma = \sqrt{\left(e^{2\mu_{x'} + \sigma_{x'}^2}\right)\left(e^{\sigma_{x'}^2} - 1\right)}$$

EXAMPLE 6.29

The times to failure for a product are known to be lognormally distributed. The times to failure in cycles of a sample of six parts are 850, 925, 1250, 1550, 1800, and 2750 cycles. Find the PDF for the distribution.

Solution:

Find the ln of each of the given values:

x	$x' = \ln x$
850	6.75
925	6.83
1250	7.13
1550	7.35
1800	7.50
2750	7.92

Find the mean and standard deviation of the values in the second column:

$$\bar{x}' = 7.25$$

$$\sigma_{x'} = 0.44$$

Substituting into the PDF formula:

$$f(x) = \frac{e^{-0.5\left(\frac{x'-7.25}{0.44}\right)^2}}{x(0.44)\sqrt{2\pi}}$$

Statistical software packages such as Minitab and JMP can be used to find the distribution that best fits a given data set.

Descriptive Characteristics of Distributions

Software programs often calculate values of two characteristics of distributions. *Skewness* is defined as

$$\text{Skewness} = \frac{n}{(n-1)(n-2)}\sum\left(\frac{x_j - \bar{x}}{s}\right)^3$$

where

n = Sample size

s = Sample standard deviation

x_j = Sample values

If the skewness value is 0, the distribution is symmetric about its mode. If skewness < 0, the distribution is left-skewed; that is, the histogram extends farther to the left of the mode than it does to the right. If skewness > 0, the distribution is right-skewed.

Kurtosis is a measure of flatness and is defined as

$$\text{Kurtosis} = \frac{n(n+1)}{(n-1)(n-2)(n-3)} \sum \left(\frac{x_j - \bar{x}}{s}\right)^4 - \frac{3(n-1)^2}{(n-2)(n-3)}$$

where

n = Sample size

s = Sample standard deviation

x_j = Sample values

A normal distribution has kurtosis = 0. If kurtosis < 0, the distribution is flatter than a normal distribution, and if kurtosis > 0, the distribution is more peaked than a normal distribution.

5. SAMPLING PLANS FOR STATISTICS AND RELIABILITY TESTING

> Use various theories, tables, and formulas to determine appropriate sample sizes or testing time for statistical and reliability testing. (Apply)
>
> Body of Knowledge III.A.5

In some cases the width of the interval is specified in advance. It is then necessary to calculate the sample size that will meet that specification. Table 6.2 lists formulas for this task. The formulas use E to denote *margin of error*, which is half the width of the confidence interval. The confidence level is $1 - \alpha$.

EXAMPLE 6.30

Determine the sample size required to construct a 95% confidence interval (CI) for the mean if the CI is to be 0.020 wide given that $\sigma = 0.028$.

In this case the first formula is appropriate because a confidence interval for the mean is sought. The value of $z_{\alpha/2}$ is found in the normal table. For 95% confidence, $\alpha = 0.05$, $\alpha/2 = 0.025$, and $z_{\alpha/2} = 1.96$. The margin of error E = 0.010.

$$n = \left(\frac{z_{\alpha/2}\sigma}{E}\right)^2 = \left(\frac{1.96 \times 0.028}{0.010}\right)^2 \approx 30.1$$

So, use a sample size $n = 31$ (always round up).

The justification for the use of the normal table is the central limit theorem. As discussed in the first section of this chapter, this theorem states that the means are normally distributed.

Suppose the sample of 31 was selected with due care for randomness, and the sample mean $\bar{x} = 25.6$. The 95% confidence interval would be 25.6 ± 0.01. That is, there is 95% confidence that the population mean is between 25.59 and 25.61.

Table 6.2 Formulas for sample size.

Confidence interval for	Sample size n Round up to the nearest whole number
μ, population mean	$\left(\dfrac{z_{\alpha/2}\sigma}{E}\right)^2$
p, population proportion	$\left(\dfrac{z_{\alpha/2}}{E}\right)^2 \hat{p}\left(1-\hat{p}\right)$ $\hat{p}$ denotes an estimate for p
p, population proportion	$0.25\left(\dfrac{z_{\alpha/2}}{E}\right)^2$ Use when no estimate for p is available
$\mu_1 - \mu_2$, the difference between two population means	$n_1 = n_2 = \dfrac{\left(z_{\alpha/2}\right)^2\left(\sigma_1^2 + \sigma_2^2\right)}{E^2}$
$p_1 - p_2$, the difference between two population proportions	$n_1 = n_2 = 0.5\left(\dfrac{z_{\alpha/2}}{E}\right)^2$

EXAMPLE 6.31

Determine the sample size to construct a 95% confidence interval that is 0.06 wide for the proportion of defectives in a batch, assuming the historic proportion has been 5%.

The second formula in Table 6.2 deals with a proportion:

$$n = \left(\frac{z_{\alpha/2}}{E}\right)^2 \hat{p}\left(1-\hat{p}\right) = \left(\frac{1.96}{0.03}\right)^2 (0.05)(0.95) \approx 202.75$$

So, use sample size $n = 203$.

Although the justification is not provided here, statistical theory states that the normal table is appropriate. If a sample of 203 is polled and the sample proportion is $p_o = 0.042$, the 95% confidence interval is 0.042 ± 0.03.

EXAMPLE 6.32

Determine the sample size needed to construct a 95% confidence interval that is 0.06 wide for the proportion of defectives in a batch when no estimate is available.

The third formula in Table 6.2 is appropriate in this case:

$$n = 0.25\left(\frac{z_{\alpha/2}}{E}\right)^2 = 0.25\left(\frac{1.96}{0.03}\right)^2 \approx 1067.1$$

So, use sample size $n = 1068$.

This illustrates why it is best to use an estimate if available.

EXAMPLE 6.33

A vendor claims that product A has an average thickness at least 2 mm larger than that of product B. How many of each product type should be sampled to construct a 95% confidence interval to check the vendor's claim? Assume the two populations have standard deviations of 3.3 mm and 3.8 mm, respectively.

The fourth formula in Table 6.2 deals with the difference between population means:

$$n = \frac{\left(z_{\alpha/2}\right)^2 \left(\sigma_1^2 + \sigma_2^2\right)}{E^2} = \frac{1.96^2 \left(3.3^2 + 3.8^2\right)}{2^2} \approx 24.3$$

So, use sample size $n = 25$.

If samples of size 25 are selected from each product type, and $\bar{x}_A = 45.6$ and $\bar{x}_B = 37.6$, then the difference of the sample means is $\bar{x}_A - \bar{x}_B = 8$, and the confidence interval for the difference is 8 ± 2; that is, there is 95% confidence that the difference is between 6 mm and 10 mm. Therefore, there is 95% confidence that the vendor's claim is valid.

EXAMPLE 6.34

A reliability engineer has two competing designs that are stress-tested for 100 hours. Let p_A = the proportion of design A that fails, and p_B = the proportion of design B that fails. It is necessary to calculate the 95% confidence interval with width = 0.4 for the difference $p_A - p_B$.

Using the fifth formula in Table 6.2:

$$n_1 = n_2 = 0.5\left(\frac{z_{\alpha/2}}{E}\right)^2 = 0.5\left(\frac{1.96}{0.2}\right)^2 \approx 48.02$$

So, use $n_1 = n_2 = 49$.

The results of testing 49 items of each design are $p_{Ao} = 0.29$ and $p_{Bo} = 0.02$.

So, $p_{Ao} - p_{Ao} = 0.27$ and the confidence interval is 0.27 ± 0.2.

For example, there is 95% confidence that the difference between the two proportions is between 0.07 and 0.47, which means that design B is significantly better than design A.

---

6. STATISTICAL PROCESS CONTROL (SPC) AND PROCESS CAPABILITY STUDIES (C_p, C_{pk})

> Define and describe SPC and process capability studies (C_p, C_{pk}, etc.), control charts, and how each is related to reliability. (Understand)
>
> Body of Knowledge III.A.6

Control Charts for Continuous Process Monitoring

Control charts are an essential tool to satisfy continuous process monitoring requirements for validated process. *Control charts* are decision-making tools that provide information for timely decisions concerning recently produced products. Control charts are also problem-solving tools that help locate and investigate the causes of poor or marginal quality. The data from control charts can provide useful information when performing revalidation or retrospective validation activities. Control charts contain a centerline—usually the mathematical average of the samples plotted—upper and lower statistical control limits that define the constraints of common cause variation, and performance data plotted over time.

Control Chart Types and Selection

There are two general classifications of control charts: variables charts and attributes charts (see Table 6.3). *Variables* are things that can be measured: length, temperature, pressure, weight, and so on. *Attributes* are things that are counted: dents, scratches, defects, days, cycles, yes/no decisions, and so on.

Control Chart Interpretation

A process is said to be *in control* when the control chart does not indicate any out-of-control condition and contains only common causes of variation. If the common cause variation is small, then a control chart can be used to monitor the

Table 6.3   Variables and attributes control charts selection.

Variables control charts

Type	Distribution	Sample	Application
$\bar{X}$ and R	Normal	$2 \le 10$	Measurement subgroups
$\bar{X}$ and s	Normal	> 10	Measurement subgroups

Attributes control charts

Type	Distribution	Sample	Application
c	Poisson	Constant	Count number of defects per item
u	Poisson	Varies	Count number of defects per item
np	Binomial	Constant	Count of defective items
p	Binomial	Varies	Count of defective items
g	Binomial	Individual	Interval between rare events

Variables or attributes control charts

Type	Distribution	Sample	Application
X and mR	Normal	1	Individual counts or measurements

Source: Mark Durivage, *Practical Engineering, Process, and Reliability Statistics* (Milwaukee, WI: ASQ Quality Press, 2014).

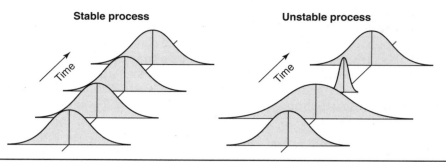

Figure 6.8 Stable and unstable variation.

Source: Adapted from Stephen A. Wise and Douglas C. Fair, *Innovative Control Charting: Practical SPC Solutions for Today's Manufacturing Environment* (Milwaukee, WI: ASQ Quality Press, 1997), Figures 3.3 and 3.5. Used with permission.

process. See Figure 6.8 for a representation of stable (in control) and unstable (out of control) processes. If the common cause variation is too large, the process will need to be modified.

When a control chart indicates an out-of-control condition (a point outside the control limits or matching one or more of the criteria below), the assignable causes of variation must be identified and eliminated.

Improper control chart interpretation can lead to several problems, including blaming people for problems they cannot control, spending time and money looking for problems that do not exist, spending time and money on process adjustments or new equipment that are not necessary, taking action where no action is warranted, and asking for worker-related improvements where process or equipment improvements need to be made first.

The following rules should be used to properly indicate that a process is out of control.

- Rule 1—One point beyond the 3σ control limit

- Rule 2—Eight or more points on one side of the centerline without crossing

- Rule 3—Four out of five points in zone B or beyond

- Rule 4—Six points or more in a row steadily increasing or decreasing

- Rule 5—Two out of three points in zone A

- Rule 6—Fourteen points in a row alternating up and down

- Rule 7—Any noticeable/predictable pattern, cycle, or trend

Please note that depending on the source, these rules can vary. See Figure 6.9 for control chart interpretation rules.

The target value (which is hopefully the control chart centerline) is closely related to process *accuracy*. The range chart is closely associated with process *precision* (spread or dispersion) (see Figures 6.10 and 6.11).

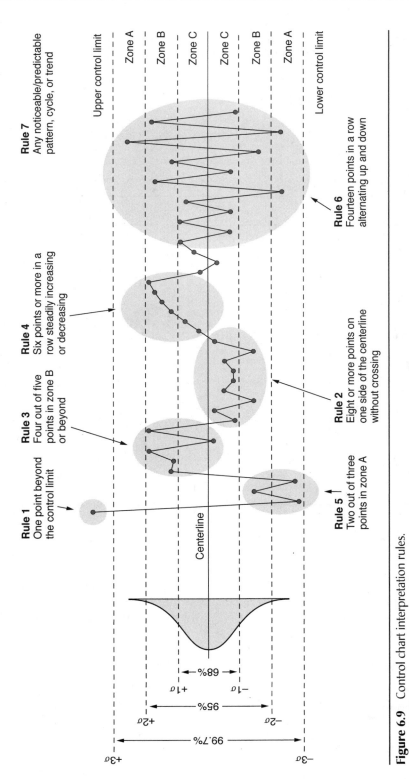

Figure 6.9 Control chart interpretation rules.

Source: Adapted from Stephen A. Wise and Douglas C. Fair, *Innovative Control Charting: Practical SPC Solutions for Today's Manufacturing Environment* (Milwaukee, WI: ASQ Quality Press, 1997), Figures 3.3 and 3.5. Used with permission.

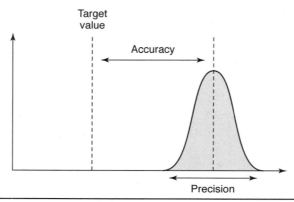

Figure 6.10 Control chart accuracy and precision.

Source: Mark Durivage, *Practical Engineering, Process, and Reliability Statistics* (Milwaukee, WI: ASQ Quality Press, 2014).

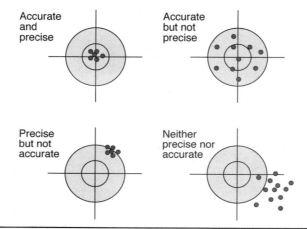

Figure 6.11 Accuracy versus precision.

Source: Mark Durivage, *Practical Engineering, Process, and Reliability Statistics* (Milwaukee, WI: ASQ Quality Press, 2014).

$\bar{X}$ and R Control Charts

$\bar{X}$ and R control charts assume a normal distribution and are usually used with a subgroup size of less than 10 (typically 3–5). A minimum of 25 subgroups is necessary to construct the chart (Figure 6.12).

$\bar{X}$ and s Control Charts

The $\bar{X}$ and s control charts assume a normal distribution and are usually used with a subgroup size of greater than 10. A minimum of 25 subgroups is necessary to construct the chart (Figure 6.13).

c-Charts

c-charts assume a Poisson distribution and are usually used with a constant sample size, counting the number of defects per item. A minimum of 25 subgroups

Figure 6.12 $\bar{X}$ and R chart.

is necessary to construct the c-chart, centerline, and the upper and lower control limits (Figure 6.14).

u-Charts

u-charts assume a Poisson distribution and are usually used with a variable sample size (although a constant sample size may be used), counting the number of defects per item. A minimum of 25 subgroups is necessary to construct the chart. The control limits will vary for each subgroup because the sample size n varies from group to group (Figure 6.15).

np-Charts

np-charts assume a binomial distribution and are usually used with a constant sample size, counting the defective items. A minimum of 25 subgroups is necessary to construct the chart (Figure 6.16).

Part III.A.6

Figure 6.13 $\overline{X}$ and *s* chart.

Figure 6.14 *c*-chart.

Figure 6.15 *u*-chart.

Figure 6.16 *np*-chart.

p-Charts

p-charts assume a binomial distribution and are usually used with a variable sample size (although a constant sample size may be used), counting the defective items. A minimum of 25 subgroups is necessary to construct the chart (Figure 6.17). The control limits will vary for each subgroup because the sample size *n* varies from group to group.

X and mR (Moving Range) Control Charts

X and mR (moving range) control charts assume a normal distribution and are used with individual values. A minimum of 25 observations is necessary to construct the chart (Figure 6.18).

Part III.A.6

Figure 6.17 *p*-chart.

Figure 6.18 *X* and mR chart.

Process Capability

There are three potential process capability indices for variables data: C_r, C_p, and C_{pk}. Additionally, there are three process capability indices for variables data: P_r, P_p, and P_{pk}.

The main difference between the "C" and "P" indices is that C_r, C_p, and C_{pk} are used with sample data to determine if the process is capable of meeting customer specifications (short term), whereas P_r, P_p, and P_{pk} are used with population data to determine if the process is capable of meeting customer specifications (long term).

These indices compare the process statistical control limits to the product specifications to determine the process capability. Figure 6.19 demonstrates the relationship between statistical control limits and product specifications.

Short-term capability **Desired ratio**

$$C_r = \frac{6s}{USL - LSL} \qquad\qquad <1$$

$$C_p = \frac{USL - LSL}{6s} \qquad\qquad >1$$

$$C_{pk} = \text{Minimum of } \frac{\bar{X} - LSL}{3s}, \frac{USL - \bar{X}}{3s} \qquad >1$$

Long-term capability **Desired ratio**

$$P_r = \frac{6\sigma}{USL - LSL} \qquad\qquad <1$$

$$P_p = \frac{USL - LSL}{6\sigma} \qquad\qquad >1$$

$$P_{pk} = \text{Minimum of } \frac{\bar{X} - LSL}{3\sigma}, \frac{USL - \bar{X}}{3\sigma} \qquad >1$$

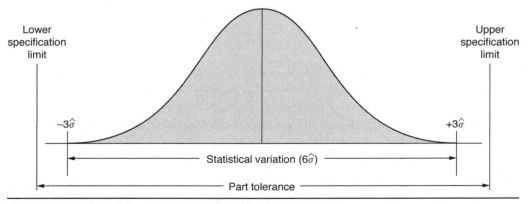

Figure 6.19   Control chart accuracy and precision.

Source: Mark Durivage, *Practical Engineering, Process, and Reliability Statistics* (Milwaukee, WI: ASQ Quality Press, 2014).

7. CONFIDENCE AND TOLERANCE INTERVALS

> Compute confidence intervals and tolerance
> intervals, draw conclusions from the results, and
> describe how point estimates are used to determine
> the interval. (Evaluate)
>
> Body of Knowledge III.A.7

Suppose an estimate is needed for the mean coating thickness of a population of 1000 circuit boards received from a supplier. Rather than measure all 1000 boards, a random sample of 40 is selected for measurement. The mean of the 40 values is 0.003 inches. Based on this sample, the estimate for the mean coating thickness for the entire lot of 1000 boards is 0.003 inches. This value is called the *point estimate*.

In this case the sample mean is an estimator of the population mean. Stated in other words, a statistic, in this case the sample mean, is used to estimate the parameter, in this case the population mean (keep in mind that *statistic* refers to a value obtained from a sample and *parameter* is a value from the population). An estimator is called *unbiased* if the mean of all possible values is equal to the parameter being estimated. The sample mean is an unbiased estimator for the population mean as a result of the central limit theorem. An example of a *biased* estimator is the sample standard deviation s. That is, s ≠ σ. One estimator for a parameter is called more *efficient* than another if it requires fewer samples to obtain an equally good approximation. If two estimators A and B are unbiased, A is defined to be more efficient than B if it has a smaller variance.

The efficiency E of A relative to B is defined as

$$E = \frac{\sigma_A^2}{\sigma_B^2}$$

In control chart calculations the population standard deviation is often calculated from the range of the sample. This method is unbiased. However, as sample size gets larger it is better to use the sample standard deviation because the relative efficiency of the range method decreases. That is, it takes more samples to obtain an equally good estimate for *s*. For sample sizes smaller than $n = 6$, however, the relative efficiency is greater than 0.95.

Maximum Likelihood Estimates

In some cases a distribution has a known PDF type with an unknown parameter Y for which an estimator is needed. The values of the elements of the distribution depend on the PDF type and the value of the parameter Y. That is, the PDF can be written $f(x,Y)$.

Let $x_1, x_2, \ldots, x_n$ be a random sample from the distribution. The likelihood function is defined as the probability that these *n* values will be the ones selected. The probability that the first value is selected is $f(x_1,Y)$, the probability that the second is selected is $f(x_2,Y)$, and so on. So the probability that this sample will be drawn is the product of these values:

$$L(Y) = f(x_1,Y)\, f(x_2,Y) \ldots f(x_n,Y)$$

This product is known as the *likelihood function*. In order to find the value of Y that will maximize $L(Y)$ we will set its derivative equal to zero and solve the resulting equation for Y; that is, solve $L'(Y) = 0$. This will produce the value of Y that maximizes the probability that the randomly selected numbers will have values $x_1, x_2, \ldots, x_n$.

EXAMPLE 6.35

Suppose the PDF is the Bernoulli distribution:

$$f(x) = p^x(1-p)^{1-x} \quad x = 0 \text{ or } 1 \quad 0 \le p \le 1$$

Given a random sample $x_1, x_2, \ldots, x_n$ we want a value of Y that is a good estimate of p. In other words, the question is, "What value of p would have the highest likelihood of producing this set of random values?" The answer is found by differentiating the likelihood function:

$$L(p) = f(x_1, p) f(x_2, p) \ldots f(x_n, p)$$

$$= p^{x_1}(1-p)^{1-x_1} p^{x_2}(1-p)^{1-x_2} \ldots p^{x_n}(1-p)^{1-x_n}$$

$$= p^{x_1 + x_2 + \ldots + x_n}(1-p)^{1-x_1 + 1-x_2 + \ldots + 1-x_n}$$

$$= p^{\sum x_i}(1-p)^{n - \sum x_i}$$

Setting the derivative of this expression equal to zero and solving leads (eventually) to the conclusion that

$$p = \frac{\sum x_i}{n} = \bar{x}$$

So the value of p that maximizes the likelihood that this sample will be drawn is the mean of the sample values.

Point Estimates

A *point estimate* of a population parameter can be made using the values of a sample from that population. One population parameter often estimated is the mean. It is also sometimes desirable to estimate the population standard deviation.

Consistency

It is important for estimators to be *consistent*. Consider a series of estimators for some parameter E and denote the elements of the series $E_1, E_2, \ldots, E_n$. The estimator is called consistent if E_n approaches E as n gets larger.

The Estimate of the Mean

The population mean μ can be estimated using the sample mean $\bar{x}$. If the sample consists of n values, $x_1, x_2, \ldots, x_n$, the estimate of the population mean can be calculated as

$$\hat{\mu} = \bar{x} = \frac{\sum x(i)}{n}$$

The Estimate of the Standard Deviation

The population standard deviation (σ) can be estimated using the sample standard deviation (s). If the sample contains n values, $x_1, x_2, \ldots, x_n$, the estimate of the population standard deviation can be calculated as

$$\hat{\sigma} = s = \sqrt{\frac{\sum (x_i - \bar{x})^2}{n-1}}$$

EXAMPLE 6.36

A sample of five units from a population is tested to failure.

Unit number 1 failed at 162 hours.
Unit number 2 failed at 157 hours.
Unit number 3 failed at 146 hours.
Unit number 4 failed at 173 hours.
Unit number 5 failed at 155 hours.
Total = 793 hours.

The point estimate of the mean of the failure times of the population can be calculated as

$$\hat{\mu} = \bar{x} = \frac{793}{5} = 158.6 \text{ hours}$$

EXAMPLE 6.37

Assume the units in Example 6.36 were checked every five hours for failure. The exact time of failure is not known.

Unit 1 failed between 160 and 165 hours.
Unit 2 failed between 155 and 160 hours.
Unit 3 failed between 145 and 150 hours.
Unit 4 failed between 170 and 175 hours.
Unit 5 failed between 150 and 155 hours.
Totals = 780 and 805 hours.

An interval estimate of the mean can be calculated. The interval end points can be obtained using the two totals:

$$\text{Upper estimate: } \hat{\mu} = \frac{805}{5} = 161 \text{ hours}$$

$$\text{Lower estimate: } \hat{\mu} = \frac{780}{5} = 156 \text{ hours}$$

The interval estimate for the mean of the population is between 156 and 161 hours.

EXAMPLE 6.38

The point estimate of the population standard deviation using the data in Example 6.36 can be calculated as

$$\hat{\sigma} = \sqrt{\frac{(162 - 158.6)^2 + (157 - 158.6)^2 + \ldots + (155 - 158.6)^2}{4}}$$

$$\hat{\sigma} = 9.915$$

Any scientific calculator will perform the calculations for estimating the mean and standard deviation using sample data. Be sure to use the function key with $n - 1$ in the denominator when calculating the estimate for standard deviation.

Note that the denominator in the estimate of the population standard deviation is one less than the sample size.

The point estimates of the population mean and the population standard deviation are distribution free. This means they are valid regardless of the population distribution. What meaning these values have, however, is very much dependent on the distribution of the population.

Confidence Intervals

A statistical confidence interval incorporating a given risk (α) can be placed about the point estimate of any population parameter made from a sample taken from the population. The statement can then be made that the true parameter of the population is within that interval with a confidence of $1 - \alpha$. The risk denoted as α is known as the *significance*.

Usually, the mean is the parameter of interest. However, confidence intervals can be set about other estimates, such as the standard deviation. The central limit theorem can be used to set a confidence interval about the estimate of the mean regardless of the population distribution if the sample size is large. It can also be used with small samples if the population distribution does not differ greatly from the normal distribution. In general, the criterion is that the population is unimodal (one peak) and is somewhat symmetrical. This is not always the case for reliability data. If the test is to determine failure times, and if the units are designed not to fail, there is usually not enough time or enough units available to get a significant number of failures. Also, some of the distributions used to model reliability data, especially the exponential, are significantly different from a normal distribution. If the population distribution is known (or assumed), exact confidence limit values can be calculated.

The Normal Distribution

Confidence interval for the mean: standard deviation known. If the population distribution is normal and the standard deviation (σ) is known, the confidence interval for the mean is:

$$\bar{x} \pm \frac{Z_{\alpha/2}}{\sqrt{n}} \sigma$$

where

α = Probability that the population mean is not in the interval (called α risk)

$1 - \alpha$ = The confidence level

$Z_{\alpha/2}$ = The value from the Z-table (area under the normal curve) with an area of $\alpha/2$ in the tail of the distribution

The upper confidence limit on the mean is $\bar{x} + \dfrac{Z_{\alpha/2}}{\sqrt{n}}\sigma$

The lower confidence limit on the mean is $\bar{x} - \dfrac{Z_{\alpha/2}}{\sqrt{n}}\sigma$

Minimal error will be incurred using the above formulas, even if the standard deviation must be estimated, if the sample size is at least 30 ($n \geq 30$).

When a confidence interval for the mean of a population is calculated, the margin of error is given by the formula

$$E = \frac{Z_{\alpha/2}}{\sqrt{n}}\sigma$$

To determine the sample size necessary to obtain a given margin of error, solve for n rounded to a whole number:

$$n = \left(\frac{Z_{\alpha/2}\sigma}{E}\right)^2$$

EXAMPLE 6.39

Calculate the 0.90 confidence limits for the mean of the coating thickness of the circuit boards.

The coating thickness of 40 circuit boards is measured in order to make an estimate of the coating thickness of the entire population of 1000 circuit boards. The coating process is known to have a standard deviation of 0.0005 inches.

$\bar{x} = 0.003$ inches

$\sigma = 0.0005$

$\alpha = 0.10$ (the risk)

$1 - \alpha = 0.90$ (the confidence)

$Z_{(\alpha/2)} = Z_{(0.05)} = 1.645$ (from the normal tables in Appendix E)

Since the standard deviation is known, the Z distribution can be used to calculate the confidence limits.

Confidence interval $= \bar{x} \pm \dfrac{Z_{\alpha/2}}{\sqrt{n}}\sigma$

Confidence interval $= 0.003 \pm \dfrac{1.645}{\sqrt{40}}(0.0005) = 0.003 \pm 0.00013$

Upper confidence limit $= 0.003 + 0.00013 = 0.00313$ inches

Lower confidence limit $= 0.003 - 0.00013 = 0.00287$ inches

With a confidence of 0.90, the true mean of the population is between 0.00287 and 0.00313 inches.

EXAMPLE 6.40

For Example 6.39, calculate the required sample size to obtain a 0.99% confidence interval ($\alpha = 0.01$) with the same margin of error:

$$E = \frac{Z_{\alpha/2}}{\sqrt{n}}\sigma = \frac{(1.645)(0.0005)}{\sqrt{40}} = 0.00013$$

$$Z_{\alpha/2} = Z_{0.05} = 2.575$$

$$n = \left(\frac{Z_{\alpha/2}}{E}\sigma\right)^2 = \left[\frac{(2.575)(0.0005)}{0.00013}\right]^2 = 98 \text{ (rounded value)}$$

To reduce the margin of error or to increase the confidence level, increase the sample size.

Confidence interval for the mean: standard deviation unknown. If the standard deviation of the population is not known and must be estimated from the sample data, the t distribution is used to set the confidence limits. The t distribution is similar to the Z distribution in that it is symmetrical about the mean. The t value is larger than the corresponding Z value because of the uncertainty involved in the estimate of σ. The smaller the sample size, the more the uncertainty. The value of t depends on the sample size. Statisticians define a value called the *degrees of freedom* (v). For the t distribution the degrees of freedom are $n - 1$. A table of t values is in Appendix J. It should be stressed that the use of the t-table is valid only under the assumption that the population distribution is normal. However, the formulas work fairly well for moderate sample sizes and nearly normal populations. Statisticians say the procedure is robust to the normality assumption:

$$\text{Confidence interval for the mean} = \bar{x} \pm \frac{t_{\alpha/2,v}}{\sqrt{n}}s$$

where:

s is the estimate of the population standard deviation.

$t_{\alpha/2,v}$ is the value from the t-table for a risk of α and $v = n - 1$ degrees of freedom.

$$\text{Upper confidence limit} = \bar{x} + \frac{t_{\alpha/2,v}}{\sqrt{n}}s$$

$$\text{Lower confidence limit} = \bar{x} - \frac{t_{\alpha/2,v}}{\sqrt{n}}s$$

Note: The difference in the use of the Z distribution and the t distribution to calculate confidence limits on the mean is of significance to the statistician. The difference may be of little practical importance to the practicing reliability engineer. The student is encouraged to pay close attention to the difference in the use of the two distributions and to the way the questions are stated.

EXAMPLE 6.41

Assume that the sample in Example 6.36 is from a population that can be approximated by a normal distribution. Find the 0.90 confidence interval for the mean:

$n = 5$

$\bar{X} = 158.6$ hours

$s = 9.915$ hours

The standard deviation is estimated from the sample; therefore, the t distribution is used to calculate the confidence limits:

$t_{(\alpha/2=0.05, v=n-1=4)} = 2.132$

$$\text{Upper confidence limit} = 158.6 + \frac{(9.915)(2.132)}{\sqrt{5}} = 168.05$$

$$\text{Lower confidence limit} = 158.6 - \frac{(9.915)(2.132)}{\sqrt{5}} = 149.15$$

The true mean of the population is between these limits with a confidence of 0.90.

$$149.15 < 168.05 \text{ with a confidence of } 0.90$$

Whenever sampling is used to estimate the value of population parameters, it is possible to calculate an interval of risk. When journalists report the results of sampling polls, they add a margin of error, which is another format for a confidence interval, usually with the default confidence level of 95%. For instance, suppose the results state that 43% of the respondents answered "A" and 46% responded "B" with a ± 3.5% margin of error. This is equivalent to saying that there is 95% confidence that the percent of the population that would have answered "A" is between 39.5% and 46.5%, while the percent that would have answered "B" is between 42.5% and 49.5%. Since these intervals overlap, one can't be 95% confident which answer is most popular, a so-called statistical dead heat.

Some statistical software packages will produce curves with associated confidence intervals. Figure 6.20 displays a plot from Minitab showing 95% confidence interval curves for the survival plot of a variable named "Start."

Confidence Interval on the Standard Deviation

The *chi-square* (χ^2) *distribution* is used to calculate confidence limits on the standard deviation of the normal distribution. The chi-square distribution is not symmetrical; therefore, both the upper and lower values must be found from the tables. The chi-square values are also defined using degrees of freedom. The chi-square value is dependent on the sample size. Values of the chi-square distribution are given in Appendix I.

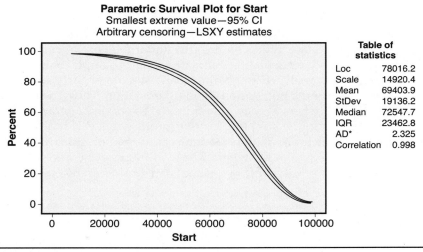

Figure 6.20   Plot of a curve with confidence interval.

The confidence interval for the population standard deviation is given by

$$\sqrt{\frac{n-1}{\chi^2_{(\alpha/2, v=n-1)}}}\, s < \sigma < \sqrt{\frac{n-1}{\chi^2_{(1-\alpha/2, v=n-1)}}}\, s$$

χ^2 is the value from the chi-square table using $n-1$ degrees of freedom.

Part III.A.7

EXAMPLE 6.42

Calculate the 0.90 confidence interval for the population standard deviation using the data from Example 6.36.

$n = 5$

$\hat{\sigma} = s = 9.915$ hours

From the chi-square tables:

$\chi^2_{(0.05,4)} = 9.488$

$\chi^2_{(0.95,4)} = 0.711$

Lower confidence value $= \sqrt{\dfrac{4}{9.488}}\,(9.915) = 6.44$

Upper confidence value $= \sqrt{\dfrac{4}{0.711}}\,(9.915) = 23.5$

$6.44 < 23.5$ with a confidence of 0.90.

Statistical Tolerance Interval

Statistical tolerance intervals, sometimes called *statistical tolerance limits,* are used to determine confidence values on the area under the normal curve when using a mean and a standard deviation estimated from a sample. Sample data from the population are analyzed to obtain $\overline{X}$, an estimate of the population mean, and s, an estimate of the population standard deviation. The two-sided tolerance interval is $\overline{X} \pm Ks$, where K is a value from the two-sided tolerance table and is dependent of the sample size, the desired confidence level, and the proportion of the area to be included within the interval. If the one-sided limit is desired, the tolerance value is $\overline{X} - Ks$, where K is a value from the one-sided tolerance table. Tables for one-sided and two-sided statistical tolerance factors are given in Appendix K.

EXAMPLE 6.43

Fifteen units from a population assumed to be normal are tested to failure. The sample mean and the sample standard deviation are calculated:

$n = 15$

$\overline{X} = 1076$ hours

$s = 45.6$ hours

a. What is the estimate of the reliability for a mission time of 1000 hours?

The reliability $[R(t_1)]$ is the area under the failure distribution to the right of t_1.

$$Z = \frac{(1000 - 1067)}{45.6} = -1.47$$

$R(t = 1000) = 0.93$ (using the normal table in Appendix E)

b. How many hours can be accumulated on a unit and maintain a reliability of at least 0.99?

It is necessary to find Z from the normal tables such that 99% of the area is to the right of that value:

$Z = -2.33$

$t = 1067 - (2.33)(45.6) = 961$ hours

c. With a confidence of 0.95, how many hours can be accumulated on a unit and maintain a reliability of at least 0.99?

From the one-sided tolerance interval table with a confidence of 0.95 and a sample size of 15:

$K = 3.520$

$t = \overline{X} - Ks = 1067 - (3.520)(45.6) = 906$ hours

d. What time interval will contain 99% of the failures?

It is necessary to find Z values from the normal tables such that 0.5% of the area is in each tail of the distribution:

$|Z| = 2.57$

$t_{(Upper)} = 1067 + (2.57)(45.6) = 1184$ hours

$t_{(Lower)} = 1067 - (2.57)(45.6) = 950$ hours

99% of the failures are expected to occur between 950 and 1184 hours of use.

e. With a confidence of 0.95, what interval will contain 99% of the failures?

From the two-sided tolerance table with a confidence of 0.95 and a sample size of 15:

$K = 3.878$

$t_{(Upper)} = \overline{X} + Ks = 1067 + (3.878)(45.6) = 1244$ hours

$t_{(Lower)} = \overline{X} - Ks = 1067 - (3.878)(45.6) = 890$ hours

99% of the failures will occur between 890 and 1244 hours of use with a confidence of 0.95.

Exponential Distribution

The exponential distribution is expressed as

$$f(t) = \frac{1}{\theta} e^{\frac{-t}{\theta}}$$

The mean of the exponential distribution is equal to θ, and is referred to as the mean time to failure (MTTF) if the units are not repairable and the mean time between failures (MTBF) if the units are repairable.

The exponential distribution is unique in that its failure rate (λ) is constant. The failure rate is equal to the reciprocal of the mean:

$$\lambda = \frac{1}{\theta}$$

Because the failure rate is constant, the probability of failure is not dependent on the age of the unit, but only on the length of the mission time. Also, because of the constant failure rate property, the mean can be estimated using censored data. It is not necessary for each unit in the sample to fail in order to make an estimate. A test can be terminated on a given failure, referred to as *failure censored*, or at a given time, referred to as *time censored*. To make an estimate of the mean, it is only necessary to know the total time (T) accumulated on the units and the number of failures (r). The total time is accumulated using the units that fail as well as the units that do not fail. The estimate of the mean is given as

$$\hat{\theta} = \frac{T}{r}$$

EXAMPLE 6.44

Ten units from a distribution assumed to be exponential are placed on a life test. Four of the units failed at the times shown. The units were not replaced when they failed. The test ended at 5000 hours (time censored) with six units still operating. Estimate the population mean:

$t(1) = 1150$ hours

$t(2) = 2150$ hours

$t(3) = 3350$ hours

$t(4) = 4950$ hours

Total of the failure times $\Sigma t(i) = 11{,}600$ hours

Number of units on test $n = 10$

Number of failures $r = 4$

The total accumulated test time (T):

$T = \Sigma t(i) + (n - r)(5500) = 11{,}600 + (6)(5000) = 41{,}600$ hours

$$\hat{\theta} = \frac{T}{r} = \frac{41{,}600}{4} = 10{,}400 \text{ hours}$$

This also gives an estimate of failure rate (λ).

$$\hat{\lambda} = \frac{1}{\hat{\theta}} = \frac{1}{10{,}400} = 96 \times 10^{-6} \text{ failures per hour (96 failures per million hours)}$$

Confidence Interval for the Mean of the Exponential Distribution

The chi-square (χ^2) distribution is used to calculate the confidence limits on the mean of the exponential distribution.

For the two-sided $1 - \alpha$ confidence interval, the lower limit is given by

$$\theta_L = \frac{2T}{\chi^2_{(\alpha/2, v=2r+2)}}$$

if the test is time censored (ended at a given time), and

$$\theta_L = \frac{2T}{\chi^2_{(\alpha/2, v=2r)}}$$

if the test is failure censored (ended on a given failure).

The difference in the equations is in the number of degrees of freedom for the (χ^2) term. If the test is time censored, the number of degrees of freedom is $2r + 2$, and if the test is failure censored, the number of degrees of freedom is $2r$.

The upper limit for both time-censored and failure-censored tests is

$$\theta_U = \frac{2T}{\chi^2_{(1-\alpha/2, v=2r)}}$$

EXAMPLE 6.45

Calculate the 0.90 confidence interval for the data in Example 6.44:

The test is time censored

$T = 41,600$ hours

$r = 4$

$\alpha = 0.10$

$\hat{\sigma} = 10,400$ hours

The lower confidence limit is $\theta_L = \dfrac{2T}{\chi^2_{(\alpha/2, v=2r+2)}}$

From the chi-square tables (Appendix I),

$$\chi^2_{(\alpha/2, v=2r+2)} = \chi^2_{(0.05, 10)} = 18.307$$

$$\theta_L = \frac{2(41,600)}{18.307} = 4545 \text{ hours}$$

The upper confidence limit is $\theta_U = \dfrac{2T}{\chi^2_{(1-\alpha/2, v=2r)}}$

From the chi-square tables,

$$\chi^2_{(1-\alpha/2, v=2r)} = \chi^2_{(0.95, 8)} = 2.733$$

$$\theta_U = \frac{2(41,600)}{2.744} = 30,320 \text{ hours}$$

$$4545 \text{ hours} < \theta < 30,320 \text{ hours}$$

The true mean of the population is between 4545 and 30,320 hours with a confidence of 0.90.

To set the one-sided confidence limit with a confidence of 0.90:

$$\theta_L = \frac{2T}{\chi^2_{(\alpha, v=2r+2)}}$$

$$\chi^2_{(\alpha, v=2r=2)} = \chi^2_{(0.10, 10)} = 15.987$$

$$\theta_L = \frac{2(41,600)}{15.987} = 5200 \text{ hours}$$

$$\theta > 5200 \text{ hours}$$

The true mean of the population is greater than 5200 hours with a confidence of 0.90.

For the one-sided confidence limit, the full α risk is placed in the lower tail:

$$\theta_L = \frac{2T}{\chi^2_{(\alpha, v=2r+2)}}$$

if the test is time censored, and

$$\theta_L = \frac{2T}{\chi^2_{(\alpha, v=2r)}}$$

if the test is failure censored.

Binomial Distribution

The binomial is a discrete distribution. This means the distribution is only defined for integer values. The binomial distribution gives the probability of exactly x success outcomes out of n possible outcomes if the probability (p) of success remains the same for each trial.

The PDF for the binomial is

$$P(x) = C_n^x p^x (1-p)^{n-x}$$

C_n^x is the number of combinations that can be made from n items taken x at a time.

$$C_n^x = \frac{n!}{x!(n-x)!}$$

When the binomial is used to model reliability data, x could be the number of units that fail, and is denoted as r. If x becomes the number of units that do not fail, it is denoted as $n - r$. The probability of success on each trial is p, which is the mean of the distribution.

EXAMPLE 6.46

Find the number of combinations that can be made using 10 items if you take them four at a time:

$$C_4^{10} = \frac{10!}{4!6!} = 210$$

This problem can be worked on most scientific calculators using the factorial key or using the combinations key to find the solution directly.

EXAMPLE 6.47

It is known that units have a 0.92 probably of surviving a given test. Twenty units are subjected to the test.

a. What is the probability that exactly 18 units will survive (not fail)?

$p = 0.92$ (Probability the unit does not fail)

$n = 20$

$r = 2$ $n - r = 18$ (Number of units that do not fail)

$$P(18) = C_{18}^{20} (0.92)^{18} (1 - 0.92)^2 = 0.2711$$

This problem could be worked by finding the probability that exactly two of the units fail and then subtracting from one:

$P = 0.08$ (Probability the unit fails)

$n = 20$

$r = 2$ (Number of units that fail)

$$P(18) = 1 - C_2^{20} (0.08)^2 (0.92)^{18} = 0.2711$$

b. What is the probability that at least 18 units will survive the test?

The probabilities are mutually exclusive and therefore can be added:

$$P(n-r \geq 18) = P(18) + P(19) + P(20)$$

$$= C_{18}^{20}(0.92)^{18}(0.08)^2 + C_{19}^{20}(0.92)^{19}(0.08) + C_{20}^{20}(0.92)^{20}$$

$$= 0.2711 + 0.3282 + 0.1887$$

$$= 0.788$$

Estimating the Binomial Mean from a Sample

An estimate of p can be made using data from a test. The data must be recorded as unit success or unit failure. This is known as attribute data, as the exact times of the failures are not known. If n units are tested and r units fail ($n - r$ units do not), the estimate of the probability of unit success, p, is the number of successes divided by the number tested. This probability is the reliability of the unit for a mission equivalent to the test:

$$\hat{p} = \frac{n-r}{n}$$

EXAMPLE 6.48

Thirty sensors are tested to determine if they will detect a given force. Two of the sensors failed to detect the force. What is the estimate of the reliability of the sensor to detect the force?

$$\hat{p} = \hat{R} = \frac{(30-2)}{30} = 0.933$$

Confidence Interval for the Mean of the Binomial Distribution

Reliability test data are usually very limited. Sample sizes are small, and if the units have high reliability, there will be few failures. The exact relationships should be used to calculate the confidence limit for the mean. Excessive error can be introduced using the normal approximation. To calculate the confidence limit for the mean of the binomial, it is necessary to use the F distribution. The F value is the ratio of two chi-square values and has two sets of degrees of freedom.

The lower $1 - \alpha$ confidence limit is given as

$$R_L = \frac{n-r}{(n-r) + (r+1)F_{\alpha, v_1, v_2}}$$

$F_{\alpha, v1, v2}$ is a value from the F distribution table with a risk of α and v_1 degrees of freedom for the numerator and v_2 degrees of freedom for the denominator:

$$v_1 = 2(r + 1)$$

$$v_2 = 2(n - r)$$

Part III.A.7

F-tables are in Appendix F, Appendix G, and Appendix H. The *F*-tables can be confusing to read. It is important that the student studying for and taking the CRE exam have tables they can read quickly and correctly.

Success Testing

If there are no failures during a test, a point estimate of the mean cannot be made. A lower confidence value for the mean can be calculated. The lower $1 - \alpha$ confidence value for a no-failure test is given as

$$R_L = (\alpha)^{\frac{1}{n}}$$

EXAMPLE 6.49

Calculate the lower 0.90 confidence limit on the mean estimated in Example 6.48:

$n = 30$

$r = 2$

$n - r = 28$

$\alpha = 0.10$

$F_{\alpha,v1,v2} = F_{0.10,6,56} = 1.88$

When the number of degrees of freedom exceeds 30, the *F*-tables require interpolation. The lower 0.90 confidence limit is

$$R_L = \frac{28}{[28 + 3(1.88)]} = 0.832$$

$$R > 0.832$$

The reliability is greater than 0.832 with a confidence of 0.90.

For graphs that can be used to make this calculation, see Appendix B of Ireson, Coombs, and Moss, *The Handbook of Reliability Engineering and Management*.

EXAMPLE 6.50

Calculate the lower 0.90 confidence limit for the reliability for the sensors in Example 6.48 if the 30 units were tested with no failures:

$$R_L = (0.10)^{\frac{1}{30}} = 0.926$$

$$R > 0.926$$

The reliability of the sensor is greater than 0.926 with a confidence of 0.90.

A frequently asked question is, "What sample size is required to obtain a given reliability with a given confidence?" If the test can be run with no failures, the required sample size can be found from the above equation.

Solve for *n*:

$$n = \frac{\log(\alpha)}{\log(R_L)}$$

n is usually rounded to the next higher integer.

EXAMPLE 6.51

How many no-failure tests are required to demonstrate a reliability of 0.95 with a confidence of 0.90?

$$n = \frac{\log(0.10)}{\log(0.95)} = 45$$

Note: The logarithms used here can be either base 10 or base e. Base 10 logarithms are denoted as log. Base e logarithms, called natural logarithms, are usually denoted as ln.

Chapter 7
B. Data Management

1. SOURCES AND USES OF RELIABILITY DATA

Describe sources of reliability data (prototype, development, test, field, warranty, published, etc.), their advantages and limitations, and how the data can be used to measure and enhance product reliability. (Analyze)

Body of Knowledge III.B.1

A good warranty program reaches into many different organizational functions:

- *Product pricing* must include allowances for warranty costs

- *Advertising* can use warranties as inducements to purchase

- *Supply chain agreements* should spell out warranty liabilities and procedures

- *Accounting procedures* should include accruals or sinking funds to cover future warranty costs

- *Operation instruction manuals* should include preventive maintenance recommendations that will mitigate failures

- *Engineering and reliability functions* have responsibilities for determining causes and determining product/process corrective actions as required

The breadth of warranty considerations implies that improvements in warranty management have the potential for substantial financial impact. Finding and executing these improvements begins with an understanding of terms.

Warranties should spell out:

- Effective initial date and duration of the warranty

- Definitions of parts and defects to be covered

- Warranty procedures, including return routes, replacement/ reimbursement policies, and policies that will be followed when no defect is found

- Conditions of use such as environmental specifications (ranges for temperature, vibration, salinity, electronic parameters) and operation procedures

- Conditions of storage, transportation, and installation

If suppliers are involved, effective warranty management requires agreements as to all these aspects with each supplier, regardless of tier.

Collection and Analysis of Warranty Data

The data collection process should include an effective method for identifying the failure conditions, including the following information:

- Traceability of each component so that its supplier, date, and conditions of manufacture and assembly are available

- Conditions of use such as environment, handling, maintenance, and operation

- Failure parameters, including type of failure, symptoms, condition of other components, and action taken (replacement, repair, refund, and so on)

Effort should be made to get beyond the "125 failures during Q3" or "$7.5M in warranty costs" type of warranty data. Obtaining useful warranty information may require expenditure of considerable resources to determine the validity of the warranty claims and the causes of the failures. These expenditures can be justified if the follow-up action results in product improvements that avoid future costs. In addition, the data may yield cost avoidance if current practices result in paying for warranty claims that are not valid or that should properly be assessed to suppliers.

Investigations of causes may require extensive study using FMEA and other tools. Consideration should be given to analyzing data for correlations with geography, place of manufacture, installer, type of application, environmental conditions, and other groupings as appropriate. Trend analyses are also useful. In some situations, sampling techniques may be employed rather than studying the entire population.

Warranty information can be used in various ways to improve customer satisfaction, including:

- Product design changes

- Process/manufacturing changes

- Changes in installation/operation documentation

- Product recalls

- Improvement in supplier performance

- Improvement of FMEA processes

In addition, warranty data can be used to refine reliability prediction for future product designs.

Sources of Reliability Data

Reliability data are generally available to a manufacturer from several sources, both external and internal to the company. A valuable external source of component reliability data is the supplier. Other users of the same component can also supply reliability data. A comprehensive external data source available to military contractors is the Government–Industry Data Exchange Program (GIDEP). This program generates and distributes reliability data on commercially available off-the-shelf units that are used by the various contractors. Failure data for units such as motors, pumps, relays, and so on, are exchanged through the GIDEP program. Information can be obtained from GIDEP Operations Center, Corona, California. Professional organizations such as the Institute of Electrical and Electronics Engineers (IEEE) develop and maintain reliability data on hardware of various types. The IEEE can be contacted at 3 Park Avenue 17th Floor, New York, New York 10016-5997.

Information on nonelectrical parts (NPRD) can be obtained from the Rome Air Development Center, National Technical Information Service, Springfield, Virginia. Many times, internally generated data are given higher credibility; the conditions used to generate the data are known and can be controlled. Capabilities of the manufacturing process, the quality control methods employed, and the specified operation environment of the design, as well as other factors specific to the manufacturer, are reflected in internally generated data.

One example of internally generated data is from analysis of prototypes. Early in the design process it is often useful to produce a model of the item and use it for reliability testing. Prototype testing can provide early warning of design flaws, material requirements, and other changes that can improve reliability. Throughout the development process, the reliability engineer can be subjecting proposed parts to preliminary stress studies and other tests. Testing of final products provides another opportunity to collect data for warranty calculations, preventive maintenance, and possible future designs.

Another valuable source of reliability data is the field service facility. Most manufacturers maintain data on the repair and maintenance services provided to their customers. This could be warranty data, data from dealers or distributors, or data from customers or users of the product. Each return or maintenance activity should result in a report. These data should be collected and distributed. Failure analyses performed on failed parts, if they are available, will provide data as to the root cause of the failure. It is a reliability engineering function to collect and distribute field failure data. The data need to be available to reliability engineering, quality engineering, product design, testing, marketing, service, and other appropriate engineering and support functions.

Care must be taken to use the data appropriately. The conditions under which data generated internally are developed will be known. The true test time, the test acceleration numbers if used, the environment of the test, the actual failure mode, and other conditions will be documented. Data that are generated externally might be suspect, as the actual test or use conditions may not be known.

The various sources are summarized in Table 7.1.

Table 7.1 Sources of reliability data.

Source	Comments	Advantages	Limitations	Potential contribution to product reliability
Prototype	Early in design process	Provides visible and testable item	Spending effort on preliminary design	Can head off early design flaws
Development	Throughout development process	Can track reliability changes with each design	Time/ resources required	Can head off early design flaws
Final product	Test as soon as available from manufacturing	Early basis for warranty calculations	May not be able to simulate environmental conditions	More extensive testing may flag weaknesses
Field warranty	Need complete data	Customer viewpoint	Data often sketchy	Helps put dollar sign on reliability

2. TYPES OF DATA

> Identify and distinguish between various types of data (e.g., attributes vs. variable, discrete vs. continuous, censored vs. complete, and univariate vs. multivariate). Select appropriate analysis tools based on the data type. (Evaluate)
>
> Body of Knowledge III.B.2

Discrete (attributes) data are obtained when the characteristic being studied can have either a finite number or countably infinite number of possible values. For example, the results of a leak test might be designated as zero or one to indicate failed or passed. Another example would be the count of the number of scratches on an object. In this case the possible values are 0, 1, 2, . . ., a so-called countably infinite set. Attribute control charts (for example, p, np, u, and c) are used to plot discrete data.

Continuous (variables) data are obtained when the characteristic being studied can have any value in a range of numbers. For example, the length of a part can be any value above zero. Between each two values on a continuous scale there are infinitely many other values. For example, between 2.350 and 2.351 inches the values 2.3502, 2.350786, and so on, occur. Variables control charts (for example, $\overline{X}$ and R, ImR) are used to plot continuous data. These charts are used to plot a single variable and are referred to as *univariate* charts. Output variables such as a dimension, hardness, pH, and so on, and input variables such as pressure, temperature, and voltage are often plotted on these charts.

If two or more input variables influence the process, it is usually best to use a *multivariate* chart rather than several univariate charts. The multivariate chart most like the $\bar{X}$ and R chart is called the T_2 *generalized variance chart*. Multivariate charts are usually plotted with the help of software packages. A disadvantage of multivariate control charts is that the scale does not directly relate to the input variables individually.

When collecting failure data, there are several possible ways the tests may be administered. Consider the testing of several pumps. Timers might be placed on each pump so that *exact failure times* can be recorded. The test might be terminated while some pumps are still functioning. In this case it is known only that these pumps' failure times are longer than the test time. Such data are called *right censored*. Another testing protocol would require that the pumps be checked every 100 hours. If a pump was operating at hour 400 but not at hour 500, it would only be known that the failure occurred between these two times. These data are called *interval censored*. If a pump is found to have failed at the first check at hour 100, it is known only that the failure occurred before hour 100. Such data are called *left censored* rather than interval censored because the failure may have occurred before the interval started, assuming a check of the pump was not conducted at time zero.

3. DATA COLLECTION METHODS

> Identify and select appropriate data collection methods (e.g., surveys, automated tests, automated monitoring and reporting tools) in order to meet various data analysis objectives and data quality needs. (Evaluate)
>
> Body of Knowledge III.B.3

One approach to data collection emphasizes the importance of the *cleanliness* of the information. This view holds that the best data are those that are uncontaminated by changes in outside factors. This can be accomplished by maintaining strict laboratory conditions, perhaps using an environmental chamber. The downside of this course of action is that very few products or processes operate in an environment in which all outside factors are controlled. This technique is most appropriate for early-stage investigation in which fundamental design cause-and-effect relationships are being determined. Some data, such as temperature, time, pressure, and so on, can be collected automatically. Data that attempt to measure qualities such as taste or pain are called *subjective* data, as opposed to *objective* data such as length or weight.

At the other end of the spectrum are *field service* data. This refers to information gathered from products in use by customers. This information is often impacted by differences in installation, environment, operator procedures, and similar factors that make analysis difficult. On the other hand, field service data represent realistic applications of the product and therefore must be taken into account as part of reliability analysis. In most cases this approach is used in the feedback process to aid in determining the accuracy of other reliability analysis methods and to provide input to future revision and design initiatives. Various other methods of data collection have been devised. Perhaps the most powerful technique is to study the failure modes and mechanisms that can occur.

When considering data sources, special attention must be paid to the conditions under which the product will be transported, stored, and used. These conditions include differences in such factors as geographic location, operator habits, lubricants, possible chemical, radiological, or biologic exposure, vibration, electromagnetic environment, and so on.

Reliability data are often stated in binary terms, such as failed or non-failed. Some contemplation should also be given to any degradation of satisfaction from the user's viewpoint—short of failure—that may occur. This contemplation should occur in the light of rising user expectations.

Once the sources of data have been determined, it is necessary to form the data collection plan. This plan needs to provide answers to such questions as:

- *Who will collect the information?* Data collectors must be familiar with the measuring equipment and the product itself. If failure data are to be collected, a well-defined and understood definition of failure is essential. If possible, more than one person should be involved to provide some cross-checking and coverage when one must be away.

- *When will the data be collected?* The plan needs to specify at what stage of design or use the data will be collected. Dates and times help planning by other team members.

- *In what format will the data be collected?* The best step here is to design a data collection sheet and specify the format for summarizing the data.

- *What measurement equipment will be employed?* The plan should specify equipment and recording devices if appropriate.

- *What measures will be used to verify data accuracy and integrity?* The plan may specify units of measurement, calibration of equipment, or recording of ancillary information that might impact the data. If data are transmitted or stored digitally, the use of error correction systems may be specified.

4. DATA SUMMARY AND REPORTING

> Examine collected data for accuracy and usefulness. Analyze, interpret, and summarize data for presentation using various techniques, based on data types, sources, and required output. (Create)
>
> Body of Knowledge III.B.4

Data analysis must be followed by communication of the results to decision makers. Good decisions are not made on the basis of poorly understood information. This makes the analysis → evaluate → summarize sequence the basis for any impact the data will have on products and processes.

The first steps in summarizing data are to construct a histogram and a run chart or a control chart. These help determine whether the process is stable as well as provide estimates of the mean and standard deviation. For example, if a sequence of batches of electrical components were tested in a chemical bath for one hour each, and the number of failures at one hour recorded, these numbers could be the basis for a *p*-chart as well as a histogram. The control chart can be helpful in spotting a trend line. Linear regression may be used to fit a line to the data. Example 7.1 illustrates the use of a histogram, control chart, and linear regression.

EXAMPLE 7.1

A reliability engineer has collected failure rates per thousand cycles as shown below:

Cycles	1000	2000	3000	4000	5000	6000	7000	8000	9000	10,000
Failure rate	0.002	0.003	0.002	0.002	0.003	0.004	0.002	0.003	0.003	0.004

Cycles	11,000	12,000	13,000	14,000	15,000	16,000	17,000	18,000	19,000	20,000
Failure rate	0.003	0.003	0.004	0.005	0.004	0.006	0.005	0.007	0.007	0.008

Cycles	21,000	22,000	23,000	24,000	25,000	26,000	27,000	28,000	29,000	30,000
Failure rate	0.010	0.009	0.010	0.011	0.009	0.008	0.008	0.011	0.010	0.011

Cycles	31,000	32,000	33,000	34,000
Failure rate	0.009	0.011	0.010	0.009

The engineer constructs a histogram:

The histogram has an interesting bimodal pattern. The engineer decides to also construct a run chart:

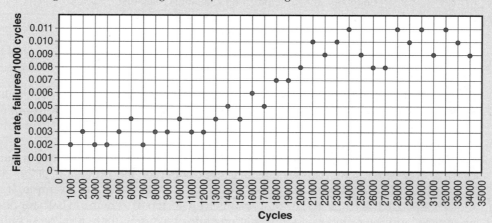

Collecting additional data seems to confirm a pattern of a low failure rate for about the first 12,000 cycles, increasing to a higher rate at about 24,000 cycles and continuing at that higher failure rate level. This would indicate that there is some additional failure mode that begins to occur at 12,000 cycles. The accountants working with warranty projections ask the engineer to provide a formula that can be used for predicting the failure rate during the transition period from 12,000 to 24,000 cycles. The engineer uses linear regression to produce the formula:

Failure rate = 0.000 000 648 × (cycles elapsed) – 0.00482

An important concern when using linear regression is that the procedure generates the best-fitting straight line even though the relationship may not be linear. The resultant line will not fit the data.

To determine how well the formula fits the given data, the engineer produces the following table:

| Cycles | Failure rate | | Error |
	Predicted	Actual	
12,000	0.0030	0.003	0.0000
13,000	0.0036	0.004	0.0004
14,000	0.0043	0.005	0.0007
15,000	0.0049	0.004	0.0009
16,000	0.0056	0.006	0.0004
17,000	0.0062	0.005	0.0012
18,000	0.0069	0.007	0.0001
19,000	0.0075	0.007	0.0005
20,000	0.0081	0.008	0.0001
21,000	0.0088	0.010	0.0012
22,000	0.0094	0.009	0.0004
23,000	0.0100	0.010	0.0000
24,000	0.0107	0.011	0.0003

This formula is provided to the warranty personnel with the caveat that it is only useful in the 12,000 to 24,000 cycle range and will not make valid predictions if it is extrapolated beyond these values.

Of course, the main concern at this point is to identify and correct the failure mode that apparently occurs at 12,000 cycles. We wish the engineer well in that endeavor.

Once failure data have been collected, it is often useful to display them in graphical format using key reliability metrics:

- *Probability density function* (PDF) can be plotted as a histogram showing the number of failures in each time block.

- *The hazard function* shows the failure rate as a function of time. It is convenient to use the following formula for the hazard function:

$$\lambda(t) = \frac{\text{Fraction of failures during the time period}}{\text{Amount of time during the period}}$$

- *The reliability function* plots reliability as a function of time, using the formula:

$$R(t) = \frac{\text{Number surviving at the end of the period}}{\text{Number of units tested}}$$

The Weibull distribution takes on many shapes depending on the value of β, the shape parameter. This feature makes the distribution an extremely flexible tool for solving reliability problems and displaying results.

EXAMPLE 7.2

A total of 283 products are tested for 1100 hours. The number of failures in each 100-hour block of time is recorded.

Time	Number of failures	Number surviving	$\lambda(t)$	$R(t)$
0–99	0	283	0	1.00
100–199	2	281	0.0001	0.99
200–299	10	271	0.0004	0.96
300–399	30	241	0.0011	0.85
400–499	48	193	0.0020	0.68
500–599	60	133	0.0031	0.47
600–699	50	83	0.0038	0.29
700–799	42	41	0.0051	0.14
800–899	30	11	0.0073	0.04
900–999	8	3	0.0073	0.01
1000–1099	3	0	0.0100	0.00

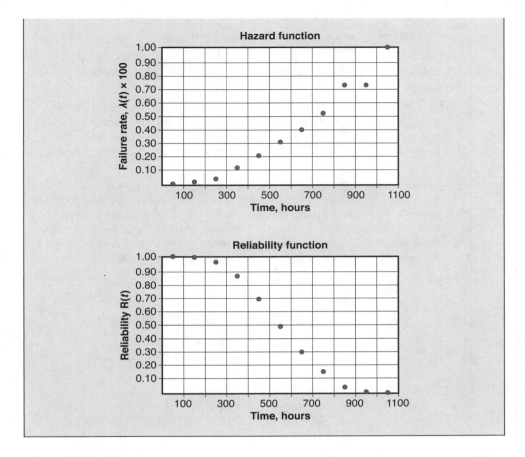

Example 7.3 illustrates a method for plotting data on Weibull probability paper. Various versions of this graph paper can be downloaded from Weibull.com.

EXAMPLE 7.3

Twenty products are tested for 1000 hours. Fourteen products fail at the following times, respectively:

70, 128, 204, 291, 312, 377, 473, 549, 591, 663, 748, 827, 903, 955 hours

Estimate the shape parameter β and the characteristic life η.

Solution:

1. Form a table listing the times to failure in ascending order in the first row. Fill the second row from the median ranks table in Appendix Q using the first 14 entries in the column labeled "20."

Hrs	70	128	204	291	312	377	473	549	591	663	748	827	903	955
MR	0.034	0.083	0.131	0.181	0.230	0.279	0.328	0.377	0.426	0.475	0.525	0.574	0.623	0.672

Continued

2. Plot the first column on the horizontal axis and the second column on the vertical axis of Weibull graph paper (see Figure 7.1).

3. Use a transparent straightedge to sketch a best-fit straight line for the points.

4. Draw a line parallel to the best-fit line that passes through the point labeled O along the left margin of the graph paper. This line is shown as a heavy dashed line in Figure 7.1. Note the value on the β scale where this line crosses the top line of the graph paper. This is the estimate for the shape parameter β. In this example $\beta \approx 1.3$.

5. Note that the vertical axis is labeled "unreliability." This means that the values on this axis are (1 − Reliability). Recall that we use 0.368 on the reliability scale to find η. This would translate to 0.623 on the unreliability scale. This value is indicated on the graph paper as a horizontal dashed line with η at its right end. The horizontal coordinate of the point where this line crosses the best-fit line is the estimated value for η.

In this example it appears that $\eta \approx 900$ hours.

Figure 7.1 Weibull probability graph.

EXAMPLE 7.4

In the previous example, find:

- The reliability function
- The reliability at 200 hours, and compare with the graphical result in Figure 7.1
- The time at which 95% reliability will occur

Solution:

The reliability function with $\eta = 900$ and $\beta = 1.3$ is

$$R(t) = e^{-\left(\frac{t}{900}\right)^{1.3}}$$

Substituting into this formula:

$$R(200) = e^{-(0.222)^{1.3}} \approx 0.87$$

In order to solve for time (t), take the natural log of both sides of the reliability equation.

$$(t/\eta)^\beta = -\ln(0.95)$$

$$t = \eta[-\ln(0.95)]^{1/\beta}$$

$$t = 900[-\ln(0.98)]^{1/1.3} = 91.6 \text{ hours.}$$

The Weibull reliability function is

$$R(t) = e^{-\left(\frac{t}{\eta}\right)^\beta}$$

In Figure 7.1, the vertical line at 200 hours crosses the best-fit line at an unreliability of about 14%, making reliability $\approx$ 86%.

To find the time at which reliability of 95% occurs, locate 5% on the vertical axis. Move across to the best-fit line. The crossing point has a time value of about 90 hours.

5. FAILURE ANALYSIS METHODS

Describe failure analysis tools and methods (e.g., mechanical, materials, physical analysis, and scanning electron microscopy [SEM]) that are used to identify failure mechanisms. (Understand)

Body of Knowledge III.B.5

It is important to have as much information as possible about each failure. This section discusses some approaches that have proved useful.

Part III.B.5

The first step in failure analysis is to determine why the item has been classified as failed. This investigation should begin with the warranty report, but it should not end there. The item should be examined for failure in its construction, but further study should be made of the application and installation—things that should be included in a warranty report but often aren't. Traceability and other documentation should be examined for clues as to the root cause of the failure. If the item did not physically fail, thorough study of the environment in which it functioned is required.

If the part has become deformed or broken, two questions arise:

- Has the part failed to meet designed strength?

- Has the part been subjected to stress beyond its designed strength?

One approach to resolving this dichotomy is to subject a number of identical parts to various stresses. Of course the word "identical," while critical, is impossible to attain. This means a thorough examination of the failed part is necessary to determine whether it has some unique property that makes it more vulnerable to stress. This may involve techniques ranging from a visual study to chemical/ metallurgical analysis. Nondestructive tools such as ultrasound, eddy current, X-ray, liquid penetrant, and magnetic particle testing may be helpful. In some cases grain structure analysis and electron microscope examination are appropriate.

If this analysis shows that the part has been subjected to stress outside its designed strength, new questions are raised, including:

- Is the design strength adequate?

- Was the part applied inappropriately?

- Did the environment (thermal, chemical, electromagnetic, vibration, and so on) contribute to the failure?

The reliability program should support a traceability system that will identify materials, methods, processes, and supplier information for each item. This will help determine whether other items in the field are vulnerable.

After determining the root cause of a failure, a report should be generated that includes any recommendations for changes that will help reduce this type of failure in the future.

EXAMPLE 7.5

A residential window has failed and has been replaced by the local representative. The warranty report states "leaker." The following list shows questions that were raised, along with answers that were obtained with some effort.

Question	Answer
Where did the leak occur?	Two places along the vertical edges.
Was the glass cracked or chipped?	No.
Did the sash have flaws that could cause leaks?	No.
Was the caulking compound deteriorated?	Yes.

Question	Answer
Was there evidence of abrasion on caulking?	No.
What type of deterioration was observed?	General pitting and some crumbling.
What direction did the window face?	North.
Where was the residence?	One block from the Oregon coastline.
Was the window rated for saline environment?	Yes.
Was the caulk rated for saline environment?	Yes.
Does the saline-rated caulk in stock resist saline deterioration?	No, upon testing, it degrades much as that on the failed window.
(To the caulk supplier) Why is your saline-rated caulk failing to resist salt?	We have mislabeled some regular caulk to indicate it is safe for saline environment.
(To the caulk supplier) Do you want our continued business bad enough that you will provide a quick method for us to check each barrel of caulk for saline resistance since we apparently can't depend on your labeling?	Yes.
(To manufacturing) Can you locate and fix windows that were caulked with the mislabeled product?	We're on it.

6. FAILURE REPORTING, ANALYSIS, AND CORRECTIVE ACTION SYSTEM (FRACAS)

> Identify elements necessary for FRACAS, and demonstrate the importance of a closed-loop process. (Evaluate)
>
> Body of Knowledge III.B.6

Despite the efforts that are put into identifying and preventing failure modes, some unanticipated failures occur. These failures are often of an insidious nature, having eluded the team during FMEA activities or else occurring despite corrective/preventive actions that were prescribed. For these reasons there may be a tendency toward lax reporting of these failures.

Failure reporting and corrective action systems (FRACAS) provide an organized, disciplined approach to this problem. The first step is to establish a *failure review board*. This group is responsible for implementing these guidelines:

- Require prompt and complete failure reporting.

- Begin the reporting with the earliest tests of products and processes, and continue through the life of the product.

- Determine root causes and appropriate corrective/preventive action in the analysis and corrective action phase of each report. This phase should be completed within a prescribed period of time, usually 30 days.

- Use a closed-loop corrective action process, as shown in Figure 7.2. Implement audits to determine whether corrective actions have been taken and whether they are effective. When corrective actions do not resolve the problem, the failure review board is responsible for a restudy of the failure mechanism and implementation of additional corrective actions.

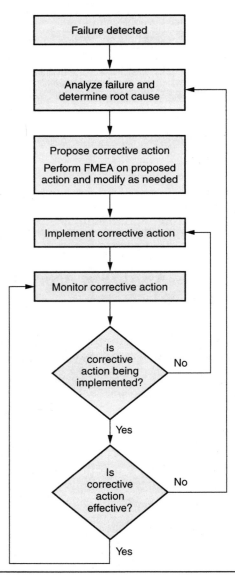

Figure 7.2 FRACAS flowchart.

Part III.B.6

Part IV

Reliability Planning, Testing, and Modeling

Part IV

Chapter 8
A. Planning

1. RELIABILITY TEST STRATEGIES

> Develop and apply the appropriate test strategies
> (e.g., truncation, test-to-failure, degradation, growth
> plan, and test, analyze, and fix [TAAF]) for various
> product development phases. (Evaluate)
>
> Body of Knowledge IV.A.1

The *reliability* of a unit is a characteristic related to time or some other measure of product use. The results of some reliability tests are used to estimate reliability, to set confidence limits on the estimate, or to demonstrate conformance to some specified reliability value. These tests must be performed over an extended period of time. The results of other reliability tests are used to improve the reliability of a unit and may not require testing over long periods of time. If the primary strategy of a testing program is to use the results for any purpose related to reliability, the test is classified as a reliability test. It is also possible to obtain reliability information from other types of tests such as feasibility tests, functional tests, or quality assurance tests.

The strategies for various reliability tests are primarily determined by the stage of product development during which the testing is performed. During early development of a new product, no units are available; therefore, no reliability testing can be performed. As the preliminary design is available and prototypes or engineering models are built, a *highly accelerated life testing* (HALT) program can begin. The strategy for this reliability testing program is to stress the units beyond the design limits in order to cause failures. A reliability improvement program to eliminate the weak components is then initiated based on analysis of these failures. The resulting design will become more robust, and failures due to marginal components will be eliminated, thus improving product reliability. Results from HALT testing cannot be used to estimate reliability values since the applied stresses are beyond the design limits.

Reliability tests with a strategy to estimate the failure rate or mean time between failures (MTBF) of the product can begin once production units become available. These tests, referred to as *life tests*, accumulate test time on several units while recording failures. These tests are required to run for a period of time. In many cases the test time could be prohibitive, making some type of acceleration necessary.

Before the product is delivered to the customer, a *highly accelerated stress screening* (HASS) test should be performed. The strategy is to stress the entire production run to eliminate defective product from the population and to detect any shift in the production process. Units that pass this test are shipped to the customer. HASS is usually considered to be a quality engineering function. The test, however, has a positive effect on reliability by limiting early-life failures from reaching the customer.

If a *compliance test* is required, it must be performed before the product can be delivered to the customer. The strategy of this type of test is to verify that the product conforms to some minimum reliability value. This is done by accumulating time on several units, requiring this test to be performed over a span of time. Compliance testing cannot be performed until the final design is set, production tooling is in place, and units have been produced. The strategy of compliance testing is *not* product improvement.

Planning for an integrated reliability test program must start at the beginning of the project. Planning must be thorough and timely if all the necessary elements are to be in place when they are needed. Planning must be done to assure that the number of units to be tested, the test facilities—including any special equipment—and the necessary time are available when the tests are to be performed. Scheduling of the various reliability tests is necessary so that the results can be used in a timely manner based on the strategy of the test. It is much more efficient to make a design change before the product is released to production.

A test plan needs to include the following: objectives of the testing program; provision of resources for facilities, test equipment and equipment calibration information, the time and necessary personnel to conduct the testing; test requirements and schedule, including the number of units to be tested and the test environments; procedures to make changes in the testing program as necessary; and documentation of the test results. If the strategy of the test is to record failures over time, a precise definition of product failure must be available to the test engineer as the output of some products can deteriorate over time.

Many sources list the necessary steps in developing a reliability test plan. The number of steps and the words describing the steps differ, but all essentially contain the same information. Dimitri Kececioglu (1993) lists nine steps:

1. Determine the test requirements and objectives.

2. Review existing data to determine if any requirements can be met without testing.

3. Review the list of tests to determine whether combining any tests would be economically feasible.

4. Determine the necessary tests.

5. Allocate the resources necessary to perform the tests.

6. Develop test specifications and data handling and storage procedures. Review acceptance and qualification criteria. Establish procedures for making future changes in the test specifications.

7. Assign the responsibility for conducting the tests, analyzing the results, and providing the overall integration of the testing program.

8. Develop forms and procedures for reporting the test results.

9. Develop procedures for maintaining the test status information throughout the entire testing program.

Reliability tests can be placed in several different classifications. One way to classify tests is by the phase of the development/production cycle in which they are conducted. Four major test categories classified in this manner are:

- Product development tests
- Reliability performance tests
- Reliability acceptance tests
- Reliability verification tests

These tests have different objectives and are conducted at different times during the process of product development and production.

Product Development Tests

These tests are performed with the intent of taking action to improve the design in the event of failures, and to evaluate the system design, including the compatibility of subsystems. Results from product development testing may be used to demonstrate the functional capabilities of the product but not to determine reliability parameters such as failure rate or MTBF. The objective of product development testing is to cause failures. Only by analyzing failures and taking appropriate action to change the design can improvement be made to the product. Testing units for long periods of time and observing no failure is costly and does not result in product improvement.

Reliability Performance Tests

Sometimes referred to as *reliability qualification tests,* these tests are performed after the design is completed. They will demonstrate that the system can meet the specified requirements under the specified conditions of operation (including environmental). Generally, these tests do not provide the data to determine reliability parameters, but only to give assurance that performance under stated conditions can be met.

Reliability Acceptance Tests

Conducted during the production phase, these tests will demonstrate that reliability parameters of the design have not been compromised by the production emphasis on the reliability parameters.

Reliability Verification Tests

These tests are performed to show compliance to stated reliability parameters such as MTBF or failure rate and may be required to demonstrate compliance at a given confidence level. This type of testing is formal, statistical in nature, and requires standard procedures. Many units or long periods of test time could be required for these tests, making some form of acceleration necessary. These tests are based on acceptable and rejectable reliability values, such as MTBF or failure rate, and decision risks.

Reliability tests could be classified according to the way the tests are conducted and the type of results that are recorded. The type of data to be taken and the way in which they are reported must be a part of the overall reliability test plan. Reliability tests can be continuous or they can be pass/fail. Results of continuous tests are recorded as variables data, and the results of pass/fail tests are recorded as attribute data.

Attribute data are recorded as success or failure for a given test. The units being tested might not have active operating times. These units are referred to as *one-shot* items. They are units that perform successfully or fail when they are called on to operate, such as sensors or fuses. Estimates of the reliability or the probability of success of one-shot items can be made from the attribute data. Confidence limits on the reliability can also be calculated using the data. Attribute data might also be recorded even if the units being tested have active operating times. Units being cycled in an environmental chamber may pass or fail the test. Unless each unit is metered separately, it will not be known until the test is complete which units were successes and which units failed. The data that are recorded are the number of units that passed and the number of units that failed the test; the actual time to failure of the units that failed is not known. Confidence limits and estimates of the reliability of these units for a mission time equal to the equivalent time of the test can be calculated using the data.

The results of continuous tests are recorded as variables. The actual times to failure of each failed unit and the total time accumulated on the non-failed units is known. Life tests are conducted to determine reliability parameters such as MTBF or failure rate. The data from these tests should be recorded as variables. Estimates of the parameters can be made and confidence limits can be calculated from the variables data. Continuous testing may be conducted as *replacement tests* or as *non-replacement tests*. The advantage of a replacement test is that the number of units on test is constant, therefore generating data at a faster rate. In a non- replacement test, units that fail are not replaced, and the test population becomes smaller.

Compliance tests are performed to show that units have achieved some reliability value. Results of these tests could be recorded as variables data or as attribute data. Compliance to an MTBF or failure rate can be shown using variables data from a fixed-time test or from sequential testing. If required, the compliance could be shown at a given confidence level. Sequential testing will require, on the average, about one-half the total unit test time as a fixed-length test. The consequence of this is fewer units required or a decrease in the actual test time. The disadvantage of sequential testing is that the actual time required for the test is not known at the beginning of the test. Attribute data from a pass/fail test can be used to demonstrate compliance to a reliability value or a probability of success value for one-shot items at a given confidence level. The test requiring the fewest number of units is a no-failure test. This is sometimes referred to as *success testing*.

Reliability tests can be classified as to the strategy and the types and levels of accelerations that are used. The strategy for a HALT program is product reliability improvement. The design is in the early development stage and is not finalized. Units are tested at stresses exceeding the design limits. The stresses usually are environmental, such as temperature or vibration, but could be other loading stresses such as voltage. Stress is increased until some component in the product fails, resulting in product failure. A design change is made to eliminate the weak component. The process is then repeated on the product incorporating the new design. Reliability improvement is achieved as the marginal design is improved by eliminating the weak components. In some cases these types of tests are also used to extend the beginning of wear-out, known as the end of useful life. The HALT program, along with other early product development reliability functions, will ensure that a robust and reliable design is released to production. The test failures are not typical, however, of the normal use of the product. Therefore, the results from the HALT program cannot be used to estimate the reliability of the product.

The amount of time and the number of units required for a life test can become prohibitive. Unlike Example 8.1, few projects will have 50 units available for reliability testing, and the 1000 hours of testing in Example 8.2 is more than 40 days. If the product has high inherent reliability, it would not be unusual to need several thousand hours of total unit test time to get meaningful results. To perform these tests it becomes necessary to use some type of acceleration.

EXAMPLE 8.1

Fifty integrated circuits (ICs) are cycled in an environmental test chamber for a test that is equivalent to 1000 hours of operation. At the completion of the test, it is found that two of the units failed during the test.

The binomial distribution is used for the estimate of reliability, and the F distribution is used to calculate the confidence limit.

The estimate of the reliability of the IC for a mission time of 1000 hours is

$$\hat{R}_{(t=1000)} = \frac{n-r}{n} = \frac{50-2}{50} = 0.96$$

From the F distribution: $F_{(0.10)6,96} = 1.82$.

The lower 90% confidence limit on the reliability of the IC for $t = 1000$ hours is

$$R_{L(\alpha=0.10)} = \frac{48}{48 + 3(1.82)} = 0.90$$

EXAMPLE 8.2

A non-replacement life test that is of 1000 hours duration is conducted on 10 units in order to estimate the MTBF and set a lower 90% confidence limit.

One unit failed at 450 hours and a second unit failed at 800 hours. Eight units did not fail during the test. The test was time-censored at 1000 hours.

The exponential distribution is used to estimate the MTBF and the χ^2 distribution is used to set the confidence limit.

The total unit test time:

$$T = 450 + 800 + (8)(1000) = 9250 \text{ hours}$$

The estimate of MTBF:

$$\hat{\theta} = \frac{T}{r} = \frac{9250}{2} = 4625$$

From the χ^2 distribution:

$$\chi^2_{(0.10)(6)} = 10.645$$

The lower 90% confidence limit:

$$\theta_{L(\alpha = 0.10)} = \frac{2(9250)}{10.645} = 1740 \text{ hours}$$

HASS is performed on 100% of the production units before shipment to the customer. To perform HASS testing, the product is subjected to elevated stresses. Some of these stress levels may exceed the limits set by the customer requirements and stress the product beyond the levels expected in normal use. It is assumed that good units are unaffected by the test. All the units that pass the test are released for shipment. The product must be robust to the stresses; therefore, HASS testing cannot be performed unless a HALT program has been part of the product development. HASS testing will remove early-life failure units from the population, but the primary strategy of the test program is to detect any shift in the production process. Before a HASS program can be successful, it is necessary that the production process has already proven to be capable and in statistical control. The stresses, usually environmental, must be determined. The test equipment, including any special test chambers, must be available and in sufficient quantity and test time allotted as part of the process in order not to slow production.

Life testing requires that the test be run on several units over a period of time to accumulate a total unit test time. Using the assumption of a constant failure rate, 100 units tested for 100 hours, 50 units tested for 200 hours, and 10 units tested for 1000 hours all result in 10,000 hours total unit test time. The data from these tests can be used to make estimates of product reliability measures, such as failure rate or the MTBF, and to determine the confidence limits of the estimate. It is important that the units tested be typical of the production units. Any changes in the design will affect the testing program, probably requiring more time or test units.

Before beginning a test, it is necessary to decide how the test will be terminated. Several possibilities are in use by reliability engineers. *Truncation* refers to terminating the test at some specified amount of time or other stress metric. For example, a part or sample of parts may be cycled a million times or cryogenically exposed for a certain amount of time and then analyzed. *Test-to-failure* refers to studies that record data about failure type and time. Some such tests continue until all units have failed. A *truncated test-to-failure* would test a sample of items until a certain number had failed (the truncation point). A *degradation test* terminates when a product reaches a predetermined reduced level of performance. The analysis of data from these different protocols requires special techniques. Statistical software packages typically are used.

Reliability Growth Testing

Reliability growth is the improvement in product reliability over a period of time. This improvement in reliability is due to changes in the product design. In the early stage of new product development, problems exist in the design that negatively affects reliability. Early-development reliability activities such as FMEA, design reviews, reliability prediction, and early testing on prototype and engineering models will begin to identify these problems. Changes to the product design will begin to eliminate these problems. Tests will then be run on the product of the new design and other problems will be identified and eliminated. This activity when repeated is referred to as *test, analyze, and fix* (TAAF) and will result in reliability growth. *Military Handbook: Reliability Growth Management* (MIL-HDBK-189) provides an understanding of the concepts and principles of reliability growth testing.

The most frequently used models to track reliability growth are the *Duane model*, developed by James Duane in 1962, and the *Army Materiel Systems Analysis Activity* (AMSAA) *model* developed by Larry Crowe in 1978. Both use the observed linear relationship between the logarithm of cumulative MTBF and cumulative test time. The Duane model is based on observation and uses a deterministic method to track reliability growth. The AMSAA model allows for statistical procedures to be used to model reliability growth.

The data are cumulated as the TAAF process progresses. A quantity called the *cumulative MTBF* (θ_m) is calculated:

$$\theta_m = \frac{T}{r}$$

where:

T = Total unit test time, including all testing

r = Total number of failures, including all testing

In the Duane model,

$$\theta_m = K(T)^b$$

As the TAAF process continues and T increases, θ_m will increase, reflecting reliability growth. This growth can be tracked:

$$\log \theta_m = \log K + b \log T$$

This linear equation in logarithms will plot as a straight line on log-log graph paper. Measuring b from the graph will give the reliability growth rate. The value of b can also be calculated. θ_0 is an initial value for the cumulative MTBF at cumulative unit test time of T_0. θ_1 is a cumulative MTBF value after a total unit test time of T_1 $(T_1 > T_0)$:

$$b = [\log (\theta_1/\theta_0)/\log (T_1/T_0)]$$

In the Duane model, the true MTBF will grow at the same rate as the cumulative MTBF value. At any time during the testing, the true MTBF (θ) can be found as

$$\theta = \theta_m/(1 - b).$$

The growth rate b can be used to compare the growth of a given project with the growth of other similar projects. A higher than average growth indicates that resources are being used aggressively for that project. A lower than average growth is an indication that the use of reliability improvement resources is limited for the project.

A growth rate of about 0.25 to 0.4 is average for most projects. A higher growth rate shows that the effort to eliminate design weaknesses has been given top priority. A lower growth rate indicates that reliability improvement actions are taken to eliminate only the most obvious design flaws.

EXAMPLE 8.3

A new speed sensor and control module for an ABS braking system is in development. Units are subjected to three cycles of growth development testing. After each set of tests the results are analyzed and corrective action is implemented. After each design change, new units are built for the subsequent test. Each test is conducted as a replacement test utilizing 20 units. The equivalent test time for each test is 1000 hours, resulting in a total test time of 20,000 hours.

The following results were obtained.

Test Cycle 1

Equivalent test time $T_{(1)}$ = 20,000 hours. The cumulative test time T = 20,000 hours.

Number of failures $r_{(1)}$ = 20. The cumulative number of failures r = 20.

$$\theta_{C(1)} = 20{,}000/20 = 1000 \text{ hours}$$

Test Cycle 2

Equivalent test time $T_{(2)}$ = 20,000 hours. The cumulative test time T = 40,000 hours.

Number of failures $r_{(2)}$ = 12. The cumulative number of failures r = 32.

$$\theta_{C(2)} = 40{,}000/32 = 1250 \text{ hours}$$

The calculation of $\theta_{(2)}$ uses the data from test cycle 1 and test cycle 2.

Test Cycle 3

Equivalent test time $T_{(3)}$ = 20,000 hours. The cumulative test time T = 60,000 hours.

Number of failures $r_{(3)}$ = 8. The cumulative number of failures r = 40.

$$\theta_{C(3)} = 60{,}000/40 = 1500 \text{ hours}$$

The calculation of $\theta_{(3)}$ uses the data from test cycle 1, test cycle 2, and test cycle 3.

A plot of the data on log-log graph paper is shown in Figure 8.1. Cumulative MTBF (θ_C) is plotted on the y-axis versus cumulative time (T) on the x-axis. A linear measure of the slope of the line shows a growth rate of about 0.37.

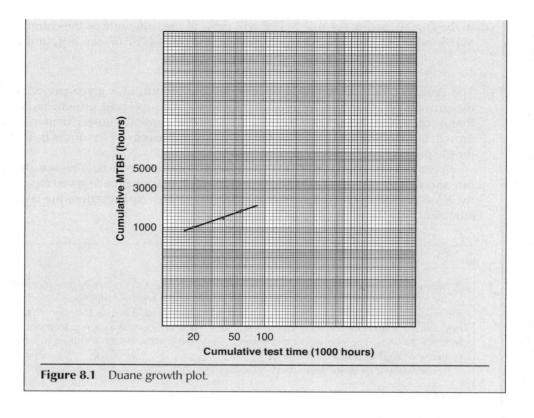

Figure 8.1   Duane growth plot.

2. ENVIRONMENTAL AND CONDITIONS OF USE FACTORS

> Identify environmental and use factors (e.g., temperature, humidity, and vibration) and stresses (e.g., severity of service, electrostatic discharge (ESD), throughput, and duty cycle) to which a product may be subjected. (Analyze)
>
> Body of Knowledge IV.A.2

Understanding the use environment and use condition of a product is a prerequisite for designing effective reliability tests. Note that, by the definition of reliability, a reliable product is the product that functions under its intended use conditions during the required mission time. Therefore, carefully defining and characterizing the product's environmental and use factors will not only help designers make informed decisions but also assist the company in developing a better warranty policy. Other purposes for characterizing environmental and use factors are:

- To design the product that meets customer expectations
- To determine product safety and durability

- To plan an effective reliability test that can provide useful information for reliability prediction

- To evaluate the product transportation, storage, installation, and use condition

- To design product monitoring schemes

- To effectively mitigate or reduce stress effects

If the product intends to be used outdoor, the environmental stress variables are often climate variables, such as temperature, humidity, UV, wind, hail, salt, precipitation, and snow, etc. Characterizing the use condition of such products requires collecting climate data at their use locations, which are often available from public resources at the National Oceanic and Atmospheric Administration (NOAA) and the Department of Energy (DOE). However, modeling these climate variables may not be an easy task. For example, to characterize the use environment of a photovoltaic module the Jet Propulsion Laboratory (JPL) suggests an environmental cell model that discretizes temperature, humidity, and UV and counts their occurrence at a location over a year. Then, the distributions of these environmental variables can be found. Knowing the stress variable distribution, instead of merely an average value, is important to reliability test planning, as a good test plan should mimic the real use environment and may even elevate the stress level based on the environmental data. Oftentimes, reliability engineers would like to know how the product performs under an environmental condition that is more severe than normal, or in a worst-case scenario, so as to give a conservative lifetime estimation or to expose any design weakness for future product improvement.

Besides climate-related variables, other environmental stress variables include:

- Pressure

- Electrical current and voltage

- Magnetic

- Vibration

- Friction

- Drop and shock

- Radiation

- Electrostatic discharge (ESD)

In general, any external factor that may induce product failure should be investigated. Therefore, identifying environmental factors should be product specific, and the corresponding test plan should be built on specific failure mechanisms.

The use factor of a product also needs to be fully understood before planning a reliability test. Each product is designed for a specific market segment and the product use intensity of different market segments could be drastically different. For example, a household washing machine may be used once or twice a week and one hour per use, but an industrial-grade washing machine that is to be installed in a laundry facility should expect everyday usage and at least eight hours per day. Therefore, the choice of motor in these machines should be quite different.

Without a clear understanding of use factor, engineers may either under-design or over-design a product.

Traditionally, a customer survey and market analysis are the typical ways to obtain the data of product use severity. However, with more and more sensors being embedded into products to make them "smart," manufacturers and service providers today have more sophisticate real-time tools for monitoring a product's use condition. For example, a computer can automatically record its power on and off time, its CPU unitization and temperature, its memory writing frequency, etc., and these data can be transmitted to a third party for fault diagnosis. The internet-connected automobile, such as the Tesla car, is another example. Aggregating these use data will give a realistic picture of how these products are actually used in the real world and whether there is a gap between design intention and actual use. Similarly, reliability tests can be better designed to simulate the real use conditions.

Lastly, consider another example—borrowed from Ullman Sails (http://ullmansails.com/sail-care/environmental-use-factors/)—of environmental and use factors that are primary causes for sail deterioration. Environmental factors that can weaken the sail include UV and saltwater. UV exposure, which affects all sail materials to varying degrees, weakens fibers. Saltwater exposure can result in electrolytic corrosion of sail fastenings. Corrosion, the result of contact of dissimilar metals, causes slides, clew and tack rings, and even headboards to fail over time. Use factors encompass the inevitable stress that sails endure while in use. They include the impacts of luffing, sails hitting the rig, and the typical loads required to harness the power of the wind under sail. Flogging, fluttering, and the sails hitting the rig will damage sailcloth and sail membranes. Understanding these damaging effects of environmental and use factors will help designers take actions to mitigate them. For example, UV inhibitors and top coatings are applied on the sailcloth to improve UV resistance; dissimilar materials are isolated to reduce corrosion potentials. All sailcloth can be subject to a range of assessments, such as "flutter and impact" tests and "fold and flex" tests, which simulate the real-world scenarios and use conditions.

3. FAILURE CONSEQUENCE

> Describe the importance of identifying the consequences of failure modes when establishing reliability acceptance criteria. (Understand)
>
> Body of Knowledge IV.A.3

Reliability analysis provides estimates of the probability of failure. The reliability engineer must go beyond these calculations and examine the consequences of failure. These consequences typically represent the loss of system function and costs to the customer. The customer finds ways of sharing these costs with the producer through the warranty system, loss of business, decrease in reputation, or civil litigation. Therefore, an important reliability function is the anticipation of possible failures and the establishment of reliability acceptance goals that will limit their occurrence and consequent costs.

Identifying failure consequences requires considerable product domain knowledge and the system function view. Most of the time, not only the direct impact of a failure mode on product functionality needs to be assessed, but its second or third order of impacts on the related parts and the surrounding system, including human beings, must also be fully understood. Any potential harm to users due to the failure of a product may lead to serious civil lawsuits. These litigations can be very damaging to a company's bottom line and, more importantly, its reputation. For example, in April and May of 2013, multiple car manufacturers recalled the airbags manufactured by the Takata Monclova Plant in Coahuila, Mexico. By that time, at least 16 deaths were linked to the defective airbags and a total of 3.6 million cars were recalled (Tabuchi and Jensen 2014). As a result, BMW announced plans to move any orders from the Mexican plant to a Takata plant in Germany (Klayman 2014). On January 13, 2017, the United States charged three Takata executives for the exploding airbag. The company agreed to plead guilty and to pay $1 billion to resolve the investigation, which includes a $25 million fine, $125 million for victim compensation, and $850 million to compensate automobile manufacturers (Reuters 2017). As shown in this example, the consequence of a product failure could be very severe in terms of system failure, human safety endangerment, loss of customers, and costs to the company, etc. Consumer product failures often invite wide media coverage and regulatory actions that are extremely damaging to the company's reputation.

Analytical techniques can be used to understand and define the failure consequence. Expert judgment should be considered from groups or individuals with specialized training or knowledge on the subject area, such as product designers and product managers, system engineers, reliability engineers, industry groups and consultants, consumer relation specialists, and customers themselves. Meetings can be held with all stakeholders to brainstorm the possible consequences of a product failure to the whole system on the company's and customer's loss. Each risk needs to be ranked accordingly based on the probability of its occurrence and its impact. Therefore, identifying failure consequences will help prioritize the resource allocation for preventing failure.

Both qualitative and quantitative tools have been used for assessing failure consequences, including:

- Document review

- Delphi method

- Root cause analysis

- Probability and impact matrix

- FMEA

In particular, the FMEA technique explicitly requires the numerical ranking of the consequence of each failure mode and the probability of its occurrence. This ranking may come from expert judgment or from historical data from same or similar products or from industrial standards. Then, we can use the ranking to prioritize the strategies for preventing or mitigating failures and failure impacts. Product redesign is often mandated for improving reliability, but other strategies, such as specifying use conditions and warranty conditions, are also common in mitigating failure impacts in practice.

4. FAILURE CRITERIA

> Define and describe failure criteria based on system requirements and warranty terms and conditions. (Understand)
>
> Body of Knowledge IV.A.4

Understanding product failures and failure consequences will lead to a proper definition of product failure criteria; that is, what is defined as a success or failure? First, a reliability goal must be established according to customer expectations, industrial standards, and the company's social responsibility. These goals are usual set for the whole system or for the company's overall performance. Therefore, they need to be broken down to the acceptance criteria for individual products or components. The acceptance criteria associated with these goals generally fall into three categories:

- *Functional requirements* (such as 20 gallons per minute for a pump)

- *Environmental requirements* (such as temperature, radiation, pH)

- *Time requirements* (such as failure rate during useful life, time elapsed before wear-out phase begins)

Functional requirements concern the designed functions of a product. Whether or not a product can be accepted depends on if it can deliver these intended functions. The required performance must be quantifiable and measurable. Reliability engineers often need to translate these requirements into specific testing tools and testing goals. Environmental requirements specify the normal or accelerated stress conditions based on the environmental and use factors of the product (as discussed previously), while time requirements specify the expected lifetime of the product under these conditions. Both environmental and time requirements should be connected to the company's warranty program, reflecting what has been promised to customers in the warranty contract. For example, if a product is under full warranty for two years, its reliability requirement should have an expected lifetime of two years and longer. We typically specify the lower percentile time, such as 5th percentile or 10th percentile of product lifetime, to meet the reliability requirement such that most of products will be guaranteed to be acceptable. If there is a large variation in lifetime distribution, this could lead to a very long mean lifetime requirement.

In addition to defining failure criteria, a good warranty program reaches into many different organizational functions:

- *Product pricing* must include allowances for warranty costs

- *Advertising* can use warranties as inducements to purchase

- *Supply chain agreements* should spell out warranty liabilities and procedures

- *Accounting procedures* should include accruals or sinking funds to cover future warranty costs

- *Operation instruction manuals* should include preventive maintenance recommendations that will mitigate failures

- *Engineering and reliability functions* have responsibilities for determining causes and determining product/process corrective actions as required

The breadth of warranty considerations implies that improvements in warranty management have the potential for substantial financial impact. Finding and executing these improvements begins with an understanding of terms. Warranties should spell out:

- Effective initial date and duration of the warranty

- Definitions of parts and defects to be covered

- Warranty procedures, including return routes, replacement/ reimbursement policies, and policies that will be followed when no defect is found

- Conditions of use such as environmental specifications (ranges for temperature, vibration, salinity, electronic parameters) and operation procedures

- Conditions of storage, transportation, and installation

Therefore, the design of warranty would definitely require the inputs from engineers on the product's designed functions and its intended use conditions. The influence between warranty policy and failure criteria definition flows in both directions. If suppliers are involved, effective warranty management requires agreements as to all these aspects with each supplier, regardless of tier.

Once component, product, and system reliability goals have been set, a testing protocol should be implemented to provide validation that these goals will impact the failure rates and the associated consequences as planned. These reliability goals typically impose specifications on the product. In anticipation of the start of production, reliability engineers provide further testing procedures to provide *verification* that these specifications are being met.

5. TEST ENVIRONMENT

> Appraise the environment in terms of system location and operational conditions, and designate the environment in the test plan to ensure an appropriate test strategy is implemented. (Evaluate)
>
> Body of Knowledge IV.A.5

The strategy of the reliability test and the product itself will determine the environment of the test. If the desired result of the test is to produce failures typical of product use, the test must be conducted in an environment that reflects the environment of use. Sometimes, increased environmental stress can be used to accelerate these tests. Not all products react the same to a given environmental stress.

Part IV.A.5

Solid-state electronics are very sensitive to increased temperature. Mechanical units might be affected by vibration or increased contaminants such as salt spray or dust. Magnetic units might be affected by radiation. Electronic circuit boards could be exposed to vibration to detect poor soldering, inadequate strength, or other mechanical defects. Radiation will also affect solid-state electronics and could be used to verify that shielding is adequate. Humidity, rapid temperature ramps, and shock are other environmental stresses used during reliability testing.

If the strategy of the reliability testing is to eliminate design weaknesses from the product, environmental stresses in excess of normal use may be used. The test strategy is to produce failures so that design changes can be introduced to improve reliability. The unit will fail in ways not typical of normal use. The elimination of the weak components will increase product reliability. The level of these stresses can greatly exceed the design limits of the product. No reliability information can be obtained by testing units at stress levels lower than the normal use environment.

Test chambers capable of the appropriate test environments are required. Test equipment is now available that will allow the simultaneous application of multiple environments. *Combined environmental reliability testing* (CERT) is an application of multiple environmental stresses simultaneously. The simultaneous application of temperature cycling and vibration is an example of CERT. Harry W. McLean (2002) gives detail as to the maximum level of environmental stresses that are appropriate. The maximum levels are specific to the product, but typical operation ranges are:

Temperature: –70°C to + 100°C

Temperature rate: 60°C per minute

Vibration: Up to 30 Grms

The most advanced vibration systems utilize six degrees of freedom at frequencies from 2 to 5000 Hz. Low-frequency energy is used to excite components with high mass; higher frequencies excite low-mass components. Solid-state components can be burned-in at 150°C. Integrated circuits should withstand temperature ramp rates of 90°C per minute. More typical test environments perform vibration using three degrees of freedom and a temperature ramp rate of 20°C per minute. If the environmental testing is sequential, the order needs to be determined and might be important. Combined thermal and vibration testing eliminates this requirement. The results of the testing should be both accurate and precise. *Accuracy* implies that the data are on target, and *precision* relates to the tolerance limits of the equipment. This requires that the calibration of the test chambers, the measuring equipment, and the data recording devices be traceable to a standard. Periodic calibration is necessary and should be stated as part of the overall reliability test plan.

Chapter 9
B. Testing

0. TESTING

> Describe the purpose, advantages, and limitations
> of each of the following types of tests, and use com-
> mon models to develop test plans, evaluate risks,
> and interpret test results. (Evaluate)
>
> Body of Knowledge IV.B

There are several different tests used to assess the reliability of parts, components, systems, and software including:

- *Accelerated life tests* (single-stress, multiple-stress, sequential stress, step-stress, HALT, margin tests)

- *Stress screening* (environmental-stress screening [ESS], HASS, burn-in tests)

- *Qualification/demonstration testing* (sequential tests, fixed-length tests)

- *Degradation testing* (wear-to-failure)

- *Software testing* (white-box, black-box, operational profile, and fault-injection)

1. ACCELERATED LIFE TESTS

> Accelerated life tests (single-stress, multiple-stress,
> sequential stress, step-stress, HALT, margin tests)
> (Evaluate)
>
> Body of Knowledge IV.B.1

The length of time required for a reliability life test can be prohibitive. To reduce the actual time of the test, accelerated life testing can be employed. The strategy is to increase the rate at which failures occur, not cause new types of failures.

167

Basically you want to compress time to gain an understating about the reliability of the item being tested. The assumption of accelerated life testing is that the failure modes are unchanged by the increased stress. Failure analysis can be used to determine whether new modes of failure result from the increased stress. This would be a reason to reduce the level or change the stress used to effect the acceleration.

Single-Stress Tests

Some devices can be accelerated in time by simply using them at a rate that exceeds the normal use rate. Automatic test facilities can be built that will continuously operate the units. The time of use and the times of failure can be recorded. A fixture operating at 120 strokes per minute could exercise keys on a computer keyboard one million times in less than six days. A home appliance such as a dishwasher that is cycled every two hours will accumulate 1200 cycles (average for eight years) in 100 days (less than three and one-half months).

Increased stress is often used to accelerate time or cycles. Suppose it is known that under normal use 5% of the population will fail in a time $t_{(n)}$. If the units are operated under an increased environmental stress, the same 5% will fail in a time $t_{(s)}$ ($t_{(s)} < t_{(n)}$). The ratio $t_{(n)}/t_{(s)}$ is defined as the *acceleration factor* (A_F). The actual time of the test (t) is referred to as the *test time* or *clock time* (also can be *test cycles*) of the test. The equivalent time of the test is $t_{(Eq)}$ and is equal to the product of the acceleration factor and the test time:

$$t_{(Eq)} = (A_F) \times t$$

The acceleration factor is assumed to remain constant over the time of the test. The models used to accelerate time will depend on several factors. Electrical and mechanical failure modes will need different models. Increasing the constant failure rate or reducing the time to the onset of wear will involve different models. A few commonly used models in electronics are the *Arrhenius model*, when temperature is used to accelerate time; the *power law model* (sometimes referred to as the *inverse power law*), when stresses other than temperature are used; and the *Peck model*, where the combination of temperature and humidity are used.

The acceleration factors are usually derived from the models using physics-of-failure analysis for the various failure modes, testing to determine the value of the acceleration factor, and then verifying the acceleration factor. Many times, the verification may be delayed until results from the field can be obtained and analyzed. The determination of acceleration factors can be a lengthy and costly process.

The Arrhenius Model

The Arrhenius acceleration model is based on the Arrhenius equation (Savanti Arrhenius, 1858–1927). The Arrhenius equation states that the rate of a chemical reaction increases as the temperature increases:

$$R = Ae^{\frac{-E_A}{KT}}$$

where:

R is the reaction rate of the chemical reaction

A is a scaling factor and will divide out of the final result

K is Boltzmann's constant (8.617×10^{-5} electron volts/degree Kelvin)

T is the temperature in degrees Kelvin (°C + 273 degrees)

E_A is the activation energy in electron volts

Reaction rate can be thought of as being synonymous with failure rate. Increasing the test temperature will increase the constant failure rate of the units, which has the effect of accelerating time. The acceleration factor is the ratio of the reaction rate at the increased temperature (T_S) and the reaction rate at the use temperature (T_U):

$$A_F = \frac{R_S}{R_U}$$

This reduces to

$$A_F = \exp[(E_A/K)(1/T_U - 1/T_S)]$$

The key to using the Arrhenius model is determining the appropriate activation energy. An approximation that can be used in the absence of knowing the activation energy is that every 10°C increase in temperature doubles the failure rate. For electronics, activation energies usually fall in the range 0.5 electron volts (eV) to 2.0 eV. The activation energy is assumed to be constant for a given failure mode.

EXAMPLE 9.1

An electronic device that normally operates at a temperature of 50°C is subjected to a stress temperature of 100°C. The activation energy for the failure mode is 0.8 eV.
What is the acceleration factor using the Arrhenius equation?

$$A_F = \exp[(E_A/K)(1/T_U - 1/T_S)]$$

$$A_F = \exp[(0.8/8.617 \times 10^{-5})(1/323 - 1/373)] = 47$$

Assuming that the increased temperature did not cause new failure modes, two days of testing at 100°C is equivalent to about three months of use.

To verify the value, it may be necessary to test units at various stress (temperature) levels. For example, units may be tested at a high temperature (C, Figure 9.1), an intermediate temperature (B, Figure 9.1), and a low temperature (A, Figure 9.1). The low temperature should represent the normal use value, but be high enough to result in a few failures during the test. The high temperature should be near the upper limit over which the failure modes remain unchanged. The intermediate temperature should be significantly different from the two other values. More units need to be assigned to the lower temperatures to ensure that failures will occur during the test. If a total of 100 units were available for test, a 4-2-1 allocation

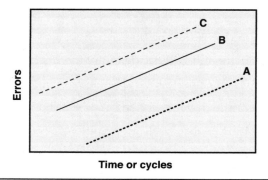

Figure 9.1 Weibull plot.

would result in 57 units tested at the low temperature, 29 units tested at the intermediate temperature, and 14 units tested at the high temperature. It may require more than one test to find these values. Failures should occur at a faster rate at the higher temperatures. If an analysis of the results shows that the same failure modes occurred at each temperature, then an acceleration factor could be determined by comparing the time for a given percentage of failures to occur. If 5% of failures occur at t_S for the high temperature and 5% of failures occur at t_L for the low temperature, the acceleration factor is t_L/t_S. This analysis could be done graphically assuming the Weibull distribution (see Meeker and Hahn 1985).

Note: It is important to perform good root cause analyses after the tests to ensure the failure root cause is the same. If the failure root causes are the same, the acceleration can be assumed. When failure root causes are not the same the analysis needs to be split up into different Weibull distributions (one distribution per failure root cause).

The Power Law Model

The power law model applies to units subjected to accelerating stresses that are not thermal. The law states that the life of the product is inversely proportional to the increased stress:

$$\text{(life at rated stress)}/\text{(life at accelerated stress)} =$$
$$[\text{(accelerated stress)}/\text{(rated stress)}]^b$$

Testing at two stress levels will give data to solve for b. It is then assumed that b will remain constant over the range of applied stress.

Multiple-Stress Tests

Other models can be used with combined stresses. Temperature and humidity or temperature and vibration are examples of combined stresses that can be applied to accelerate failures and reduce the actual test time. The *Eyring model* can also be used when temperature is the acceleration stress. The Eyring model, the Arrhenius model, and the power law model can be combined to be used with multiple stresses. For an excellent discussion of combined stress models see Kececioglu (2001). For example, the Peck model is widely used in a temperature of 85°C and a humidity of 85% relative humidity (Peck 1986).

Figure 9.2   Step–stress testing.

Step-stress testing is sometimes used to further accelerate a reliability test. This technique involves increasing the stress level at fixed points and recording the failures or degradation levels (see Figure 9.2). For example, a test might apply five amps of current for the first 100 hours, then 10 amps for the next 100 hours, and so on, recording product performance at each step. The statistical analysis of the data is somewhat involved and is covered in Tseng and Wen (2000). Other stressors such as current can be used with this technique, step stressing.

EXAMPLE 9.2

A device that normally operates with 5 volts applied is tested at two increased stress levels: $V_1 = 15$ volts and $V_2 = 30$ volts.

    Analysis of the data from the tests indicates that 5% of the population failed at 150 hours when the high stress voltage of 30 volts was used. When the stress voltage of 15 volts was applied, 5% of the population failed at 750 hours.

    At what time t would 5% of the population be expected to fail under the normal stress of 5 volts?

$$[750/150] = [30/15]^b$$

$$\log [750/150] = b \log [30/15]$$

$$b = 2.3$$

$$[t/150] = [30/5]^{2.3}$$

$$t = 9240 \text{ hours}$$

This means that an hour of testing at 30 volts is equivalent to 62 hours of use at 5 volts. This results in an acceleration factor of 62.

Highly accelerated life testing (HALT) is a reliability test program used in the early stages of product development. HALT is not a new concept. HALT testing grew out of the step-stress or overstress testing programs and uses the same strategy. The procedure is to continue to increase stress on a unit until failure occurs. The intent is to identify the weak link in the design in order to make a change to improve the design. The unit is not expected to fail when exposed to stresses that are within the design limits. The stresses that are applied exceed the specification limits of the design, forcing the unit to fail. Failure analysis and design improvement follow each failure. The process ensures that a robust design is created during the design and development phase, and eliminates the need for design changes during the production phase. HALT testing many times uses combined environments utilizing temperature cycling, humidity, and vibration.

To improve the reliability of the product, HALT testing must be employed early in product development. It is much more efficient and cost-effective to make changes before the design is completed, parts are ordered, and the processing tooling is set.

Product failures are analyzed for product improvement purposes. These failures may not be typical of the product when it is operated within its design specifications. The intent is to cause failures to occur quickly, using a small number of units for the test.

Times to failure are not recorded—only stress levels are recorded—and all the products tested might fail. Therefore, reliability measures such as *mean time between failures* (MTBF), *mean time to failure* (MTTF), or failure rate cannot be calculated using the results of the test. The amount of reliability improvement due to the design change cannot be quantified using the results of HALT. The product design will be robust, with a strength that not only exceeds the normal stresses it is expected to experience during use, but also exceeds the stresses in the tails of the stress distributions. It is these stresses that cause failure in otherwise well-designed products.

Highly accelerated life testing should be a standard component of the design and development phase if there is an expectation that the delivered product will perform with zero or very few failures. The details of the HALT program will differ with the product. The stresses to be used, the limits on the stresses, whether the testing is cycled or static, and other details are product dependent. The HALT stresses used during the design of a new type of stepper motor and radar antenna servo system will be different from those used during the design of an autopilot for a new military aircraft. Testing as an entire unit might be appropriate for some products, while the testing of subsystems might result in quicker reliability improvement for other products. The test plan and the test procedures need to be developed with input from reliability engineering, test engineering, product engineering, and design to ensure the most efficient use of test time for the HALT process. McLean (2002) describes three distinct phases of the HALT process.

Phase 1: Pre-HALT Phase
During this phase, testing procedures are documented. Test equipment is procured and made ready. Procedures for recording of data are in place. The availability of necessary resources is assured. Figure 9.3 provides a view of robustness knowledge of the item before HALT testing.

Phase 2: HALT Phase
The testing is performed during this phase. The test procedures developed in the pre-HALT phase are followed. The operating units are subjected to elevated stresses. The tests are monitored, the results are analyzed, and the data recorded as previously determined.

Phase 3: Post-HALT Phase
Each issue uncovered during the HALT phase is subjected to root cause analysis and corrective action. A person is assigned responsibility for each action. Each action is open-ended until it is closed by reliability engineering. Phase 2 and Phase 3 can then be repeated as necessary. Figure 9.4 provides a view of robustness knowledge after HALT testing.

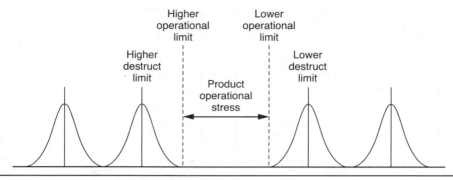

Figure 9.3 Robustness knowledge before HALT test.

Figure 9.4 Robustness knowledge after HALT test.

Margin tests apply increasing stress levels in an effort to develop a margin above specification for a particular failure mode. When a failure occurs, the cause is remedied and the test continues until a design results that has a predetermined margin above design specification. The larger the margin, the lower the probability that that particular failure mode will occur under design stress.

2. STRESS SCREENING

> Stress screening (ESS, HASS, burn-in tests) (Evaluate)
>
> Body of Knowledge IV.B.2

Stress screening, also called *burn-in testing*, describes final tests performed on production units prior to release to the customer. Burn-in testing is allowing the product to accumulate use time before it is delivered. A burn-in or screening test program will reduce the occurrence of early-life failures after the product is delivered. During the burn-in, manufacturing-related nonconformities that cause early failure will be detected.

To accelerate the rate at which the weak units fail (early-life failures), some stress (usually environmental) is applied during the test. This is referred to as *environmental stress screening* (ESS). This stress should not damage an acceptable unit. Units that do not fail will be delivered to customers.

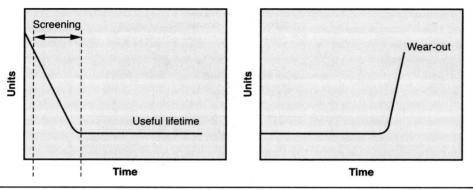

Figure 9.5 Stress screening in the "bathtub" curve.

Highly accelerated stress screening (HASS) is a stress screening program to ensure that the final product will exceed its environmental requirements. Figure 9.5 provides the location of stress screening in the "bathtub" curve. The design has been proven to be robust using a HALT program. The environmental stresses of a HASS program may exceed the product design specifications. A HASS program can only be used if a HALT program was used during product development. The HASS program will detect problems in the process that negatively affect product reliability. The HASS "program is not intended to detect ongoing process problems. Its purpose is detecting a shift in a process that has previously been shown to be capable. HASS testing is not intended to compensate for a production process that is less than capable. Before HASS can be used successfully, accepted process quality procedures must be applied to the process.

Processes must have capability measures, such as C_{pk}, at acceptable levels. Suitable statistical process control (SPC) procedures must be in place. Modern test equipment allows the testing to be done using combined environments.

Once the process has demonstrated statistical control, it may be possible to replace the HASS test program, which is performed on 100% of the production units, with a stress audit program. This would reduce costs as it would require less test equipment and fewer personnel. It could also reduce time to market for high-volume production. A statistical approach to the audit that would involve stress screening a sample of the production units is called *highly accelerated stress audit* (HASA). A HASA test program will detect a process shift but has the risk of allowing some early-life failures to reach the customer.

3. QUALIFICATION/DEMONSTRATION TESTING

> Qualification/demonstration testing (sequential tests, fixed-length tests) (Evaluate)
>
> Body of Knowledge IV.B.3

Qualification/demonstration reliability testing is commonly referred to as *compliance testing*. Compliance tests are used to demonstrate that a product parameter conforms to a given requirement. In reliability compliance testing, the parameter could be MTBF or MTTF, a failure rate (failure intensity), or a reliability value. IEC standard 61124-2006 *Reliability Testing—Compliance Tests for Constant Failure Rate and Constant Failure Intensity* contains procedures for testing values of failure rate or MTBF/MTTF, and IEC standard 61123-1997 *Reliability Testing—Compliance Plans for Success Ratio* contains procedures for testing reliability values for success/fail items. IEC standard 61124 contains fixed-time test plans, and IEC 61123 contains fixed-trial test plans. Both standards contain truncated sequential test plans. The best-known military standard for reliability demonstration or compliance testing is MIL-HDBK-781 *Reliability Test Methods, Plans, and Environments for Engineering Development, Qualification, and Production.* The assumption for all compliance test plans that use time as the continuous variable is that the failure model is the exponential. This implies that the failure rate is constant and that MTBF/MTTF is equal to the reciprocal of the failure rate. The assumed failure model for the fixed-trial/failure test plans is the binomial.

All compliance test plans are described by an operating characteristic (OC) curve. An *operating characteristic curve* is a graph showing the probability of demonstrating compliance given the true value of the product parameter. For a test with time as the continuous variable, the OC curve will have the true value of the required parameter (failure rate $[\lambda]$ or MTBF $[\theta]$) and the probability of success for each trial on the x-axis, and the probability of demonstrating compliance on the y-axis for fixed-trial test plans.

If failure rate is used as the compliance requirement, the probability of demonstrating compliance will be high if the true failure rate is equal to or less than the requirement. The probability of demonstrating compliance will decrease as the true value of the failure rate increases. If MTBF is the compliance requirement, the probability of demonstrating compliance will be high if the true MTBF is equal to or greater than the requirement. The probability of demonstrating compliance will decrease as the true MTBF decreases. IEC standard 61124 uses MTBF as the compliance value.

A typical OC curve for failure rate is shown in Figure 9.6. The OC curve shown uses failure rate (λ) as the compliance value. The test is defined by two points on the OC curve: an accept point defined by λ_0 and $1 - \alpha$, and a reject point defined by λ_1 and β. The product is in compliance if the true failure rate is equal to or

Figure 9.6 Operating characteristic curve for sampling plan.

better (less) than λ_0, and should pass the test. There is a risk of failing the test even though the product is in compliance with the requirement.

This risk is α and is known as the *probability of α type I error*. The product is not in compliance if the true failure rate is worse (greater) than λ_1, and should fail the test. There is also a risk of passing the test even though the product is not in compliance with the requirement. This risk is β and is known as the *probability of a type II error*. The ratio of the two λ values (λ_1/λ_0) is referred to as the *discrimination ratio*. As the discrimination ratio approaches 1, the required amount of testing will increase. This could result in an increase of both the test time and the number of units on test.

MTBF/MTTF could be used as the compliance value. The accept point for this OC curve is defined by m_0 and $1 - \alpha$, and the reject point is defined by m_1 and β. The ratio m_0/m_1 is the discrimination ratio.

The Basics

Fixed-Time Test Plans

A fixed-time compliance test consists of placing units on test to accumulate test time (T) while recording failures. The criterion for acceptance (compliance) is based on accumulating a given amount of test time and having an acceptable number of failures. The maximum number of allowable failures for compliance is usually specified as c. The test is continued until either the required amount of test time has been accumulated (accept) or the allowable number of failures has been exceeded (reject).

Both the required amount of test time and the allowable number of failures are determined by the accept and reject points on the OC curve. Once the two points are defined, the amount of cumulative test time T required and the allowable number of failures c is set. The cumulative test time T is the total of the operating time of all the units during the test, including the units that fail as well as the units that do not fail.

Either a replacement test or a non-replacement test can be performed to acquire the required cumulative test time. In a replacement test, the units that fail are replaced with good units. This essentially keeps the same number of units on test at all times. If a non-replacement test is used, the units that fail are not replaced and the test population becomes smaller with each failure. The cumulative test time is the total of all the operating times of all the units during the test, no matter which type of test is used.

EXAMPLE 9.3

Ten units are on test. The units are not replaced when they fail (non-replacement).

One unit fails at $t_1 = 685$ hours, and a second unit fails at $t_2 = 1690$ hours.

The test is ended at $t = 2500$ hours with no additional failures.

What is the total accumulated test time?

$$T = 685 + 1690 + (8)(2500) = 22{,}375 \text{ hours}$$

EXAMPLE 9.4

An example using IEC standard 61124 will be shown.

It is desired to show compliance of a product MTBF.

The acceptable value m_0 = 3000 hours, and the rejectable value m_1 = 1000 hours.

The discrimination ratio m_0/m_1 = (3000)/(1000) = 3.

The α and β risks are both set to 0.10.

From Table 3 of IEC standard 61124 (see Table 9.1) test plan B.7 can be used.
The OC curve for this plan is shown in Figure B.6 of the standard (see Figure 9.7).
The test requires a cumulative test time of 9300 hours, and the allowable number of failures is five.

$$T = (3.1) \times (m_0) = (3.10) \times (3000) = 9300 \text{ hour}$$

$$c = 5$$

Table 9.1 Table of fixed-time test plans.

Test plan no.	Characteristics of the plan			Test time for termination	Acceptable number of failures	True risks for	
	Nominal risks		Discrimination ratio			$m = m_0$	$m = m_1$
	$\alpha\%$	$\beta\%$	D	T_1/m_0	c	$\alpha\%$	$\beta\%$
B.1	5	5	1.5	54.10	66	4.96	4.84
B.2	5	5	2	15.71	22	4.97	4.99
B.3	5	5	3	4.76	8	5.35	5.40
B.4	5	5	5	1.88	4	4.25	4.29
B.5	10	10	1.5	32.14	39	10.00	10.20
B.6	10	10	2	9.47	13	10.00	10.07
B.7	10	10	3	3.10	5	9.40	9.90
B.8	10	10	5	1.08	2	9.96	9.48

Source: IEC standard 61124 *Reliability Testing—Compliance Tests for Constant Failure Rate and Constant Failure Intensity.*

The accept and the reject points on the OC curve can be verified. Using the constant failure rate concept the expected number of failures is $\lambda \times T$. If the true MTBF is 3000 hours, $\lambda \times T = (1/3000) \times (9300) = 3.1$. This is the accept point. Using the cumulative Poisson tables, which can be justified because of the constant failure rate, the probability of five or fewer failures is 0.90. At the reject point, $\lambda \times T = (1/1000) \times (9300) = 9.3$. Again from the cumulative Poisson tables, the probability of five or fewer failures is 0.10.

Continued

Figure 9.7 OC curves for fixed–time test plans.

Source: IEC standard 61124 *Reliability Testing—Compliance Tests for Constant Failure Rate and Constant Failure Intensity.*

EXAMPLE 9.5

If the rejectable MTBF is changed to 1500 hours ($m_1 = 1500$ hours), the discrimination ratio is now 2, and test plan B.6 can be used.

The required cumulative test time is 28,410 hours [(9.47) × (3000)] and the allowable number of failures is 13.

It is important to note the increase in required cumulative test hours as the discrimination ratio approaches 1. This is in spite of the fact that the MTBF value to be demonstrated remains the same.

The time required to perform a demonstration test can become excessive. If accelerated testing can be used, the actual time required can be reduced. For Example 9.5, the required cumulative test time is 28,410 hours. This could be accomplished by placing 20 units on test and running the test for about 1420 hours (approximately two months). If a non-replacement test is performed, the test time would be extended with each failure. If an acceleration factor of 60 can be applied to the test, the actual test time (t) could be reduced to 23.7 hours to get the same cumulative test time (approximately one day using 20 units on test): $T = A_F(t)(n) = 60(23.7)(20) \approx 28410$ hours.

Sequential Test Plans

Sequential test or *probability ratio sequential test* (PRST) plans are different from the fixed-time test plans. For a fixed-time test, the decision to accept cannot be made until the test is completed and the required cumulative test time is reached.

$\alpha = 0.10; \beta = 0.10; D = 3.0$

Figure 9.8 Sequential test plan.

The results of sequential tests are continuously assessed to arrive at one of three alternative decisions. Sequential testing results in a decision to accept compliance, reject compliance, or continue testing at every value of cumulative test time. The intention is to make a decision to accept or reject compliance in the minimum amount of test time. A graph of a sequential test plan is shown in Figure 9.8.

The alternatives, described by the three regions on the graph, are *accept compliance*, *reject compliance*, or *continue testing*. The three regions are defined by parallel straight lines constructed using the values m_0 (acceptable MTBF) and m_1 (rejectable MTBF) along with α and β from a predetermined OC curve if MTBF is to be demonstrated. Acceptable failure rate (λ_0) and rejectable failure rate (λ_1) are used if the compliance value is a failure rate.

In order to ensure that the test does not continue for an indefinite time, there are rules for ending the test. The test could be terminated at a given time or on a given number of failures if a decision to accept or reject compliance has not been reached. This is referred to as a *truncated sequential test*. The sequential test plan from IEC standard 61124, shown in Figure 9.8, has α and β risks equal to 0.10 and a discrimination ratio of 3. The OC curve for this test is shown in Figure 9.7 (test B.7). The equations for constructing the straight lines that identify the accept, reject, and continue testing regions, as well as the rules for termination, are included in the standard. On average, an accept or reject decision will be reached with less cumulative test time than with fixed-time test plans.

4. DEGRADATION

> Degradation (wear-to-failure) testing (Evaluate)
>
> Body of Knowledge IV.B.4

It may be necessary to test units to determine the end of useful life. This is the beginning of wear-out. Some products may be expected to have extremely long

Part IV.B.4

lives. It is not uncommon to expect 150,000 miles of operation for some automotive systems or 10 years for some electronic systems. To test for these times, some form of acceleration to increase the rate of wear is necessary. Rapid cycling to increase the rate of fatigue, salt spray to increase the rate of corrosion, and temperature to increase the rate of degradation of solid-state electronics are a few of the acceleration stresses.

The failure rate of solid-state electronics will increase as the temperature increases. Good design practice for solid-state electronics dictates that heat be kept to a minimum and removed from the system. If the objective is to have units fail at a faster rate during testing, the addition of heat causes faster degradation, which can be equated to increasing the amount of test time. The Arrhenius model is often used to determine the equivalent time the unit is on.

It is sometimes possible to extrapolate to a failure time by observing the amount of degradation a unit has experienced in a given time. This would reduce the amount of test time necessary to determine the end of life. Information gained from measuring the amount of wear on a bearing, or the intensity of crack propagation due to fatigue at a given time, could be used to predict the time to failure if the model for the rate of degradation is known or assumed. Models that are often used are the linear, exponential, and power law models. The model could be derived using physics of failure. Each product could be unique.

For example, suppose the specification for the fabric covering of an office chair seat is 100,000 cycles of a 250-pound weight moving across then off the fabric. The failure mode is the visible color change when the backing surface shows. Previous testing has shown that the relationship of number of cycles versus fabric thickness lost is approximately linear. The problem is to find the fabric thickness that will meet the specification. To obtain the first estimate for the answer, a fabric is tested for 10,000 cycles and the thickness loss is measured. This would indicate that the first estimate for the design fabric thickness is 10 times the measured wear loss.

Other techniques for degradation testing are dust testing, where a control amount of dust is sprayed in a test room where the product is present, and solar testing, where radiation of the sun is being subjected to the product.

5. SOFTWARE TESTING

> Software testing (white-box, black-box, operational profile, and fault-injection) (Evaluate)
>
> Body of Knowledge IV.B.5

Various software testing strategies are used. To be the most effective at removing faults or "bugs" from the software, testing should be a function of each development phase. *White-box testing*, also referred to as *structural testing*, implies that the tests are designed and implemented with complete knowledge of the inner structure of the system being tested. It is testing the internal functions that must collectively result in the specified external output. The intent is to cover all paths and to test all branches within the system. White-box testing focuses on how the software works.

It is desired to predict the amount of testing required to remove the majority of faults from a new software package. The fault rate decreases as faults are found and eliminated from the software. To make a prediction as to the number of faults remaining at any given time in the testing program, it is necessary to have a prediction of the number of faults at the start of the testing program. One method, referred to as *fault injection*, is to seed the program with known faults and measure the test time to uncover a given percentage of these faults. Compare that to the number of true program faults that have been found in a given test time and, using the fault rate, make a prediction as to the number of original faults in the program.

Many of the faults contained in large software programs are due to poorly stated or misunderstood specifications. The focus of software reliability should be on defect prevention instead of defect detection and removal. A specification review and a design review should be part of every software development project. A testing program is required to ensure that software is released with a minimum number of embedded faults. Testing is the most efficient method of finding and eliminating faults from software. O'Connor (2002) states that more than 50% of programming errors are due to the lack of understanding of the specifications.

Good design controls and well-stated specifications reduce the probability of a programming error. Not introducing an error into the program is much preferred over trying to remove the error from the program.

As faults are found and eliminated, the probability of finding additional faults decreases. This is the early-failure part of the software bathtub curve. This testing activity is a part of the development phase and differs from the early-failure part of the hardware bathtub curve. The early-failure part of the hardware bathtub curve occurs after the production phase. It is desirable to test the software package for every possible input under every condition. Error-free software would then be delivered to the customer if every fault that is uncovered is eliminated without adding additional faults. For complex software packages, all possible conditions may not be anticipated and the elimination of faults could result in the creation of new faults. It is generally accepted that the most extensive testing programs will uncover and eliminate about 95% of the faults in a software program.

Testing software programs with respect to their external specifications is referred to as *black-box testing* or *functional testing.* Representative inputs are inserted and the resulting outputs are compared to the requirements. The intent is to determine whether the software responds as intended and to test the completed system to determine whether the original requirements are met. Black-box testing is not concerned with internal functions. Black-box testing should be performed in the operating environment using the actual interface units.

Software testing should begin as the programs are written. Testing smaller programs is efficient and less complicated. Testing should continue as the programs are integrated into a system. White-box testing is concerned with how the system works. The individual programmers may be best suited for this type of testing as they understand their own codes. The program can be immediately corrected as errors are found.

Errors that are found by the customer after the software is released may not be immediately corrected. The customer may require use of the software in ways not anticipated by the test engineer. If the customer could test the software before release, these faults might be found and eliminated. For some applications, it is possible to involve the customer in testing the software before it is released. This is referred to as *beta testing*. For a flight control software package, this testing might be done on a flight simulator instead of an actual aircraft.

Operational profile testing exercises the software package under all the anticipated conditions of the users. Faults that remain in the software are obscure and difficult to detect. These faults are experienced in a random manner and will not immediately be corrected. This is the justification for considering the fault rate constant and for using the exponential distribution to model the reliability of software after it is released.

Regression testing is selective retesting to detect earlier solved faults that did not cause unintended behavior of the software or other faults: verify if the fault is solved, verify if previous solved problems are still fixed, and test if the software doesn't have unwanted side effects due to the fix.

Other well-known methods in software testing (possible complementary) include:

- *Field testing*: testing in the customer final environment

- *Random-input testing* (or *monkey testing*): random entering of possible inputs to the software

- *Boundary value testing*: testing at the boundaries of the software input values

- *Automated software testing*: writing another software routine replacing the users, or recording user routines (key logger) and playing them back (at a different pace if desired) to be able to stress the software routines automatically

Chapter 10
C. Modeling

1. RELIABILITY BLOCK DIAGRAMS AND MODELS

> Generate and analyze various types of block dia-
> grams and models, including series, parallel, partial
> redundancy, and time-dependent. (Evaluate)
>
> Body of Knowledge IV.C.1

A system can be modeled for reliability analysis using *block diagrams*. A system consists of subsystems connected to perform given functions. Systems can become complex, making reliability analysis difficult. A math model reduces the system to a graphical representation of the interconnection of its subsystems. The system reliability can then be modeled using the reliability of the various subsystems.

There are several advantages to modeling the system, including predicting system reliability using reliability predictions for the various subsystems. The math model can be used to assist in making changes to the system for reliability improvement. The model can be used to identify weak links in the system and to indicate where reliability improvement activities should be introduced. The model can be used to determine test and maintenance procedures. Modeling of the system should be initiated as soon as preliminary designs are completed, and the model should be updated as design changes are made to the system.

Static System Reliability Models

Series System

A system block diagram reduces the system to its subsystems and provides a tool for understanding the effect on the system of a subsystem failure. The most basic of the static block diagrams is the *series model*. A reliability series model block diagram shows that the successful operation of the system depends on the successful operation of each of the subsystems. The failure of any subsystem will result in the failure of the system. This is a natural way to design and build systems. Consequently, most systems are series systems unless some effort is made to incorporate redundancy into the design.

Figure 10.1 The series system.

In the series system block diagram, each block represents a subsystem, as shown in Figure 10.1. There is only one path for system success. If any subsystem fails, the system will fail. It is important not to overlook the subsystem interfaces as they may be a source of failure.

To analyze the system reliability using a series block diagram, it is necessary to assume that the probabilities of failure for the individual subsystems are independent. The assumption of independence is reasonable and need only apply until the time of first failure. Any secondary failure, although it may be a safety consideration, does not affect the reliability analysis. The system has already failed. This is not true of all models. Other models require the user to assume that the probabilities of subsystem failure are completely independent for the entire mission.

It is necessary that all subsystems survive the mission if the system is to survive the mission. This is the joint occurrence of the success of the subsystems, and the product law for the joint occurrence of independent events is used to calculate system reliability.

The reliability of the system $[R_{System}(t)]$ is the probability of success of the system for the mission time, t. The reliability of a subsystem i $[R_i(t)]$ is the probability of the success of that subsystem for a mission of time t. If there are n subsystems, and the reliability of each subsystem is known, the system reliability can be found as

$$R_{System}(t) = [R_1(t)] \times [R_2(t)] \times \ldots \times [R_n(t)]$$

The reliability of each subsystem is less than 1. See Example 10.1. The reliability of the system will be less than the reliability of any subsystem:

$$R_{System}(t) < R_i(t)$$

System modeling will assist in identifying reliability problems and the implementation of a reliability improvement effort. If significant reliability improvement is to be made to a series system, the subsystem with the minimum reliability must be improved. Maximum improvement in system reliability will be achieved by increasing the reliability of the subsystem with the minimum reliability.

If the reliability of subsystem 1 in Example 10.1 is improved to 0.999, the improvement in system reliability is marginal:

$$R_{System}(t) = (0.999)(0.98)(0.94) = 0.92$$

Regardless of the amount of improvement in subsystems 1 and 2, the system reliability cannot exceed 0.94. The focus for system reliability improvement should be on subsystem 3.

EXAMPLE 10.1

A system consists of three subsystems connected in series.
The reliability for each subsystem for a mission time of t is:

$$R_1(t) = 0.99$$
$$R_2(t) = 0.98$$
$$R_3(t) = 0.94$$

The system reliability for mission time t:

$$R_{System}(t) = (0.99)(0.98)(0.94) = 0.91$$

There are other block diagram models that could result in higher system reliability. These models will be considered. However, it should be noted that there are many highly reliable series systems in use. The series design has some advantages over other designs. A series system will require a minimum number of parts, consume minimum power and therefore dissipate less heat, take up less room, add less weight, and be cheaper to build than other system configurations.

Parallel System

Redundancy can be designed into a system to increase system reliability. A parallel system provides more than one path for system success, as shown in Figure 10.2. An active redundancy system has subsystems online that can individually perform the functions required for system success. If a subsystem fails, system success can be accomplished with the successful operation of a remaining subsystem. The system fails only when all the redundant subsystems fail.

To analyze a parallel system it is necessary to assume that the probabilities of failure for the various subsystems are totally independent for the entire mission time. This requires that the redundant system design be engineered to ensure that this assumption is valid. If a single event can cause more than one subsystem to fail, or if the failure of one subsystem can cause a secondary failure of a redundant subsystem, the desired improvement in system reliability due to the redundancy is lost. For example, a single power supply failure might cause the failure of redundant

Part IV.C.1

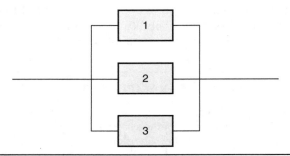

Figure 10.2 The parallel system.

navigational systems. This situation is referred to as a *single-point failure*. Also, particular attention must be given to the interconnection points of the redundant subsystems. Many times, these are the source of single-point failures. Reliability engineering tools such as FMEA that can be used to identify single-point failures or failure modes and remove them from the design.

A parallel system will fail only if all subsystems fail. If a redundant system consists of n independent subsystems, and if the reliability of each subsystem is known, then system reliability can be calculated as

$$R_{System}(t) = 1 - [1 - R_1(t)] \times [1 - R_2(t)] \times \ldots \times [1 - R_n(t)]$$

Active redundancy is an important reliability tool available to the system designer. See Example 10.2. It should not, however, be used to improve the reliability of a poor design. It is much more efficient to engineer the design for the highest possible reliability and then use active redundancy if the desired reliability is still not achieved.

EXAMPLE 10.2

An active parallel system has three independent subsystems.
The reliability for each subsystem for a mission time of t is:

$$R_1(t) = 0.99$$
$$R_2(t) = 0.98$$
$$R_3(t) = 0.94$$

The reliability of the system for mission time t is equal to

$$R_{System}(t) = 1 - (1 - 0.99)(1 - 0.98)(1 - 0.94) = 0.99998$$

It should be noted that the reliability of the system is greater than the reliability of any of the redundant subsystems.

$$R_{System} > R_i \text{ for all } i = 1 \text{ to } n$$

Series–Parallel Model

A system may be modeled as a combination of series and parallel subsystems. For this model the same assumptions apply as for individual series or parallel systems. The combined system reliability can be found by converting the system to an equivalent series or equivalent parallel model.

EXAMPLE 10.3

Figure 10.3 shows a series–parallel system. The reliabilities for each subsystem are shown on the diagram. Find the reliability for the system.
The reliability for the two parallel subsystems is:

$$R_1 = 1 - (1 - 0.99)(1 - 0.99) = 1 - (1 - 0.99)^2$$
$$R_1 = 0.9999$$

The reliability for the three parallel subsystems is:

$$R_3 = 1 - (1 - 0.89)(1 - 0.92)(1 - 0.90)$$

$$R_3 = 0.99912$$

The system is now an equivalent series system with R_1 and R_3 and $R_2 = 0.999$. The system reliability can be found as:

$$R_{System} = R_1 \times R_2 \times R_3 = (0.9999)(0.999)(0.99912)$$

$$R_{System} = 0.998$$

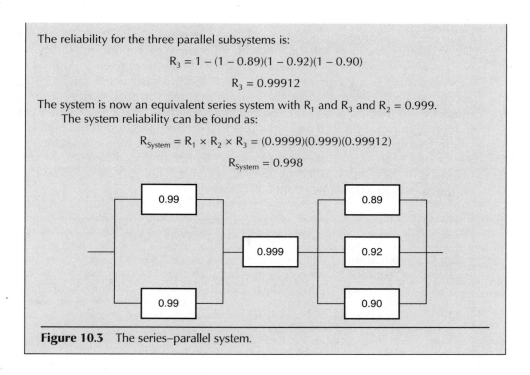

Figure 10.3   The series–parallel system.

Special Case Reliability Modeling

m *out of* n *System Model*

A special case of the parallel system is the *m* out of *n* system. This is a parallel system of *n* equivalent subsystems. System success requires that at least *m* ($m < n$) of the subsystems not fail. For this system, *m* can be any positive integer less than *n*; however, if $m = 1$, the system reduces to an active parallel system. The binomial distribution, along with the addition law for mutually exclusive events, is used to find the reliability of the system.

If R is the reliability for each of the *n* redundant subsystems, and *m* subsystems are required for system success,

$$R_{System}(t) = \sum C_i^n (R)^i (1 - R)^{n-i} \text{ for } i = m \text{ to } n$$

where:

$C_i^n = \dfrac{n!}{[i!(n-i)!]}$ is the number of combinations of *n* items taken *i* at a time

n! (defined only for nonnegative integers) is the product of all the positive integers up to and including *n*

$6! = 2 \times 3 \times 4 \times 5 \times 6 = 720$

$0! = 1$ by definition

Significance

The reliability engineer must always guard against presenting reliability results with more precision than the data warrant. All engineers need to know how to express results using correct significance. A legitimate concern might be raised about the significance of the results in the examples in this section. In order to illustrate the method of solving the problems, the results are many times carried to more significant digits than can be justified by the data used in the calculations.

In Example 10.4 and the subsequent examples, the results of the calculations are carried to the fourth decimal place and then rounded. This exceeds any significance that can be justified by the values used. This is done to show that the methods will give the same results.

EXAMPLE 10.4

Eight units each with a reliability of 0.85 are connected in a parallel configuration. At least six units are required for system success. What is the reliability of the system?

The reliability of the system is the probability that six of the units are successful and two of the units fail or that seven of the units are successful and that one of the units fails or that all eight of the units are successful. These probabilities are mutually exclusive and can be added to give the probability of system success.

$$R_{System}(t) = C_6^8 (0.85)^6 (1 - 0.85)^2 + C_7^8 (0.85)^7 (1 - 0.85) + C_8^8 (0.85)^8$$

$$= (28)(0.85)^6 (0.15)^2 + (8)(0.85)^7 (0.15) + (0.85)^8$$

$$= 0.895$$

System Model Using Bayes's Theorem

Another special case is a coherent system, a connection of subsystems that cannot be reduced to a series or parallel model. One method to solve for system reliability of such a system is known as *Bayesian analysis*.

Choose one subsystem. With that subsystem assumed to be first in a success state, then in a failed state, the remaining system should reduce into a series–parallel arrangement. If it does not, choose another subsystem. With the chosen subsystem assumed to be in a success state, find the reliability of the remaining system and multiply by the probability that the subsystem has not failed. With the chosen subsystem assumed to be in a failed state, find the reliability of the remaining system and multiply by the probability that the subsystem has failed. The sum of these two values is the system reliability.

EXAMPLE 10.5

The system model shown in Figure 10.4 cannot be reduced to an equivalent series or equivalent parallel model. Find the reliability of the system using Bayes's theorem.

The subsystem reliability values are:

$$R_A = R_B = R_C = 0.95$$

$$R_D = R_E = 0.99$$

Figure 10.4   System model for Bayesian analysis.

Choose subsystem E.
   Assume E is in a success state. The system model will reduce to

and the system reliability with E good is

$$R_{(E\ success)} = 1 - [1 - (0.99)(0.95)][1 - 0.95] = 0.9970$$

Assume E is in a failed state. The system model will reduce to

and the system reliability with E failed is

$$R_{(E\ failed)} = [1 - (1 - 0.99)(1 - (0.95)(0.95))]\ [0.95] = 0.9491$$

The system reliability is

$$R_{System} = R_{(E\ success)} \times P_{(E\ success)} + R_{(E\ failed)} \times P_{(E\ failed)}$$

$$R_{System} = (0.9970)(0.99) + (0.9491)(1 - 0.99)$$

$$R_{System} = 0.9965$$

Truth Table Method

System reliability can be found from any block diagram—when the subsystem reliabilities are known—using a systematic method to identify all the events that will result in system success. The total events can be identified by finding all the combinations of subsystem success (S) and subsystem failure (F). It can then be determined if an event will result in system success or in system failure. The probability that each event will occur can be determined. The events are mutually exclusive. The probability of system success is the sum of the probabilities of the events that result in system success. The total number of events for a system modeled using k subsystems is 2^k.

EXAMPLE 10.6

Find the reliability of the system shown in Figure 10.5 using the truth table method. Subsystem reliabilities are:

$$R_A = 0.85$$
$$R_B = 0.90$$
$$R_C = 0.92$$

The total number of events is $2^3 = 8$.
   Construct a truth table using S for success and F for failure.

Event #	Subsystem			System	Event probability
	A	B	C		
1	S	S	S	S	(0.85)(0.90)(0.92) = 0.7038
2	S	S	F	S	(0.85)(0.90)(0.08) = 0.0612
3	S	F	S	S	(0.85)(0.10)(0.92) = 0.0782
4	S	F	F	S	(0.85)(0.10)(0.08) = 0.0068
5	F	S	S	S	(0.15)(0.90)(0.92) = 0.1242
6	F	S	F	F	
7	F	F	S	F	
8	F	F	F	F	

The system reliability is the sum of the probabilities of the events that result in system success:

$$R_{System} = 0.7038 + 0.0612 + 0.0782 + 0.0068 + 0.1242 = 0.9742$$

This can be verified using the series–parallel model:

$$R_{System} = 1 - [1 - (0.90)(0.92)] \times [1 - 0.85] = 0.9742$$

For an exercise, apply this method to the problem in Example 10.5 and verify that the system reliability is 0.9965. There are $2^5 = 32$ total events. Fifteen events result in system success.

Figure 10.5   Series–parallel model for truth table method.

The method will be demonstrated on a simple system that can be easily verified. The method can be used for complex system diagrams but can become cumbersome as the number of subsystems increases. A computer model can be used for complex systems. See Example 10.6.

It should be noted that the solutions for system reliability for all of the above static math models are distribution free. This means that no assumption is made about the distributions that describe the subsystem failures. Each subsystem failure could be described by a different distribution. The subsystem reliabilities can be determined independently, and the system reliability can be calculated using the laws of probability. It might require a complex analysis to determine the distribution describing the system failures. The exception to this is the series model with subsystem failures described by the exponential distribution (constant failure rate). In this case the system has a constant failure rate, and the system failure rate is the sum of the subsystem failure rates.

Series Model (Constant Failure Rate)

A series system is shown in Figure 10.6. Assume that the failure distribution for each of the subsystems is exponential. Each subsystem i has a constant failure rate λ_i. The system failure rate is also constant and is equal to the sum of the subsystem failure rates:

$$\lambda_{System} = \sum_n \lambda_i$$

The system reliability is

$$R_{System} = e^{-(\lambda_{System})t}$$

The MTTF/MTBF of the system is

$$\theta = \frac{1}{\lambda_{System}}$$

See Example 10.7.

Figure 10.6   The series system.

Part IV.C.1

EXAMPLE 10.7

For the system in Figure 10.6:

$$\lambda_1 = 100 \times 10^{-6}\ \text{failures/hour}$$

$$\lambda_2 = 80 \times 10^{-6}\ \text{failures/hour}$$

$$\lambda_3 = 20 \times 10^{-6}\ \text{failures/hour}$$

Continued

What is the system reliability for $t = 100$ hours?

$$\lambda_{System} = \lambda_1 + \lambda_2 + \lambda_3$$

$$\lambda_{System} = (100 + 80 + 20) \times 10^{-6} = 200 \times 10^{-6} \text{ failures/hour} = 200E{-}6 \text{ failures/hour}$$

Reliability: $R_{(t=100)} = e^{-(200E{-}6 \times 100)} = 0.98$

MTBF: $\theta = 1/(200 \times 10^{-6}) = 5000$ hours

An alternate method would be to first find the reliability of each subsystem and then find the system reliability using the series model:

$$R_1 = e^{-(100E{-}6 \times 100)} = 0.99$$

$$R_2 = e^{-(80E{-}6 \times 100)} = 0.992$$

$$R_3 = e^{-(20E{-}6 \times 100)} = 0.998$$

$$R_{System} = (0.99)(0.992)(0.998) = 0.98$$

Dynamic System Models

Dynamic math models are time-dependent. To analyze a dynamic model, it is necessary to assume a failure distribution for the subsystems. For the following models the exponential distribution is assumed to describe the failures of the subsystems. Each subsystem is assumed to have a constant failure rate.

Load Sharing Model

The subsystems of an active parallel system are connected such that each shares equally in the total load. The subsystems are derated so that each is operating at less than its maximum load capacity. The failure rate of each subsystem is lowered and reliability is improved because the units are operating at a lower stress level. If a failure occurs, the remaining subsystems have enough capacity to carry the system load, but they will be operating at a higher stress level and therefore at a higher failure rate.

For the case of two units in a load-sharing configuration, each subsystem operates with a constant failure rate of λ_1 as long as both are operating. If one subsystem fails, the remaining subsystem will continue to operate but at an increased failure rate $\lambda_2 > \lambda_1$.

System success for a mission time of t would be described as both subsystems operating successfully for the entire time t at failure rates equal to λ_1, or a failure occurring at time $t_1 < t$, and the remaining subsystem operating for a time of $t - t_1$ at a failure rate of λ_2:

$$R_{System(t)} = e^{-2\lambda_1 t} + \frac{2\lambda_1 \left(e^{-\lambda_2 t} - e^{-2\lambda_1 t}\right)}{2\lambda_1 - \lambda_2} \quad \text{if } 2\lambda_1 - \lambda_2 \neq 0$$

If $2\lambda_1 = \lambda_2$, the denominator of the above equation becomes zero.
The reliability equation reduces to

$$R_{System(t)} = e^{-2\lambda_1 t} + 2\lambda_1 t e^{-\lambda_2 t}$$

The reliability equation can be expanded to include systems with more than two units.

Standby Redundant Systems

A system that has parallel units that are utilized only in the event of a failure is a *standby redundant system.*

Figure 10.7 shows a primary unit performing a function. If the primary unit were to fail, a sensor could detect the failure and a standby unit could be switched in to allow the system to continue to perform the function. The standby unit must be capable of performing the function, but it might not be identical to the primary unit. The sensing and switching system may be an automatic part of the system or may require some manual interface. An example of automatic sensing and switching and nonidentical redundant units is the backup battery in an alarm clock. An example requiring manual switching is the replacement of a failed tire on an automobile.

These are examples of standby redundant systems because the secondary units become a functioning part of the system only after the primary unit fails. A failure distribution for the subsystems must be assumed to analyze the system for reliability. Other factors to be considered are the reliability of the sensing and switching system and the probability that the secondary subsystem could fail before it is needed.

The simplest system is one with both the primary and secondary units identical, perfect sensing and switching, zero probability of failure of the secondary unit in its quiescent mode, and a constant failure rate to describe the probability of failure for the units.

For such a system, the failure rate of the primary and secondary units is λ and the mission time is t. The reliability of the system, $R_{System}(t)$, is the probability that the primary unit will operate successfully for time t, or the primary unit will fail at $t_1 < t$, and the secondary unit will operate successfully for the time $t - t_1$.

The reliability equation is

$$R_{System}(t) = e^{-\lambda t}(1 + \lambda t)$$

If the sensing and switching are not perfect ($R_{s/s} < 1$), the equation becomes

$$R_{System}(t) = e^{-\lambda t}(1 + R_{s/s}\lambda t)$$

The equation can be expanded to include multiple standby units.

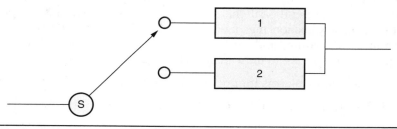

Figure 10.7 Standby redundant model.

The reliability for a system with two standby units and perfect switching is

$$R_{\text{System}}(t) = e^{-\lambda t}\left(1 + \lambda t + \frac{(\lambda t)^2}{2}\right)$$

2. PHYSICS OF FAILURE (PoF) AND FAILURE MECHANISMS

> Identify various potential failure mechanisms
> (e.g., fracture, corrosion, memory corruption) and
> describe the physical process of these failures.
> (Apply)
>
> Body of Knowledge IV.C.2

Physics of failure is a science-based approach to reliability that uses modeling and simulation to design-in reliability. This approach models the root causes of failures such as fatigue, fracture, wear, and corrosion. Computer-aided design (CAD) tools have been developed to address various loads, stresses, and failure mechanisms and sites. The two main focus areas are in electronic and mechanical systems analyses. PoF uses knowledge of basic failure processes to prevent failures through robust design and manufacturing practices and aims to:

- Design-in reliability up front

- Eliminate failures prior to testing

- Increase fielded reliability

- Promote rapid, cost-effective deployment of health and usage monitoring systems (HUMS)

- Improve diagnostic and prognostic techniques and processes

- Decrease operation and support costs

The PoF approach to reliability uses data regarding the actual environmental conditions (e.g., applied voltage and temperature in electronic components) and loading during the life of the unit to make predictions about the unit's current "health" and its expected reliability. In the case of mechanical systems, the environmental conditions may include time/cycles at temperature/pressure conditions, humidity, and previous operational characteristics of similar mechanical systems. This requires a data collection mechanism, usually via various sensors, some sort of data mining algorithm, and an analysis of the failure modes. The goals of the research in this field are to reduce lifecycle costs by:

- Generating alarms for impending failures

- Reducing unscheduled maintenance

- Extending preventive maintenance times

- Reducing inspection costs and replacement part inventory

One technique for sensing the accumulated stress on a unit is to add an additional device that will provide an alarm that a critical level has been reached. For example, to help detect the accumulated effect of oxidation on the undercarriage of a marine vessel, a separate metal tab could act as an early warning such that when oxidation of the tab reached a certain point, an alarm would be set. Other devices may be used to detect the effect of vibration, chemistry, temperature, and so on, on the unit's reliability.

There are two more or less competing approaches to the physics of failure: model based and data driven.

Model-Based Approaches

These systems attempt to derive a mathematical model to describe unit performance and to generate reliability predictions. Much of the work in this field has been done in the area of electronics and circuit board reliability. Pecht and Gu (2009) identify the circuit board failure mechanisms and their associated theoretical models, as shown in Table 10.1.

Failure Modes

Failures in engineering design and systems usually occur in the four forms: hardware failures, software failures, human failures, and organizational failures. Table 10.2 lists the failure modes in mechanical components.

Failure Mode Descriptions[1]

Force and/or temperature-induced elastic deformation failure occurs whenever the elastic (recoverable) deformation in a machine member, brought about by the imposed operational loads or temperatures, becomes great enough to interfere with the ability of the machine to satisfactorily perform its intended function.

Yield failure occurs when the plastic (unrecoverable) deformation in a ductile machine member, brought about by the imposed operational loads or motions,

Table 10.1 Failure modes and models for circuit boards.

Failure sites	Failure modes	Failure models
Fracture	Die attach, wirebond, solder leads, bond pads, traces, interfaces	Nonlinear power law
Corrosion	Metalizations	Eyring
Electromigration	Metalizations	Eyring
Conductive filament migration	Between metalizations	Power law
Stress-driven diffusion voiding	Metal traces	Eyring
Time-dependent dielectric breakdown	Dielectric layers	Arrhenius

Table 10.2   Failure modes most commonly seen in machines and machine parts.

1. Force and/or temperature-induced elastic deformation	8. Wear:
2. Yield	a. Adhesive wear
3. Brinnelling	b. Abrasive wear
4. Ductile rupture	c. Corrosive wear
5. Brittle fracture	d. Surface fatigue wear
6. Fatigue:	e. Deformation wear
a. High cycle fatigue	f. Fretting wear
b. Low cycle fatigue	9. Impact:
c. Thermal fatigue	a. Impact fracture
d. Surface fatigue	b. Impact deformation
e. Corrosion fatigue	c. Impact wear
f. Fretting fatigue	d. Impact fretting
7. Corrosion:	e. Impact fatigue
a. Direct chemical attack	10. Creep
b. Galvanic corrosion	11. Thermal relaxation
c. Pitting corrosion	12. Stress rupture
d. Intergranular corrosion	13. Thermal shock
e. Selective leaching	14. Galling and seizure
f. Erosion corrosion	15. Spalling
g. Cavitation corrosion	16. Radiation damage
h. Hydrogen damage	17. Buckling
i. Biological corrosion	18. Creep buckling
j. Stress corrosion	19. Combined creep and fatigue
k. Fretting corrosion	

Source: Dieter and Schmidt (2009), 712.

becomes great enough to interfere with the ability of the machine to satisfactorily perform its intended function.

Brinnelling failure occurs when the static forces between two curved surfaces in contact result in local yielding of one or both mating members to produce a permanent surface discontinuity of significant size. For example, if a ball bearing is statically loaded so that a ball is forced to permanently indent the race through local plastic flow, the race is brinnelled. Subsequent operation of the bearing might result in intolerably increased vibration, noise, and heating, and, therefore, failure will occur.

Ductile rupture failure occurs when the plastic deformation, in a machine part that exhibits ductile behavior, is carried to the extreme so that the member separates into two pieces. Initiation and coalescence of internal voids slowly propagate to failure, leaving a dull, fibrous rupture surface.

Brittle fracture failure occurs when the elastic deformation, in a machine part which exhibits brittle behavior, is carried to the extreme so that the primary interatomic bonds are broken and the member separates into two or more pieces. Preexisting flaws or growing cracks provide initiation sites for very rapid crack propagation to catastrophic failure, leaving a granular, multifaceted fracture surface.

Fatigue failure is a general term given to the sudden and catastrophic separation of a machine part into two or more pieces as a result of the application of fluctuating loads or deformations over a period of time. Failure takes place by the initiation and propagation of a crack until it becomes unstable and propagates suddenly to failure. The loads and deformations that cause failure by fatigue are typically far below the static failure levels.

- *High-cycle fatigue* occurs when loads or deformations are of high enough magnitude that more than about 50,000 cycles are required to produce failure, the phenomenon is usually termed fatigue caused by elastic deformation surpassing the ultimate tensile stress limit, or the yield stress limit.

- *Low-cycle fatigue* occurs when loads or deformations are of high enough magnitude that less than about 10,000 cycles are required to produce failure.

- *Thermal fatigue* occurs when load or strain cycling is produced by a fluctuating temperature field in the machine part.

- *Surface fatigue* failure, usually associated rolling surfaces in contact (but sometimes associated with sliding contact), manifests as pitting, cracking, and spalling of the contacting surfaces as a result of the cyclic contact stresses that result in maximum values of cyclic shear stresses slightly below surface. The cyclic subsurface shear stresses generate cracks that propagate to the contacting surface, dislodging particles in the process, to produce surface pitting.

Corrosion failure implies that a machine part is rendered incapable of performing its intended function because of the undesired deterioration of the material as a result of chemical or electrochemical interaction with the environment. Corrosion often interacts with other failure modes such as wear or fatigue. Some of the many forms of corrosion include the following:

- *Direct chemical attack*, perhaps the most common type of corrosion, involves corrosive attack of the surface of the machine part exposed to the corrosive medium, more or less uniformly over the entire exposed surface.

- *Galvanic corrosion* is an accelerated electrochemical corrosion that occurs when two dissimilar metals in electrical contact are made part of a circuit completed by a connecting pool or film of electrolyte or corrosive medium, leading to current flow and ensuing corrosion.

- *Crevice corrosion* is the accelerated corrosion process highly localized within crevices, cracks, or joints where small volume regions of stagnant solution are trapped in contact with the corroding metal.

- *Pitting corrosion* is a very localized attack that leads to the development of an array of holes or pits that penetrate the metal.

- *Intergranular corrosion* is the localized attack occurring at grain boundaries of certain copper, chromium, nickel, aluminum, magnesium, and zinc alloys when they are improperly heat treated or welded. Formation of local galvanic cells that precipitate corrosion products at the grain boundaries seriously degrades the material strength because of the intergranular corrosive process.

- *Selective leaching* is a corrosion process in which one element of a solid alloy is removed, such when zinc dissolves out of brass alloys or build-up of graphite in gray cast irons.

- *Erosion corrosion* is the accelerated chemical attack that results when an abrasive or viscous material flows past a containing surface continuously baring fresh, unprotected material to the corrosive medium.

- *Cavitation corrosion* is the accelerated chemical corrosion that results when, because of differences in vapor pressure, certain bubbles and cavities within a fluid collapse adjacent to the pressure vessel walls, causing particles of the surface to be expelled, baring fresh, unprotected surface to the corrosive medium.

- *Hydrogen damage* is induced by corrosion. Hydrogen damage includes hydrogen blistering, hydrogen embrittlement, hydrogen attack, and decarburization.

- *Biological corrosion* is a corrosion process that results from the activity of living organisms, usually by virtue of their processes of food ingestion and waste elimination, in which the waste products are corrosive acids or hydroxides.

- *Stress corrosion* failure occurs when the applied stresses on a machine part in a corrosive environment generate a field of localized surface cracks, usually along grain boundaries, that render the part incapable of performing its function, often because of triggering some other failure mode. Stress corrosion is a very important type of corrosion failure mode because so many different metals are susceptible to it. For example, a variety of iron, steel, stainless steel, copper, and aluminum alloys are subject to stress corrosion cracking if placed in certain adverse corrosive media.

- *Corrosion wear* failure is a combination failure mode in which corrosion and wear combine their deleterious effects to incapacitate a machine part. The corrosion process often produces a hard, abrasive corrosion product that accelerates the wear, while the wear process constantly removes the protective corrosion layer from the surface, baring fresh metal to the corrosive medium and thus accelerating the corrosion. The two modes combine to make the result more serious than the sum of the modes would have been otherwise.

- *Corrosion fatigue* is a combination failure mode in which corrosion and fatigue combine to cause failure of a machine part. The corrosion process often forms pits and surface discontinuities that act as stress raisers that in turn accelerate fatigue failure. Further, cracks in the usually brittle corrosion layer also act as fatigue crack nuclei that propagate into the base material. On the other hand, the cyclic loads or strains cause cracking and flaking of the corrosion layer, which bares fresh metal to the corrosive medium. Thus, each process accelerates the other, often making the result disproportionately serious.

Wear is the undesired cumulative change in dimensions brought about by the gradual removal of discrete particles from contacting surfaces in motion predominantly as a result of mechanical action. Wear is not a single process, but a number of different processes that can take place independently or in combination, resulting in material removal from contacting surfaces through a complex combination of local shearing, plowing, gouging, welding, tearing, and others.

- *Adhesive wear* takes place because of high local pressure and welding at asperity contact sites, followed by motion-induced plastic deformation and rupture of asperity junctions, with resulting metal removal or transfer.

- *Abrasive wear* takes place when the wear particles are removed from the surface by plowing, gouging, and cutting action of the rough edges of a harder mating surface or by hard particles entrapped between the mating surfaces.

- *Corrosive wear* occurs when the conditions for either adhesive wear or abrasive wear coexist with conditions that lead to corrosion, and they interact synergistically.

- *Surface fatigue wear* is a wear phenomenon associated with curved surfaces in rolling or sliding contact, in which subsurface cyclic shear stresses initiate microcracks that propagate to the surface to spall out macroscopic particles and form wear pits.

- *Deformation wear* arises as a result of repeated *elastic* deformation at the wearing surface that produces a matrix of cracks that grow in accordance with the surface fatigue description just given.

- *Fretting wear* failure results when the changes in dimensions of the mating parts, because of the presence of fretting action, become large enough to interfere with proper design function or large enough to produce geometrical stress concentration of such magnitude that failure ensues as a result of excessive local stress levels.

Impact failure results when a machine member is subjected to nonstatic loads that produce in the part stresses or deformations of such magnitude that the member no longer is capable of performing its function. The failure is brought about by the interaction of stress or strain waves generated by dynamic or suddenly applied loads, which may induce local stresses and strains many times greater than would be induced by static application of the same loads.

- *Impact fracture* occurs when the magnitudes of the stresses and strains are sufficiently high to cause separation into two or more parts.

- *Impact deformation* occurs when the impact produces intolerable elastic or plastic deformation.

- *Impact wear* occurs if repeated impacts induce cyclic elastic strains that lead to initiation of a matrix of fatigue cracks, which grow to failure by the surface fatigue phenomenon described above.

Part IV.C.2

- *Impact fretting* is induced by the small lateral relative displacements between two surfaces as they impact together, where the small displacements are caused by Poisson strains or small tangential "glancing" velocity components.

- *Impact fatigue* failure occurs when impact loading is repetitively applied to a machine member until failure occurs by the nucleation and propagation of a fatigue crack.

Fretting action may occur at the interface between any two solid bodies whenever they are pressed together by a normal force and subjected to small-amplitude cyclic relative motion with respect to each other. Fretting usually takes place in joints that are not intended to move but, because of vibrational loads or deformations, experience minute cyclic relative motions. Typically, debris produced by fretting action is trapped between the surfaces because of the small motions involved.

- *Fretting fatigue* failure is the premature fatigue fracture of a machine member subjected to fluctuating loads or strains together with conditions that simultaneously produce fretting action. The surface discontinuities and microcracks generated by the fretting action act as fatigue crack nuclei that propagate to failure under conditions of fatigue loading that would otherwise be acceptable. Fretting fatigue failure is an insidious failure mode because the fretting action is usually hidden within a joint where it cannot be seen, leading to premature, and often unexpected, fatigue failure of a sudden and catastrophic nature.

- *Fretting corrosion* failure occurs when a machine part is rendered incapable of performing its intended function because of the surface degradation of the material from which the part is made, as a result of fretting action.

- *Creep* failure results whenever the plastic deformation in a machine member accrues over a period of time under the influence of stress and temperature until the accumulated dimensional changes interfere with the ability of the machine part to satisfactorily perform its intended function. Three stages of creep are often observed: (1) transient or primary creep, during which time the rate of strain decreases, (2) steady-state or secondary creep, during which time the rate of strain is virtually constant, and (3) tertiary creep, during which time the creep strain rate increases, often rapidly, until rupture occurs. This terminal rupture is often called creep rupture and may or may not occur, depending on the stress-time-temperature conditions.

Thermal relaxation or *stress relaxation* failure occurs when the dimensional changes due to the creep process result in the relaxation of a prestrained or prestressed member until it no longer is able to perform its intended function. For example, if the prestressed flange bolts of a high-temperature pressure vessel relax over a period of time because of creep in the bolts, so that finally the peak pressure surges exceed the bolt preload to violate the flange seal, the bolts will have failed because of thermal relaxation.

Stress rupture failure is intimately related to the creep process except that the combination of stress, time, and temperature is such that rupture into two parts is assured. In stress rupture failures the combination of stress and temperature is often such that the period of steady-state creep is short or nonexistent.

Thermal shock failure occurs when the thermal gradients generated in a machine part are so pronounced that differential thermal strains exceed the ability of the material to sustain them without yielding or fracture.

Galling failure occurs when two sliding surfaces are subjected to such a combination of loads, sliding velocities, temperatures, environments, and lubricants that massive surface destruction is caused by welding and tearing, plowing, gouging, significant plastic deformation of surface rough edges, and metal transfer between the two surfaces. Galling may be thought of as a severe extension of the adhesive wear process. When such action results in significant impairment to intended surface sliding, or in seizure, the joint is said to have failed by galling. *Seizure* is an extension of the galling process to such a level of severity that the two parts are virtually welded together, and relative motion is no longer possible.

Spalling failure occurs whenever a particle is spontaneously dislodged from the surface of a machine part so as to prevent the proper function of the member. Armor plate fails by spalling, for example, when a striking missile on the exposed side of an armor shield generates a stress wave that propagates across the plate in such a way as to dislodge or *spall* a secondary missile of lethal potential on the protected side. Other examples of spalling failure are manifested in rolling contact bearings and gear teeth because of the action of surface fatigue as described earlier.

Radiation damage failure occurs when the changes in material properties induced by exposure to a nuclear radiation field are of such a type and magnitude that the machine part is no longer able to perform its intended function, usually as a result of the triggering of some other failure mode, and often related to loss in ductility associated with radiation exposure. Elastomers and polymers are typically more susceptible to radiation damage than are metals whose strength properties are sometimes enhanced rather than damaged by exposure to a radiation field, though ductility is usually decreased.

Buckling failure occurs when, because of a critical combination of magnitude and/or point-of-load application, together with the geometrical configuration of a machine member, the deflection of the member suddenly increases greatly with only a slight increase in load. This nonlinear response results in a buckling failure if the buckled member is no longer capable of performing its design function.

Creep buckling failure occurs when, after a period of time, the creep process results in an unstable combination of the loading and geometry of a machine part so that the critical buckling limit is exceeded and failure ensures.

Combined creep and fatigue failure is a combination failure mode in which all of the conditions for both creep failure and fatigue failure exist simultaneously, each process influencing the other to produce accelerated failure. The interaction of creep and fatigue is probably synergistic but is not well understood.

While each of the above can be analyzed from a pure engineering point of view, the probability of failure due to each of these failure modes is usually based on the collection of failure mode data and statistical failure analysis.

Summary of Data-Driven Approaches

A disadvantage of the model-based approach is that detailed knowledge about the geometry and composition of the unit are needed but not always available. The data-driven approach skirts this issue by relying on a software system that learns the data patterns that lead to failure. A disadvantage of this method is that historical data must be available to establish correlations and detect patterns.

Physics of failure is associated in the literature with *prognostics and health management* (PHM), where the word "health" refers to a methodology for continuous assessment of the remaining useful life of the unit. A good source in this field is the PHM Society (http://www.phmsociety.org).

One last word: *Memory corruption* is somewhat independent of the more physical causes of failure. This failure refers to software activity that modifies a section of computer memory. The corruption, when unintentional, is due to human error by the programmer. In some early programming systems, variables were global, meaning that programmers needed to check with each other when they wanted to use a particular variable to make sure no one else was using it. Failure to make that check produced errors that were sporadic and extremely difficult to debug. More recent examples of memory corruption are far more sophisticated but produce similarly sporadic results and, sometimes, system crashes, which again are difficult to detect and fix. In some cases malware exploits memory corruption in commercial software to cause it to execute damaging code.

3. FAILURE MODELS

> Select appropriate theoretical models (e.g., Arrhenius, S-N curve) to assess or predict failure rates. (Analyze)
>
> Body of Knowledge IV.C.3

Common Life-Stress Models

There are several common life-stress models used by reliability professionals. The most widely used life-stress models include the Arrhenius, Eyring, and the inverse power law.

- *Arrhenius*: a single stress model used when temperature is the accelerated stress

- *Eyring*: a single stress model used when temperature or humidity is the accelerated stress

- *Inverse power law (IPL)*: a single stress model typically used with a nonthermal stress, such as cyclic loading, vibration, voltage, or temperature cycling

- *Temperature–humidity*: a double-Arrhenius model used when temperature and humidity are two acceleration variables

- *Temperature–nonthermal*: a combination of the Arrhenius and IPL relationships used when one stress is temperature and the other is nonthermal (e.g., voltage)

Mathematical equations of life versus stress are:

- Linear: Life = a(Stress) + b

- Exponential: Life = $be^{a(\text{Stress})}$ or Life = $Ae^{\frac{E_a}{kT}}$

- Power: Life = $b^{(\text{Stress})a}$ or Life = $\dfrac{1}{k(\text{Stress})^n}$

- Logarithmic: Life = $a*\ln(\text{Stress}) + b$ or Life = $e^{a_0 + a_1 \text{Stress}_1 + \ldots + a_n \text{Stress}_n}$

- Combinations of these forms as well:

$$\text{Life} = \frac{1}{(\text{Stress})} e^{-\left(A - \frac{B}{\text{Stress}}\right)} \quad \text{Eyring relationship}$$

Arrhenius Temperature Acceleration Model

The Arrhenius model is one of the most used acceleration models. The Arrhenius model predicts how time-to-fail varies with temperature. This model is widely used for electronics, chemicals, and packaging industries. The time to failure and the acceleration factor is calculated using:

$$t_f = A_0 \exp\left(\frac{E_a}{kT}\right)$$

$$AF = \frac{t_{use}}{t_{test}} = \exp\left[\left(\frac{E_a}{kT}\right)\left(\frac{1}{T_{use}} - \frac{1}{T_{test}}\right)\right]$$

where:

t_f = Time to failure (hours)

A_0 = A material constant

k = Boltzmann's constant = 8.617×10^{-5} eV/°K

E_a = Activation energy for damage mechanism and material

AF = Acceleration factor

t_{use} = Number of temperature cycles in service use

t_{test} = Number of temperature cycles in laboratory test

T_{use} = Product temperature cycles in service use, °K

T_{test} = Product temperature cycles in laboratory text, °K

EXAMPLE 10.8

An electronic device that normally operates at a temperature of 50°C is subjected to a stress temperature of 100°C. The activation energy for the failure mode is 0.8 electron volts.
What is the acceleration factor (AF) using the Arrhenius equation?

Solution:

$$AF = \exp\,[E_A/k(1/T_{use} - 1/T_{test})]$$

$$AF = \exp\,[(0.8/8.617 \times 10^{-5})(1/323 - 1/373)] = 47$$

Assuming the increased temperature did not cause new failure modes, two days of testing at 100°C is equivalent to about three months of use.

Inverse Power Law for Voltage Acceleration

The most commonly used model for voltage acceleration is the *inverse power relationship* (or "inverse power rule" or "inverse power law"). Let $T(\text{volt})$ and $T(\text{volt}_U)$ be the failure times that would result for a particular unit tested at increased voltage and use-voltage conditions, respectively.

$$T(\text{volt}) = \frac{T(\text{volt}_U)}{AF(\text{volt})} = \left(\frac{\text{volt}_U}{\text{volt}}\right)^{\beta_1} T(\text{volt}_U)$$

$$\text{so, } T(\text{volt}) = \frac{\alpha}{(\text{volt})^{\beta}}$$

The relationship is known as the inverse power law because, generally, $\beta_1 > 0$. Step-stress testing is sometimes used to further accelerate a reliability test. This technique involves increasing the stress level at fixed points and recording the failures or degradation levels (see Example 10.9).

EXAMPLE 10.9

A device that normally operates with 5 volts is tested at two increased stress levels: $V_1 = 15$ and $V_2 = 30$ volts.
Analysis of the data from the tests indicates that 5% of the population failed at 150 hours when the high stress voltage of 30 volts was used. When the stress voltage of 15 volts was applied, 5% of the population failed at 750 hours.
At what time t would 5% of the population be expected to fail under the normal stress of 5 volts?

Solution:

$$[750/150] = [30/15]^{\beta}$$

$$\log\,[750/150] = \beta \log\,[30/15]$$

$$\beta = 2.3$$

$$[t/150] = [30/5]2.3$$

$$t = 9240 \text{ hours}$$

This means that an hour of testing at 30 volts is equivalent to 62 hours of use at 5 volts.

Degradation Model

Two common assumptions typically made when degradation data are modeled are the following:

1. A parameter D, which can be measured over time, drifts monotonically (upwards or downwards) towards a specified critical value DF. When it reaches DF, failure occurs.

2. The drift, measured in terms of D, is linear over time with a slope (or rate of degradation) R, which depends on the relevant stress the unit is operating under and also the (random) characteristics of the unit being measured. *Note:* It may be necessary to define D as a transformation of some standard parameter in order to obtain linearity—logarithms or powers are sometimes needed.

Figure 10.8 illustrates these assumptions by showing degradation plots of units on test. Degradation readings for each unit are taken at the same time points and straight lines fit through these readings on a unit-by-unit basis. These lines are then extended up to a critical (failure) degradation value. The projected times of failure for these units are then read off the plot.

So, the central idea is to model unit degradation paths to predict unit times to fail . . . then use the characterized times-to-failure to estimate reliability.

Steps in degradation modeling are as follows:

- Determine appropriate degradation model, e.g.,

  - Crack growth rate = $C[K(a)]^m$

  - Arrhenius model $t_f = A_0 \exp\left(\dfrac{E_a}{kT}\right)$

- Fit model to each sample degradation path

- Use parameters from degradation paths to predict reliability

Note: Degradation modeling can be more accurate than traditional maximum likelihood estimates because it includes information about how close to failure an item may be.

Part IV.C.3

Figure 10.8 Degradation plots.

Regression Approach

For the case when D = 0 at time 0 and the "degradation at failure" (DF) is the same for all units, models can be fit using all the degradation readings and linear regression. Since (rate of degradation) × (time on test) = (amount of degradation) and (rate of degradation) × (time of failure) = degradation at failure (DF), therefore, y_i = Ln(time to failure) of $unit_i$ = Ln(DF_i) – Ln(rate of degradation)$_i$/Ln(time on test)$_i$.

For an Arrhenius model analysis, with

$$t_f = A \, e^{\frac{\Delta H}{kT}}$$

$$y_{ijk} = a + bx_k$$

with the x_k values equal to $1/kT$. Here T is the temperature of the kth cell, measured in Kelvin (273.16 + degrees Celsius) and k is Boltzmann's constant (8.617 × 10^{-5} in eV/°K). Use a linear regression program to estimate a = LnA and b = ΔH. If we further assume t_f has a lognormal distribution, the mean square residual error from the regression fit is an estimate of σ^2 (with σ the lognormal sigma). Example 10.10 demonstrates linear degradation over time with varying operating temperatures.

EXAMPLE 10.10

A component has a critical parameter that studies show degrades linearly over time at a rate that varies with operating temperature. A component failure based on this parameter occurs when the parameter value changes by 30% or more. Fifteen components were tested under three different temperature conditions five at 65°C, five at 85°C and the last five at 105°C). Degradation percent values were read out at 200, 500, and 1000 hours. The readings are given in the following table:

Unit	Temp (°C)	Hour	Degrad	Unit	Temp (°C)	Hour	Degrad
Unit 1	65	200	0.87	Unit 1	85	200	1.41
Unit 2	65	200	0.33	Unit 2	85	200	3.61
Unit 3	65	200	0.94	Unit 3	85	200	2.13
Unit 4	65	200	0.72	Unit 4	85	200	4.36
Unit 5	65	200	0.66	Unit 5	85	200	6.91
Unit 1	65	500	1.48	Unit 1	85	500	2.47
Unit 2	65	500	0.96	Unit 2	85	500	8.99
Unit 3	65	500	2.91	Unit 3	85	500	5.72
Unit 4	65	500	1.98	Unit 4	85	500	9.82
Unit 5	65	500	0.99	Unit 5	85	500	17.37
Unit 1	65	1000	2.81	Unit 1	85	1000	5.71
Unit 2	65	1000	2.13	Unit 2	85	1000	17.69
Unit 3	65	1000	5.67	Unit 3	85	1000	11.54
Unit 4	65	1000	4.28	Unit 4	85	1000	19.55
Unit 5	65	1000	2.14	Unit 5	85	1000	34.84

Unit	Temp (°C)	Hour	Degrad
Unit 1	105	200	24.58
Unit 2	105	200	9.73
Unit 3	105	200	4.74
Unit 4	105	200	23.61
Unit 5	105	200	10.9
Unit 1	105	500	62.02
Unit 2	105	500	24.07
Unit 3	105	500	11.53
Unit 4	105	500	58.21
Unit 5	105	500	27.85
Unit 1	105	1000	124.1
Unit 2	105	1000	48.06
Unit 3	105	1000	23.72
Unit 4	105	1000	117.2
Unit 5	105	1000	54.97

Solution:

Fit the Arrhenius/lognormal equation $y_{ijk} = a + bx_{ijk}$ where

$$y_{ijk} = \ln(30) - (\text{Ln(Degrad)} - \text{Ln(Hour)})$$

$$x_{ijk} = \frac{100{,}000}{8.617(\text{Temp} + 273.16)}$$

Note: DF = 30 is used since >30% degradation is considered failure.

Fitted Line Plot
$y_{ijk} = -18.94 + 0.8188x_{ijk}$

S	0.561051
R-Sq	83.1%
R-Sq(ad)	82.7%

The Eyring Model

The Eyring model has a theoretical basis in chemistry and quantum mechanics and can be used to model acceleration when many stresses are involved. This model has several key features:

- It has a theoretical basis from chemistry and quantum mechanics.

- If a chemical process (chemical reaction, diffusion, corrosion, migration, etc.) is causing degradation leading to failure, the Eyring model describes how the rate of degradation varies with stress or, equivalently, how time to failure varies with stress.

- The model includes temperature and can be expanded to include other relevant stresses.

- The temperature term by itself is very similar to the Arrhenius empirical model, explaining why that model has been so successful in establishing the connection between the ΔH parameter and the quantum theory concept of "activation energy needed to cross an energy barrier and initiate a reaction."

The model for temperature and one additional stress appears as

$$t_f = AT^\alpha \exp\left[\frac{\Delta H}{kT} + \left(B + \frac{C}{T}\right)S_1\right]$$

for which S_1 could be some function of voltage or current or any other relevant stress and the parameters α, ΔH, B, and C determine acceleration between stress combinations. As with the Arrhenius model, k is Boltzmann's constant and temperature is in degrees Kelvin.

If an additional nonthermal stress term is needed, the model is

$$t_f = AT^\alpha \exp\left[\frac{\Delta H}{kT} + \left(B + \frac{C}{T}\right)S_1 + \left(D + \frac{E}{T}\right)S_2\right]$$

and as many stresses as are needed may be included by adding similar terms.

Note that the general Eyring model includes terms that have stress and temperature interactions (in other words, the effect of changing temperature varies, depending on the levels of other stresses). Most models do not include interaction terms, so that the relative change in acceleration factors includes only one stress change and does not depend on the level of the other stresses. In models with no interaction, you can compute acceleration factors for each stress and multiply them together. This would not be true if the physical mechanism required interaction terms—but, at least to first approximations, it seems to work for most examples in the literature.

Advantages of the Eyring model are:

- Can handle many stresses

- Can be used to model degradation data as well as failure data

- The ΔH parameter has a physical meaning and has been studied and estimated for many well-known failure mechanisms and materials

Disadvantages of the Eyring model are:

- Even with just two stresses, there are five parameters to estimate. Each additional stress adds two more unknown parameters.

- Many of the parameters may have only a second-order effect. For example, setting the stress term $\alpha = 0$ works quite well since the temperature term then becomes the same as in the Arrhenius model. Also, the constants C and E are only needed if there is a significant temperature interaction effect with respect to the other stresses.

- The form in which the other stresses appear is not specified by the general model and may vary according to the particular failure mechanism. In other words, S_i may be voltage or ln(voltage) or some other function of voltage.

The Eyring relationship temperature acceleration factor is

$$AF_{Ey}(\text{Temp},\text{Temp}_U,E_a) = \left(\frac{\text{Temp } K}{\text{Temp}_U\ K}\right)^m AF_{Ar}(\text{Temp},\text{Temp}_U,E_a)$$

For use over practical ranges of temperature acceleration, and for practical values of m not far from 0, the factor outside the exponential has relatively little effect on the acceleration factor and the additional term is often dropped in favor of the simpler Arrhenius relationship. Example 10.11 provides a comparison using the Arrhenius and the Eyring relationships.

EXAMPLE 10.11

An accelerated life test will be used to study a metallization failure mechanism for a solid-state electronic device. Experience with this type of failure mechanism suggests that the quasi-activation energy should be in the neighborhood of $E_a = 1.2$ eV. The usual operating junction temperature for the device is 90°C. The Eyring acceleration factor for testing at 160°C, using $m = 1$, is

$$AF_{Ey}(160,90,1.2) = \left(\frac{160 + 273.15}{90 + 273.15}\right)^{1.2} AF_{Ar}(160,90,1.2) = 1.1935 \times 494 = 589$$

where

$$AF_{Ar}(160,90,1.2) = \exp\left[\left(\frac{1.2}{8.617 \times 10^{-5}}\right)\left(\frac{1}{363} - \frac{1}{433}\right)\right] = 494$$

is the Arrhenius acceleration factor. So, for a fixed value of E_a the Eyring relationship predicts an acceleration that is 19% greater than the Arrhenius.

Proportional Hazard Models

These are models having the property that individual component hazard rate functions are proportional to each other. The proportional hazards model has been used to model the effect of secondary variables on survival. It is more like an acceleration model than a specific life distribution model, and its strength lies in its ability to model and test many inferences about survival without making any specific assumptions about the form of the life distribution model.

Proportional Hazards Model Assumption

Let $z = \{x, y, \ldots\}$ be a vector of 1 or more *explanatory* variables believed to affect lifetime. These variables may be continuous (like temperature in engineering studies or dosage level of a particular drug in medical studies) or they may be indicator variables with the value 1, if a given factor or condition is present, and 0 otherwise. Let the hazard rate for a nominal (or baseline) set $z_0 = (x_0, y_0, \ldots)$ of these variables be given by $h_0(t)$, with $h_0(t)$ denoting a hazard function (failure rate) for some unspecified life distribution model.

The proportional hazards model assumes we can write the changed hazard function for a new value of z as $h_z(t) = g(z)h_0(t)$.

In other words, changing z, the explanatory variable vector, results in a new hazard function that is proportional to the nominal hazard function, and the proportionality constant is a function of z, $g(z)$, independent of the time variable t.

In its simplest form:

$$\lambda(x) = \sum_{i=0}^{k} a_i x_i$$

Another useful form for $f(z)$ is the *log linear model*, which has the equation:

$$g(x) = e^{ax} \text{ for one variable,}$$

$$g(x,y) = e^{ax+by} \text{ for two variables, etc.}$$

EXAMPLE 10.12

A multiplicative model for predicting the failure rate of ball bearings:

$$\lambda = \lambda_b \left(\frac{L_a}{L_s}\right)^y \left(\frac{A_C}{0.006}\right)^{2.36} \left(\frac{v_0}{v_1}\right)^{0.54} \left(\frac{C_1}{60}\right)^{0.67} \left(\frac{M_b}{M_f}\right) C_W$$

where:

λ_b = Base failure rate of a bearing/10^6 hours

L_a = Actual radial load in pounds

L_s = Specification radial load in pounds

y = 3.33 for roller bearings, 3.0 for ball bearings

A_C = Alignment error in radians

v_0 = Specification lubricant viscosity

v_1 = Operating lubricant viscosity

C_1 = Actual contamination level ($\mu g/m^3$)

M_b = "Material factor" (e.g., YS) of base material (psi)

M_f = "Material factor"(e.g., YS) of operating material (psi)

C_W = H_2O contamination factor (leakage of water into the oil lubricant) = 1 + 460x (for x < 0.002) = 2.026 + 1.029x −0.0647x (for x ≥ 0.002), where x is the percent of H_2O present in the oil (actual or from experience)

Often the following multiplicative is used:

$$\lambda(x) = \prod_{i=0}^{k} e^{a_i x_i} = \exp \sum_{i=0}^{k} a_i x_i$$

Source: Adapted from Ploe and Skewis (1990).

4. RELIABILITY PREDICTION METHODS

> Use various reliability prediction methods (e.g., Monte Carlo simulation, part stress analysis, and parts count prediction) for both repairable and non-repairable components and systems, and describe the inputs into the model. (Apply)
>
> Body of Knowledge IV.C.4

Modeling a dynamic system to predict its performance can become complex. The dynamic models discussed previously assumed a constant failure rate for each block of the model, and the only parameter generated was reliability for a given mission time.

Part IV.C.4

EXAMPLE 10.13

The strength of a unit is normally distributed with a mean (μ_s) of 2600 psi and a standard deviation (σ_s) of 300 psi. The unit is exposed to a stress that is normally distributed with a mean (μ_s) of 2000 psi and a standard deviation (σ_s) of 200 psi. What is the reliability of the unit?

  A Monte Carlo simulation can be performed on the unit by randomly selecting values from the strength and stress distributions and finding their difference. Failure of the unit will occur when the difference between strength and stress is negative (the stress is greater than the strength). Table 10.3 shows a printout of the first several steps of a Microsoft Excel file using these values. The printout shows a failure at replication number 9. These steps would be replicated thousands of times. N is the number of replications. The reliability of the unit could then be estimated:

$$\hat{R} = \frac{\# \text{ failures}}{N}$$

Continued

Table 10.3 Computer-generated values for a Monte Carlo simulation.

Replication number	Stress s $\mu = 2000$ $\sigma = 200$	Strength S $\mu = 2600$ $\sigma = 300$	Difference $x(S) - x(s)$ d	Failure = 1 $d < 0 = 1$
1	1942	2278	335	0
2	2091	2566	475	0
3	1599	2196	597	0
4	2013	2572	559	0
5	1934	2842	908	0
6	2177	2416	239	0
7	1936	2788	853	0
8	1952	2110	157	0
9	2042	2029	−13	1
10	1950	2167	218	0
11	1789	2743	954	0
12	2141	2306	165	0
13	2010	2619	610	0
14	2030	2362	332	0
15	1786	2593	806	0
16	1805	2961	1156	0

System reliability may be dependent on failure distributions other than the exponential (constant failure rate), or the desired system performance parameter may include availability. Availability is a function of the probability that the system remains in a usable state (reliability) and the probability of restoring the system to a usable state in a given period of time if a failure were to occur (maintainability). To analyze these systems, a simulation technique can be used. To use simulation, the defining parameters of each distribution must be known.

In a *Monte Carlo simulation*, repeated calculations of system performance are made using randomly selected values based on the probability distributions that describe each element of the model. The large number of values of system performance generated can be used to develop a probability distribution of system performance. Monte Carlo simulation does not involve complex mathematics; however, it requires an extensive use of computer time as each possible event for each unit of the model must be repeatedly sampled over the desired mission time.

Markov Analysis

A complex system can be analyzed as a *Markov process*. The Markov process can be used to find the probability of being in a given state at some time in the future if the probability of moving from one state to another state is known and the probability remains constant. The system can exist in only one state at a time, and except for the immediately preceding state, all future states are independent of past states.

One use of a Markov analysis is to determine the future probability of a repairable system being in a success state when the failure probability and probability of restoring the system are known. A simple system consisting of one unit can be considered to be in a success state (not failed) or in a failed state. If it is in the failed state, it is waiting to be returned to the success state. The transition probability from one state to the other is determined by the failure rate and the rate at which the unit can be restored to the success state after a failure (see Figure 10.9). P_{S-F} is the probability of transition from state S (success) to state F (failure) in a given time interval. P_{F-S} is the probability of transition from state F to state S in the same time interval. $1 - P_{S-F}$ is the probability of remaining in state S if the system is in state S. $1 - P_{F-S}$ is the probability of remaining in state F if the system is in state F.

A Markov analysis is not limited to a system with only two states. There can be more than one success state. All the possible states of the system are identified. All of the transitions from one state to another state are identified, assuming one action at a time. The transition rates from one state to another state are determined.

The probability of the system being in a success state can be determined by considering all possible states and the rates of transition from state to state. A Markov analysis requires the use of differential equations, Laplace transforms, and the solution of a series of linear equations using matrix algebra. Even though the analysis is exact, the assumptions necessary can affect the credibility of the results. A tree diagram can be used to model a simple system.

Each probability path represents a mutually exclusive event. The probability of the machine being in the success state (state S) at the end of two time intervals can be calculated as the summation of the probability paths to state S:

$$P(\text{State S}) = (0.7)(0.1) + (0.9)(0.9) = 0.88$$

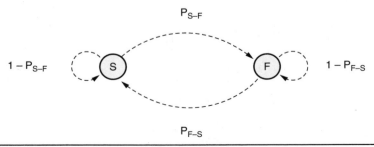

Part IV.C.4

Figure 10.9 A transition diagram for a system with two states.

EXAMPLE 10.14

Refer to the system in Figure 10.10.

A machine in state S (success) is operating successfully. There is a probability of 0.9 that the machine will remain in state S for a given time interval. There is a probability of $1 - 0.9 = 0.1$ that the machine will fail and transition to state F (failure). If the machine is in state F, there is a probability of 0.7 that it will be restored in the given time interval and transition back to state S. There is a probability of $1 - 0.7 = 0.3$ that it will not be restored in the given time interval and will remain in state F.

$P_{S-F} = 0.1$ $P_{S-S} = 0.9$
$P_{F-S} = 0.7$ $P_{F-F} = 0.3$

Figure 10.10 Tree diagram for Markov analysis for two time intervals.

As an exercise, expand the tree diagram to cover three time intervals. Verify that the probability of being in the success state (state S) at the end of three time intervals is P(State S) = (0.7)(0.3)(0.1) + (2)(0.9)(0.7)(0.1) + (0.9)(0.9)(0.9) = 0.876.

The tree diagram and the manual calculations become complex if the system has several success states. A Markov analysis will result in a transitional probability matrix that can be evaluated to find the state probabilities over many periods of time.

$$T = \begin{bmatrix} x_{1,1} & x_{1,2} \\ x_{2,1} & x_{2,2} \end{bmatrix}$$

EXAMPLE 10.15

Using the values in Example 10.14, the transitional matrix is

$$T = \begin{bmatrix} 1-P_{S-F} & P_{S-F} \\ P_{F-S} & 1-P_{F-S} \end{bmatrix} = \begin{bmatrix} 0.9 & 0.1 \\ 0.7 & 0.3 \end{bmatrix}$$

T^k will give the state probabilities after the kth time interval:

$$T^2 = \begin{bmatrix} 0.9 & 0.1 \\ 0.7 & 0.3 \end{bmatrix}^2 = \begin{bmatrix} 0.88 & 0.12 \\ 0.84 & 0.16 \end{bmatrix}$$

and

$$T^3 = \begin{bmatrix} 0.9 & 0.1 \\ 0.7 & 0.3 \end{bmatrix}^3 = \begin{bmatrix} 0.876 & 0.124 \\ 0.868 & 0.132 \end{bmatrix}$$

The value in the first row and the first column, $x_{1,1} = 0.88$ when $k = 2$ and $x_{1,1} = 0.876$ when $k = 3$, is the probability of the machine being in the success state (state S) at the end of the second and third time intervals if the original state of the machine was success. The value in the second row and the first column, $x_{2,1} = 0.84$ when $k = 2$ and $x_{2,1} = 0.868$ when $k = 3$, is the probability of the machine being in the success state at the end of the second and third time intervals if the original state of the machine was failure (state F). As k increases, these values will converge, becoming the steady-state value of the availability of the machine:

$$T^6 = \begin{bmatrix} 0.875008 & 0.124992 \\ 0.874994 & 0.125056 \end{bmatrix}$$

The values $x_{1,1}$ and $x_{2,1}$ are converging to 0.875, the steady-state value of the availability of the machine.

There are some handheld calculators and many software programs that can be used to do the matrix algebra.

Part Count Predictions and Part Stress Analysis

A *reliability prediction* is a design tool to be used early in the design and development stage. To be effective, the prediction is started before the design is completed, and completed before production tooling is set and hardware is procured for production.

Many times, the prediction is done without any actual reliability data on the particular system, although there may be data on some of the components. The reliability prediction can be used to determine the feasibility of the design to meet the system reliability goals, to focus attention to "weak links" in the design, to assess the impact of design changes on the system reliability, to compare the reliability of competing designs early in the development stage, and to assist in establishing maintenance procedures. The reliability prediction is not a reliability estimate, which requires data, and should not be used as a measure of the actual achieved system reliability.

The best known and most widely used source of predictive data for electrical/electronic systems is MIL-HDBK-217. The handbook assumes electronics can be modeled using a constant failure rate and contains failure rate data for electrical and electronic components. The handbook contains data for all passive devices: resistors, inductors, capacitors, transformers, and so on. It also contains data for active elements: transistors, diodes, field-effect transistors (FETs), and so on, as well as digital and analog integrated circuits (ICs). There are methods to adjust the base failure rate of the components depending on the number of leads, the number of gates in an IC, the use environment the component will experience, the quality control requirements the customer can impose on the supplier, and other factors that could affect the component failure rate. The multipliers used to adjust the base failure rate are referred to as π (pi) factors.

EXAMPLE 10.16

The failure rate model for a resistor is $\lambda_p = \lambda_b \times \pi_E \times \pi_R \times \pi_Q$ failures/million hours.

Tables in MIL-HDBK-217 contain λ_b, the base failure rate, based on the standard derating used by the designer. Tables also contain the pi factors:

- π_E is the environmental factor reflecting how the resistor is used.
- π_R is a factor based on the value of the resistor.
- π_Q is a quality factor and is dependent on the amount of control the customer has in the production of the component.

These factors and the base failure rate are combined to give the predicted failure rate of the resistor.

EXAMPLE 10.17

A 10,000-ohm carbon resistor is used in a communications receiver located in the crew compartment of a commercial aircraft. Assume a standard design derating of 40% at 60°C.

From MIL-HDBK-217:

$\lambda_b = 0.0012/10^6$	Base failure rate
$\pi_E = 3$	Environmental stress factor
$\pi_Q = 1$	Quality factor
$\pi_R = 1$	Resistance factor
$\lambda_p = (3)(1)(1)(0.0012/10^6) = 0.0036/10^6$	Predicted failure rate

If the same resistor were used in a radar detector located on the deck of a naval ship:

$\pi_E = 12$	Environmental stress factor
$\lambda_p = (12)(1)(1)(0.0012/10^6) = 0.0144/10^6$	Predicted failure rate

---

The handbook was last revised in 1994 and was issued as MIL-HDBK-217F. It is common knowledge that predictions made using MIL-HDBK-217 will be pessimistic and the product will have a failure rate less than the predicted value.

A circuit board (subsystem) failure rate could be predicted by adding the predicted failure rates of all the components on the board. This assumes a series model for the circuit board and will give a worst-case prediction. This is referred to as the *part count method*. A system failure rate could be predicted by adding the predicted failure rates of all the subsystems. This also assumes a series model.

Using the assumption of a series model, the system will have a constant failure rate if all the components have a constant failure rate. In an attempt to overcome some of the deficiencies of MIL-HDBK-217, the *PRISM reliability prediction method* was developed by the Reliability Analysis Center (RAC).

Instead of using just multipliers to model component failures, PRISM uses combinations of both additive and multiplicative factors. The factors are called π factors, and the model could be of the form

$$\lambda_S = \lambda_1(\pi_1\pi_2 + \pi_3\pi_4 + \pi_5)$$

where λ_i is the initial failure rate and the π values are based on the part. PRISM also allows for consideration of early-life failures as well as failures due to a constant failure rate.

The *217(plus) method* is an outgrowth of PRISM. It contains new part type failure rate models including connectors, switches, and relays.

For predicting the reliability of mechanical systems, the *Handbook for Reliability Prediction for Mechanical Systems* (NSWC-07) is available. Information can be obtained from the Naval Surface Warfare Center, Carderock Division, Bethesda, Maryland.

The handbook follows the format of MIL-HDBK-217 and contains base failure rates for mechanical components, which can be adjusted using multipliers or "c" factors depending on the type of material, physical configuration, heat treatment, the use environment, and other factors that would affect the probability of failure. Examples of specific mechanical devices included are springs, bearings, brakes and clutches, seals, pumps, and other nonelectrical devices. This handbook assumes the constant failure rate model.

Non-electronic Parts Reliability Data (NPRD-2011) contains failure rates for mechanical and electromechanical parts. This method allows the engineer to consider failures due to wear-out.

Telcordia SR-332 (once known as Bellcore) has prediction data in tables and graphs for communication equipment with commercial applications. These Telcordia models were developed by AT&T Bell Labs, and the method is based on MIL-HDBK-217.

Several international standards are also available. The methodology used in these standards is similar to that in MIL-HDBK-217.

Reliability predictions can also be based on the engineer's experience with components used in previous designs of similar systems. In some cases, the component vendor may supply typical failure rate data. The Government-Industry Data Exchange Program (GIDEP) is a source available to military contractors that contains failure reports on commercially available subsystems such as motors, compressors, pumps, and so on. System reliability values obtained using any of these sources should be treated only as prediction values.

Reliability Prediction Methods

The reliability of a product needs to be continually evaluated using the available information during all stages of design, development, and production. This is necessary to assure that the product will meet the system reliability requirements. During design, information on components and parts, along with the system model, can be used to predict the reliability. As the product moves through the development and production stages, information from tests can be used to estimate product reliability.

Part IV.C.4

Early reliability predictions using the system model can be very useful to the reliability engineer. Predictions can be used to determine weak spots in the design and initiate a redesign effort. Predictions can be used to choose between alternate designs. Predictions can be used to evaluate the effect on reliability of a design change. Predictions can be used to evaluate the feasibility of meeting the final system-level reliability requirement with the present design.

Predictions have the limitation that they are based on the simplifying assumption that each component has an inherent constant failure rate. Predictions can consider environmental stress levels, the complexity of the component, the manufacturing capability of the component manufacturer, and other factors that might affect failure. However, predictions cannot take into account the human factors that most likely cause failure. Factors such as the skill of the operator using the product, the ability of the design group to anticipate how the product will be used, the motivation of the designer to design a reliable product, the manufacturing capability of the system manufacturer, and the skill of maintenance personnel may be much more significant to product reliability.

A prediction, unlike an estimate, does not have relevant experimental data for support. A prediction has no statistical confidence. Reliability prediction is, at best, an exercise in uncertainty. Databases containing typical reliability values such as failure rates are available. However, the reliability of a specific product is not a characteristic that can be inherently predicted with high precision. It is necessary that the reliability engineer realize that even though complex models and mathematical relations exist for making predictions, the usefulness of a prediction is limited.

If testing results are available, reliability predictions can be made based on the distribution of times to failure and the estimated parameters. If the exponential distribution models the times to failure, the estimated parameter is the mean. This is called the *mean time to failure* (θ) or MTTF. If n units are tested, and during the test r units fail, the estimate of MTTF is

$$\hat{\theta} = \frac{T}{r}$$

where T is the total time accumulated on the units, including the units that failed and the units that did not fail and r is the number of failures.

The estimated failure rate

$$\hat{\lambda} = \frac{r}{T}$$

is the reciprocal of the mean.

The estimated reliability for a mission time of t is

$$\hat{R} = e^{-(t/\theta)} = e^{-\lambda t}$$

A lower confidence limit ($\theta_{(\alpha)}$) can be calculated for the estimate of the mean:

$$\alpha = 1 - \text{Confidence}$$

The estimate of reliability for a mission time t at a confidence level of $1 - \alpha$ is

$$R_{(\alpha)} = e^{-(t/\theta(\alpha))}$$

For a repairable system, if the exponential distribution model is appropriate, the above discussion is valid up to the first failure. Predicting reliability for a repairable system becomes complicated because the system can be restored to use after a failure. A system that has undergone a series of restore (repair) actions comprises subsystems and components that have acquired different operating times. Even though a repair might return a subsystem to a new state, the system is not in a new state. This means that the system cannot be modeled using a constant failure rate. Rather than making predictions of the reliability of a system that has experienced several repair cycles, predictions should be made as to the number of spare parts needed in order for the system to meet specified availability requirements.

5. DESIGN PROTOTYPING

> Describe the advantages and limitations of proto-typing to enhance product reliability. (Understand)
>
> Body of Knowledge IV.C.5

Prototyping

Prototyping is the process of rapidly putting together a working model (a prototype) in order to test various aspects of a design, show ideas or features and gather early user feedback. As examples:

- A supplier provides a model of a proposed oil filter to an automotive company so ease of filter changes can be determined.

- A hardware manufacturer provides a sample of proposed door hinges for laboratory reliability testing.

- A computer firm puts a new modeling capability out in a "beta" version to get potential customer feedback.

A key concept is that prototyping is *user-centered design*.

When prototyping, the final product is not really the concern. Instead the "prototypers" are more concerned about creating prototypes that let them think about their products and services through a physical manifestation and customer feedback. Early prototyping allows designers to fail early. By creating a prototype and putting it in the hands of users, designers can spot problems early. It's better to invest a little bit of time and effort into a prototype that fails than to invest a lot of time and effort (and money) into a final product that fails.

> *Prototyping is practice for people who design and make things. When you prototype, you allow your design, product, or service to practice being itself. And as its maker, you learn more about your designs in this way than you ever could in any other way.*
>
> —Dave Gray, XPLANE

The Product-Prototype Cycle

Production of prototypes (see Figure 10.11) provides the design team with a three-dimensional object they can examine and, in some cases, run through reliability tests. Many have said that the main disadvantage of prototyping is the cost, but the cost of a prototype seems cheap compared to the amount of money saved by making sure a safe, reliable, functional product is introduced to the customer and considering that recalls are eliminated or reduced and warranty costs are lowered.

What Is Rapid Prototyping?

Rapid prototyping refers to physical objects that are automatically constructed with the aid of additive manufacturing technology (see Figure 10.12). Rapid prototyping systems use liquid, powder, or sheet materials to form physical objects. Rapid prototyping is relatively recent invention. The first rapid prototyping machines were available in the late 1980s.

Figure 10.11   The product–prototype cycle.

Figure 10.12   Typical rapid prototype material applicator.

Figure 10.13   Example of a complex part produced with rapid prototyping technology.

Rapid prototyping in its earlier days was applied to production of models and prototype parts. But now, with the advancement in technology, rapid prototyping is used widely for many applications that include manufacturing production-quality parts. Rapid prototyping takes the virtual designs from computer-aided design (CAD) or animation modeling software (AMS). See Figure 10.13.

These designs are further transformed into thin, virtual, horizontal cross-sections, and then the process "of creating successive layers continues till the model in complete. On completion, the virtual model is almost the same as the physical model. The objective of WYSIWYG ("what you see is what you get") process is that the final product is the same as the image created. Once the layers that correspond to the virtual cross-section from CAD are formed, they are either joined or fused automatically to yield the final shape. Additive fabrication has the benefit of creating any shape or geometric feature.

Rapid prototyping technologies include:

1. *Selective laser sintering (SLS).* This technology involves the use of a high-power laser for the fusion of tiny particles of plastic, metal, etc., into a mass that represents a desired 3-D object, through the help of an SLS machine. This is an additive manufacturing technique. Materials used in this technique are metal powders and thermoplastics.

2. *Fused deposition modeling (FDM).* This additive manufacturing technology was invented in the late 1980s by S. Scott Crump and is used for modeling, prototyping, and production applications. Thermoplastics are used extensively in this method.

3. *Stereolithography (SLA).* This additive manufacturing technology is used for production of models and patterns through the stereolithography machine. Photopolymer is the principal material used in this technique.

4. *Laminated object manufacturing (LOM).* Paper is the base material used in this technology. In this method layers of adhesive-coated plastic, paper, or metal laminates are fused together and cut into shape with the aid of a knife or a laser cutter.

| Titanium additive | Steel engine tie-rod |
| 3-D printing | Laser sintering |

Figure 10.14   Products made with rapid prototyping.

5. *3-D printing.* This is an additive manufacturing technology that uses various materials and successive layers of material to create a 3-D object. 3-D printing technology actually is said to be more affordable, easy to use, and speedy than the other additive manufacturing technologies. Though production applications are actually dominated by the other technologies, 3-D has a great potential to prove useful in production applications.

Some products made with rapid prototyping are shown in Figure 10.14.

Rapid prototyping is becoming more capable (especially with additive methods for solid parts) and is already producing large products. It is therefore becoming "rapid manufacturing."

NOTE

1. This section is reprinted from Collins, Busby, and Staab (2003).

Part V
Lifecycle Reliability

Part V

Chapter 11
A. Reliability Design Techniques

1. DESIGN EVALUATION TECHNIQUES (VALIDATION AND VERIFICATION)

> Explain how validation, verification, and other review techniques are used to assess the reliability of a product's design at various lifecycle stages. (Apply)
>
> Body of Knowledge V.A.1

The reliability engineer performs evaluation functions in each step of the design process.

Concept

As the earliest design parameters are established, preliminary estimates of reliability requirements should be made.

Design Team Effort

As the more formal design phase is initiated, the reliability engineer should be prepared to provide the team with guidance and judgment regarding various options. Data on the reliability of proposed components and the implications for product reliability should be documented for the team at each design refinement. The allocation of reliability requirements to various subsystems and components should also be studied. The underlying mind-set must be to formally study every potential failure and establish cost-effective ways of preventing them. The two general approaches to failure prevention are *fault tolerance* and *fault avoidance*. A fault-tolerant approach requires design of redundant systems so that a fault does not result in a failure. Dual master cylinders in an automotive braking system is an example of a fault-tolerant system. The fault-avoidance approach requires designing the product with components that are sufficiently reliable to guarantee the minimum product reliability. This may be accomplished, for example, by using heavier structural pieces, more-reliable components, derating, and other techniques. Reliability growth during the design process should be documented.

The customer's lifecycle cost for the product can be minimized by establishing optimum reliability levels and implementing systems for obtaining them.

Design Review

Reliability engineers should provide the design team with data from testing of the final version of the product, assuring that the design meets the reliability requirements. This is often referred to as *validation*.

Preproduction

Alternative manufacturing processes and parameters should be studied for their impact on reliability in order to meet or exceed design requirements.

Production

A testing program should be established to assure that production output meets reliability requirements. This is often referred to as *verification*.

Post-Production

Once a product is released for production, a system for follow-up should be in place so that any failures, in-house or in the field, can be studied. One approach to doing this is known as *failure reporting, analysis, and corrective action system* (FRACAS).

A system that permits traceability of individual components helps establish sources of failure due to design, production, service, customer misuse, and so on. The thrust should be not to fix the *blame* but to fix the *problem*. Thorough, documented design requirements help assure customer satisfaction. The purpose of design evaluation is to verify that the product meets the requirements at each design stage. The aspects of the requirements relating to product reliability mandate special attention because the issue is not merely "does it work?" but rather "how long will it work and under what conditions?" A strong program of testing and documentation can help avoid disappointed customers.

There are four types of evaluation:

1. *Environmental stress screening.* The unit is exposed to the most severe design environmental stresses. In some cases accelerated life testing may be used. The purpose is to identify weak components.

2. *Reliability development/growth tests.* A series of tests conducted periodically from design through production phases to demonstrate the impact of corrective actions on reliability.

3. *Reliability qualification tests* (also called *reliability demonstration tests*). Conducted on a sample from production to determine whether production units meet reliability requirements, these tests serve as a basis for production approval.

4. *Product reliability acceptance tests.* A periodic test during production to determine whether the output continues to meet reliability requirements.

A product's lifecycle from the producer's viewpoint may be expanded to include these stages:

1. *Concept/design.* This is the stage at which reliability testing and analysis can have the most impact, especially on lowering the failure rate during the useful life of the product. Reliability engineers can aid in the assessment of design validation (that is, fitness for use in the intended operating conditions) by conducting accelerated life tests of components and subassemblies.

2. *Introduction.* At this stage the reliability program gathers and analyzes data on failure rate and proposes measures to reduce it. During this phase, restudy of installation and usage procedures is appropriate. In addition, reliability engineers can aid in the assessment of design validation (that is, compliance with explicit specifications).

3. *Growth.* As the market for the product grows and improvements are implemented, careful traceability becomes critical. It is important to know if these type X failures occurred on products that were produced after improvement Y was in place.

4. *Maturity.* Market growth has plateaued and the enterprise searches for new markets and applications. New environments or functions require a new assessment of reliability.

5. *Decline.* As the market for the product decreases, the costs involved with continued maintenance support must be analyzed. Typically, the support cost per item in use will grow unless carefully monitored.

2. STRESS-STRENGTH ANALYSIS

> Apply the stress-strength analysis method of calcu-
> lating probability of failure, and interpret the results.
> (Analyze)
>
> Body of Knowledge V.A.1

Failure of a part will occur when a stress exceeds the strength of the part for that stress. Accepted design practice is to design so that the strength is always greater than the expected stress. A good design will incorporate safety factors or safety margins to ensure that the strength is always greater than the stress. To use these design techniques, the stress the part will encounter as well as the strength of the part must be viewed as single-point values. To use the stress-strength analysis method, both the stress and the strength are viewed as distributions.

For example, suppose the stress and strength are normally distributed random variables. The mean of the stress distribution is μ_s, and the standard deviation of the stress distribution is σ_s. The mean and standard deviation of the strength distribution are μ_S and σ_S. Good design would dictate that $\mu_S > \mu_s$. The safety factor is

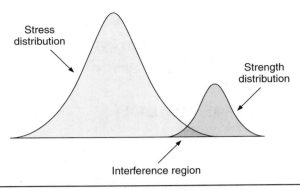

Figure 11.1   Diagram showing stress–strength interference region.

equal to μ_S/μ_s and is greater than 1. If viewed as single-point values, failure cannot occur. However, when viewed as distributions, there can be an interference region in which it is possible for stress to exceed strength (see Figure 11.1).

The *difference distribution* can be used to solve for the probability of failure. The difference distribution is the distribution of strength minus stress. The difference distribution will have a mean $\mu_D = \mu_S - \mu_s$ and standard deviation

$$\sigma_D = \sqrt{\sigma_S^2 + \sigma_s^2}$$

The area to the left of zero in the difference distribution is the probability of failure as this is the region where stress exceeds strength. The reliability is equal to 1 – (probability of failure), or the area to the right of zero.

EXAMPLE 11.1

$$\mu_{\text{Stress}} = 30{,}000 \text{ psi} \qquad \mu_{\text{Stress}} = 40{,}000 \text{ psi}$$

$$\sigma_{\text{Stress}} = 30{,}000 \text{ psi} \qquad \sigma_{\text{Stress}} = 40{,}000 \text{ psi}$$

$$Z = \frac{\mu_{\text{Stress}} - \mu_{\text{Strength}}}{\sqrt{\sigma_{\text{Stress}}^2 + \sigma_{\text{Strength}}^2}} = \frac{30{,}000 - 40{,}000}{\sqrt{3000^2 + 4000^2}} = \frac{-10{,}000}{5000} = -2.0$$

From standard normal tables, probability of failure = 0.023.

Reliability = 1 – 0.023 = 0.977

Viewing stress-strength relationships in this manner emphasizes the four basic ways the designer can improve on the reliability.

The designer usually has more control over the strength:

- *Increase the mean strength*: use different materials or different design

- *Decrease the strength variation*: reduce variation in the materials and in the process

The designer may have some control over the stress:

- *Decrease the mean stress*: control the loading
- *Decrease the stress variation*: limit the use environment

3. DESIGN OF EXPERIMENTS (DOE)

> Develop and interpret the results of a standard design of experiments (DOE) (e.g., full-factorial and fractional factorial). (Analyze)
>
> Body of Knowledge V.A.3

The objective of a designed experiment is to generate knowledge about a product or process. The experiment seeks to find the effect a set of independent variables has on a set of dependent variables. Mathematically, this relationship can be denoted $y = f(x)$, where x is a list of independent variables and y is the dependent variable.

For example, suppose a machine operator who can adjust the feed, speed, and coolant temperature wishes to find the settings that will produce the best surface finish. The feed, speed, and coolant temperature are called independent variables. The surface finish is called the dependent variable because its value depends on the values of the independent variables. Independent variables may be thought of as input variables and dependent variables as output variables. There may be additional independent variables, such as the hardness of the material or humidity of the room, that have an effect on the dependent variable. The independent variables that the experimenter controls are called *control factors* or sometimes just factors. The other factors, such as hardness or humidity, are called *noise factors*. In this example, the experimental design may specify that the speed will be set at 1300 rev/min for part of the experiment and at 1800 rev/min for the remainder. These values are referred to as the *levels of the speed factor*. The experimenting team decides to test each factor at two levels, as follows:

Feed: (*F*): 0.01 and 0.04 in/rev

Speed (*S*): 1300 and 1800 rev/min

Coolant temp (*C*): 100 and 140°F

They opt for a *full-factorial experiment* so that they can generate the maximum amount of process knowledge. A full-factorial experiment tests all possible combinations of levels and factors, using one run for each combination. The formula for number of runs is

$$n = L^F$$

where:

n = Number of runs

L = Number of levels

F = Number of factors

In this situation, $n = 2^3 = 8$ runs. The team develops a data collection sheet listing those eight runs with room for recording five repetitions for each run (see Table 11.1).

The factor-level combinations are also called *treatments*, and the repetition of runs is sometimes called *replication*. In experimenter's jargon, it is said that there are eight treatments, with each treatment replicated five times. As the data are collected, the values are recorded as shown in Table 11.2. These data are also referred to as the *response values* since they show how the process or product responds to various treatments.

Note that the five values for a particular run are not all the same. This may be due to drift in the factor levels, variation in the measurement system, and the influence of noise factors. The variation observed in the readings for a particular run is referred to as *experimental error*. If the number of replications is decreased, the calculation of experimental error is less accurate, although the experiment has

Table 11.1   A 2^3 full-factorial data collection sheet.

Run #	Feed	Speed	C temp	1	2	3	4	5
1	0.01	1300	100					
2	0.01	1300	140					
3	0.01	1800	100					
4	0.01	1800	140					
5	0.04	1300	100					
6	0.04	1300	140					
7	0.04	1800	100					
8	0.04	1800	140					

Table 11.2   A 2^3 full-factorial data collection sheet with data entered.

Run #	Feed	Speed	C temp	1	2	3	4	5
1	0.01	1300	100	10.1	10.0	10.2	9.8	9.9
2	0.01	1300	140	3.0	4.0	3.0	5.0	5.0
3	0.01	1800	100	6.5	7.0	5.3	5.0	6.2
4	0.01	1800	140	1.0	3.0	3.0	1.0	2.0
5	0.04	1300	100	5.0	7.0	9.0	8.0	6.0
6	0.04	1300	140	4.0	7.0	5.0	6.0	8.0
7	0.04	1800	100	5.8	6.0	6.1	6.2	5.9
8	0.04	1800	140	3.1	2.9	3.0	2.9	3.1

a lower total cost. If all the factors that impact the dependent variable are included in the experiment, and all measurements are exact, replication is not needed and a very efficient experiment can be used. Thus, the accurate determination of experimental error and cost are competing design properties.

Planning and Organizing Experiments

When preparing to conduct an experiment, the first consideration is, "What question are we seeking to answer?" In the previous example, the objective was to find the combination of process settings that minimizes the surface finish reading.

Examples of other experimental objectives include:

- Find the inspection procedure that provides optimum precision

- Find the combination of mail and media ads that produces the most sales

- Find the cake recipe that produces the most consistent taste in the presence of oven temperature variation

- Find the combination of valve dimensions that produces the most linear output

Sometimes, the objective derives from a question. For example, the question "What's causing the excess variation in hardness at the rolling mill?" could generate the objective "Identify the factors responsible for the hardness variation and find the settings that minimize it." The objective must be measurable, so the next step is to establish an appropriate measurement system. If there is a tolerance on the objective quantity, the rule of 10 measurement principle says that the finest resolution of the measurement system must be less than or equal to 1/10 of the tolerance. The measurement system must also be reasonably simple and easy to operate.

Once the objective and a measurement system have been determined, the factors and levels are selected. People with the most experience and knowledge about the product or process are asked to name the adjustments they would make to achieve the objective. Their responses should include the things they would change (factors) and the various values (levels) they would recommend. From these recommendations, the list of factors and the levels for each factor are determined.

The next step is to choose the appropriate design. The selection of the design may be constrained by such things as affordability and time available. At this stage, some experimenters establish a budget of time and other resources that may be used to reach the objective. If production equipment and personnel must be used, how much time is available? How much product and other consumables are available? Typically, 20% to 40% of the available budget should be allocated to the first experiment because it seldom meets the objective and in fact often raises as many questions as it answers. Typical new questions are:

- What if an additional level had been used for factor A?

- What if an additional factor had been included instead of factor B?

Therefore, rather than designing a massive experiment involving many variables and levels, it is usually best to begin with more modest screening designs whose purpose is to determine the variables and levels that need further study.

The next few sections discuss various designs.

Randomization

Returning to the surface finish example, there are eight treatments with five replications per treatment. This produces 40 tests. The tests should be performed in random order. The purpose of randomization is to spread out the variation caused by noise variables. The 40 tests may be randomized in several ways. Here are two possibilities:

1. Number the tests from one to 40 and randomize those numbers to obtain the order in which tests are performed. This is referred to as a *completely randomized design*.

2. Randomize the run order, but once a run is set up, make all five replicates for that run.

Although it usually requires more time and effort, the first method is better. To see that this is true, suppose time of day is a noise factor such that products made before noon are different from those made after noon. With the completely randomized design, each run will likely have parts from both morning and afternoon.

Blocking

If it is not possible to run all 40 tests under the same conditions, the experimenting team may use a technique called *blocking*. For example, if the 40 tests must be spread over two shifts, the team would be concerned about the impact the shift difference could have on the results. In this experiment, the coolant temperature is probably the most difficult to adjust, so the team may be tempted to perform all the 100°F runs during the first shift and the 140°F runs on the second shift. The obvious problem here is that what appears to be the impact of the change in coolant temperature may in part reflect the impact of the change in shift. A better approach would be to randomly select the runs to be performed during each shift. This is called a *randomized block design*.

For example, the random selection might put runs 1, 4, 5, and 8 in first shift and 2, 3, 6, and 7 in second shift. Another method that might be used to nullify the impact of the shift change would be to do the first three replicates of each run during the first shift and the remaining two replicates of each run during the second shift. Once the data are collected as shown in Table 11.2, the next step is to find the average of the five replication responses for each run. These averages are shown in Table 11.3.

Main Effects

The first step in calculating the main effects, sometimes called *average main effects*, is to average the results for each level of each factor. This is accomplished by

Table 11.3 A 2^3 full-factorial data collection sheet with run averages.

Run #	Feed	Speed	C temp	Average surface finish reading
1	0.01	1300	100	10
2	0.01	1300	140	4
3	0.01	1800	100	6
4	0.01	1800	140	2
5	0.04	1300	100	7
6	0.04	1300	140	6
7	0.04	1800	100	6
8	0.04	1800	140	3

averaging the results of the four runs for that level. For example, $F_{0.01}$ (feed at the 0.01 in/rev level) is calculated by averaging the results of the four runs in which feed was set at the 0.01 level. These were runs 1, 2, 3, and 4, so

$$F_{0.01} = (10 + 4 + 6 + 2) \div 4 = 5.5$$

Similarly, $F_{0.04} = (7 + 6 + 6 + 3) \div 4 = 5.5$

Runs numbered 1, 2, 5, and 6 had S at 1300 rev/min, so

$$S1300 = (10 + 4 + 7 + 6) \div 4 = 6.75$$
$$\text{and } S1800 = (6 + 2 + 6 + 3) \div 4 = 4.25$$
$$C100 = (10 + 6 + 7 + 6) \div 4 = 7.25$$
$$C140 = (4 + 2 + 6 + 3) \div 4 = 3.75$$

The main effects may be graphed as shown in Figure 11.2.

    Because the better surface finish has the lowest score, the team would choose the level of each factor that produces the lowest result. The team would suggest using a speed of 1800 rev/min and coolant temp of 140°F. What feed rate should be recommended? Since both $F_{0.01}$ and $F_{0.04}$ are 5.5, the feed rate doesn't impact surface finish in this range. The team would recommend a feed rate of 0.04 since it will result in a faster operation.

Figure 11.2 Plot of main effects.

Factors with the greater difference between the high and low results are the factors with the greatest impact on the quality characteristic of interest (surface finish, in this case). Most authors refer to the main effect as *the high-level result minus the low-level result for the factor.* For example, main effect of factor $F = F_{0.04} - F_{0.01} = 5.5 - 5.5 = 0$. Similarly, main effect of $S = S1800 - S1300 = 4.25 - 6.75 = -2.50$ and $C = C140 - C100 = 3.75 - 7.25 = -3.50$.

Using this definition of main effect, the larger the absolute value of the main effect, the more influence that factor has on the quality characteristic. It is possible that the perceived difference between high and low results is not statistically significant. This would occur if the experimental error is so large that it would be impossible to determine whether the difference between the high and low values is due to a real difference in the dependent variable or due to experimental error. This may be determined by using *analysis of variance* (ANOVA) procedures. For analysis of data from an experiment, the null hypothesis is that changing the factor level does not make a statistically significant difference in the dependent variable. The β risk is the probability that the analysis will show that there is a significant difference when there is not. The β risk is the probability that the analysis will show that there is no significant difference when there is. The *power* of the experiment is defined as $1 - \beta$, so the higher the power of the experiment, the lower the β risk. In general, a higher number of replications or a larger sample size provides a more precise estimate of experimental error, which in turn reduces the β risk.

Interaction Effects

To assess the interaction effects, return to the original experimental design matrix, replacing each high level with "+" and each low level with "–" as shown in Table 11.4.

To find an entry in the column labeled "$F \times S$," multiply the entries in the F and S columns, using the multiplication rule "If the signs are the same, the result is positive; otherwise, the result is negative." Fill the other interaction columns the same way. To fill the $F \times S \times C$ column, multiply the $F \times S$ column by the C column (see Table 11.5).

Table 11.4   A 2^3 full-factorial design using + and – format.

Run	F	S	C	$F \times S$	$F \times C$	$S \times C$	$F \times S \times C$
1	–	–	–				
2	–	–	+				
3	–	+	–				
4	–	+	+				
5	+	–	–				
6	+	–	+				
7	+	+	–				
8	+	+	+				

Table 11.5 A 2^3 full-factorial design showing interaction columns.

Run	F	S	C	F × S	F × C	S × C	F × S × C	Response
1	−	−	−	+	+	+	−	10
2	−	−	+	+	−	−	+	4
3	−	+	−	−	+	−	+	6
4	−	+	+	−	−	+	−	2
5	+	−	−	−	−	+	+	7
6	+	−	+	−	+	−	−	6
7	+	+	−	+	−	−	−	6
8	+	+	+	+	+	+	+	3

To calculate the effect of the interaction between factors F and S, first find $F \times S+$ by averaging the results of the runs that have a "+" in the $F \times S$ column:

$$F \times S+ = (10 + 4 + 6 + 3) \div 4 = 5.75$$

Similarly, $F \times S- = (6 + 2 + 7 + 6) \div 4 = 5.25$

The effect of the $F \times S$ interaction is $5.75 - 5.25 = 0.50$

Similar calculations show that $F \times C = 1.50$, $S \times C = 0$, and $F \times S \times C = -1$

Interactions may be plotted in a manner similar to main effects, as indicated in Figure 11.3. The presence of interactions indicates that the main effects aren't additive.

Now, suppose the experiment, as set up in the previous example, is considered too expensive, and the team must reduce costs. They can either reduce the

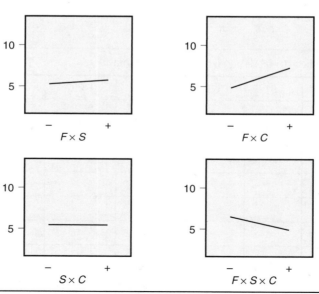

Figure 11.3 A plot of interaction effects.

number of replications for each run or reduce the number of runs by using what is called a *fractional factorial design*. It will be shown later that reducing the number of replications reduces the precision of the estimate of experimental error. So, the team decides to use a fractional factorial. They might choose the one illustrated in Table 11.6. This design uses only four of the eight possible runs; therefore, the experiment itself will consume only half the resources as the one shown in Table 11.7. It still has three factors at two levels each. It is traditional to call this a 2^{3-1} *design* because it has two levels and three factors but only $2^{3-1} = 2^2 = 4$ runs. It is also called a *half fraction of the full factorial* because it has half the number of runs as in the 2^3 full-factorial design.

Balanced Designs

In Table 11.6, note that when factor A is at its low level in runs 1 and 2, factor B is tested once at its low level and once at its high level, and factor C is also tested once at each level. Furthermore, when factor A is at its high level in runs 3 and 4, factor B is tested once at its low level and once at its high level, and factor C is also tested once at each level. Likewise, when factor B is at its low level in runs 1 and 3, factor A is tested once at its low level and once at its high level, and factor C is also tested once at each level. And when factor C is at its low level in runs 2 and 3, factor B is tested once at its low level and once at its high level, and factor A is also tested once at each level. An experimental design is called *balanced* when each setting of each factor appears the same number of times with each setting of every other factor. The fractional factorial design in Table 11.6 is balanced.

The logical next question is, "Why use a full-factorial design when a fractional design uses a fraction of the resources?" To see the answer, add a column to the design for the A × B interaction, as shown in Table 11.7, and fill it using the multiplication rule.

Table 11.6   Half fraction of 2^3 (also called a 2^{3-1} design).

Run #	A	B	C
1	–	–	+
2	–	+	–
3	+	–	–
4	+	+	+

Table 11.7   Half fraction of 2^3 design with interaction columns.

Run #	A	B	C	A × B	A × C	B × C	A × B × C
1	–	–	+	+	–	–	+
2	–	+	–	–	+	–	+
3	+	–	–	–	–	+	+
4	+	+	+	+	+	+	+

Note that the A × B interaction column has the same configuration as the C column. Isn't that scary? This means that when the C main effect is calculated, it is not clear whether the effect is due to factor C or the interaction between A × B or, more likely, a combination of these two causes. Statisticians say that the main effect C is *confounded* with the interaction effect A × B. This confounding is the principal price the experimenter pays for the reduction in resource requirements of a fractional factorial. This is the source of much of the controversy about the fractional factorial methods advocated by Taguchi and others. It is interesting to calculate the A × C and B × C interactions. More fright! So when is it safe to use fractional factorial designs? Suppose the team has completed a number of full-factorial designs and determined that factors A, B, and C do not interact significantly in the ranges involved. Then there would be no significant confounding, and the fractional factorial would be an appropriate design.

Resolution

Table 11.8 shows a full-factorial 2^4 (two levels for four factors) design. Of course, the number of runs is $n = 2^4 = 16$.

Table 11.9 illustrates a half fraction of the 2^4 full-factorial design with interaction columns added. This half fraction was carefully selected to minimize the

Table 11.8   A 2^4 full-factorial design.

Run #	A	B	C	D
1	–	–	–	–
2	–	–	–	+
3	–	–	+	–
4	–	–	+	+
5	–	+	–	–
6	–	+	–	+
7	–	+	+	–
8	–	+	+	+
9	+	–	–	–
10	+	–	–	+
11	+	–	+	–
12	+	–	+	+
13	+	+	–	–
14	+	+	–	+
15	+	+	+	–
16	+	+	+	+

Table 11.9   A 2^{4-1} fractional factorial design with interactions.

Run #	A	B	C	D	AB	AC	AD	BC	BD	CD	ABC	BCD	ACD	ABD	ABCD
1	+	−	−	−	−	−	−	+	+	+	+	−	+	+	−
2	+	+	+	−	+	+	−	+	−	−	+	−	−	−	−
3	−	+	−	−	−	+	+	−	−	+	+	+	−	+	−
4	−	−	+	−	+	−	+	−	+	−	+	+	+	−	−
5	−	−	−	+	+	+	−	+	−	−	−	+	+	+	−
6	−	+	+	+	−	−	−	+	+	+	−	+	−	−	−
7	+	−	+	+	−	+	+	−	−	+	−	−	+	−	−
8	+	+	−	+	+	−	+	−	+	−	−	−	−	+	−

confounding of main effects with two-factor interactions. Note that there are six two-factor interactions, four three-factor interactions, and one four-factor interaction. Also note that factor A is confounded with the BCD interaction because they have the same +/− pattern (although the A column has "−" signs where the BCD column has "+" signs, and vice versa).

Similarly, factor B is confounded with the ACD interaction, factor C with the ABD interaction, and factor D with interaction ABC. The big advantage of this particular fractional factorial is that, although there is confounding, main effects are confounded with three-factor interactions only. Since three-factor interactions are often small, the confounding of main effects will usually be minor. Of course, if a three-factor interaction is significant, as it sometimes is, especially in chemical and metallurgical reactions, it will be missed with this design. Another downside of this design is that two-factor interactions are confounded with each other (AB with CD, and so on). This means that an accurate picture of two-factor interactions will not be possible. Fractional factorial designs fall into three categories:

1. *Resolution III* designs have main effects confounded with two-factor interactions

2. *Resolution IV* designs have main effects confounded with three-factor interactions, and two-factor interactions confounded with each other

3. *Resolution V* designs have some two-factor interactions confounded with three-factor interactions, and some main effects confounded with four-factor interactions

Recall that full-factorial designs have no confounding.

One-Factor Experiments

A process can be run at 180°F, 200°F, or 220°F. Does the temperature significantly affect the product's moisture content? To answer the question, the experimenting team decided to produce four batches at each of the temperatures. The 12 tests could be completely randomized by numbering them from 1 to 12 and randomizing the numbers to obtain the order in which the tests are to be run. Several experimental designs are possible. The least expensive design to execute would be to run the four 180°F batches and then the four 200°F batches, followed by the four 220°F batches. This would reduce the wait time for oven cool-down that more random designs have, but would tend to confound any time-of-day effects with temperature effects. A chart showing testing order would look like the following table, where test #1 is done first, and so on:

Temperature, °F		
180	**200**	**220**
#1	#5	#9
#2	#6	#10
#3	#7	#11
#4	#8	#12

A completely randomized design would have a chart like the following to show the testing order, where test #1 is done first, and so on:

Temperature, °F		
180	**200**	**220**
#3	#11	#8
#7	#5	#1
#12	#9	#2
#6	#4	#10

If the team decided to produce one batch at each temperature each day for four days, they would randomize the order of the temperatures each day, thus using a randomized block design. The test order chart could look like the following:

	Temperature, °F		
Day	**180**	**200**	**220**
1	#3	#1	#2
2	#1	#3	#2
3	#1	#2	#3
4	#2	#1	#3

The team might decide to block for two noise variables: the day the test was performed and the machine the test was performed on. In this case, a *Latin square design* could be used. However, these designs require that the number of levels of each of the noise factors is equal to the number of treatments. Since they have decided to test at three temperatures, they must use three days and three machines. This design is shown in Table 11.10.

Assume that the team decides on the completely randomized design and runs the 12 tests with the following results:

Temperature, °F		
180	**200**	**220**
10.8	11.4	14.3
10.4	11.9	12.6
11.2	11.6	13.0
9.9	12.0	14.2

The averages of the three columns are 10.6, 11.7, and 13.5, respectively. A scatter plot of these data is shown in Figure 11.4.

The graph suggests that an increase in temperature does cause an increase in moisture content. The vertical spread of the dots on each temperature raises some concern. If the dots were spread vertically too much, the within-treatment noise

Table 11.10   Latin square design.

Day	Machine #1	Machine #2	Machine #3
1	180	200	220
2	200	220	180
3	220	180	200

Figure 11.4   Scatter plot of data. The heavy line connects the averages for each temperature.

would shed doubt on the conclusion. How much spread is too much? That question is best answered by using ANOVA procedures.

A 2^2 full-factorial experiment has two factors, with two levels for each factor. For instance, to help determine the effect that acidity and bromine have on nitrogen oxide (NOx) emissions, two levels of acidity and two levels of bromine are established. The two levels are denoted – and + in each case. One scheme for listing the $2^2 = 4$ combinations is

Run	A	B
1	–	–
2	–	+
3	+	–
4	+	+

That is, run #1 consists of measuring NOx emissions with acidity and bromine both at low levels. As stated earlier, it is important to repeat (or replicate) each run several times to get a handle on experimental error. If the measured results of the replications of a particular run are not consistent, a larger experimental error is indicated. The concept of experimental error is quantified by using ANOVA. Assume in this case that each run will be replicated three times. Once again, it is important to randomize the order in which the 12 tests are done. Following is an example of a completely randomized experimental design:

Run	A	B	Replicates		
1	–	–	11	8	5
2	–	+	2	6	4
3	+	–	7	10	9
4	+	+	1	3	12

The number 1 in the last row indicates that for the first test, acidity and bromine are both set at their high levels and the resultant NOx emission is measured.

Full-Factorial Experiments

A 2^2 full-factorial completely randomized experiment is conducted, with the results shown in Table 11.11.

The first step is to find the mean response for each run and calculate the interaction column as shown in Table 11.12.

The main effect of factor A is $(24.7 + 37.3) \div 2 - (28.4 + 33) \div 2 = 0.3$

The main effect of factor B is $(33.0 + 37.3) \div 2 - (28.4 + 24.7) \div 2 = 8.45$

The interaction effect A × B is $(28.4 + 37.3) \div 2 - (33.0 + 24.7) \div 2 = 4.0$

Table 11.11 A 2^2 full-factorial completely randomized experiment with results.

Run #	A	B	Response, y		
1	–	–	28.3	28.6	28.2
2	–	+	33.5	32.7	32.9
3	+	–	24.6	24.6	24.8
4	+	+	37.2	37.6	37.0

Table 11.12 A 2^2 full-factorial completely randomized experiment with results and mean results shown.

Run #	A	B	A × B	Response, y			$\bar{y}$
1	–	–	+	28.3	28.6	28.2	28.4
2	–	+	–	33.5	32.7	32.9	33.0
3	+	–	–	24.6	24.6	24.8	24.7
4	+	+	+	37.2	37.6	37.0	37.3

The next issue is whether these effects are statistically significant or merely the result of experimental error. The larger the effect, the more likely that it is significant. Intuitively, it appears that factor B may be significant and factor A probably isn't. It's not too clear whether the interaction A × B is significant. The definitive answer to the question can be found by conducting a two-way ANOVA on the data. The calculations are quite cumbersome, so software packages are often employed. The following illustrates the use of MS Excel. Excel requires the data in a slightly different format, as shown in Table 11.13. The values obtained when factor A is at its low level are shown in the top two boxes. The values obtained when factor A is at its high level are shown in the bottom two boxes. The values obtained when factor B is at its low level are shown in the left two boxes. So, the values obtained when A is low and B is low are in the top left corner box. These numbers and labels are put in the first rows and columns of the spreadsheet, and the two-way ANOVA function is invoked. The result is illustrated in Table 11.14.

The printout from the ANOVA function contains additional information, but the portion shown in Table 11.14 provides the statistical significance results. The P-value column contains information relating to the statistical significance of the factors. P is the probability that the source of variation is not significant. Using a hypothesis test model, the null hypothesis would be that the source of variation is not statistically significant. Assuming $\alpha = 0.05$, the null hypothesis should be rejected if $P \leq 0.05$. In

Table 11.13   Format for entering data into a Microsoft Excel spreadsheet in preparation for two-way ANOVA.

		−	B	+
		28.3		33.5
	−	28.6		32.7
		28.2		32.9
A				
		24.6		37.2
	+	24.6		37.6
		24.8		37.0

Table 11.14   ANOVA printout from Microsoft Excel. ANOVA is invoked through the Tools > Data analysis menus.

ANOVA

Source of variation	SS	df	MS	F	P-value	F criteria
Acidity	0.213333	1	0.213333	2.639175	0.142912	5.317645
Bromine	223.6033	1	223.6033	2766.227	1.89E-11	5.317645
Interaction	47.20333	1	47.20333	583.9588	9.17E-09	5.317645
Within	0.646667	8	0.080833			
Total	271.6667	11				

this case, the P-values for the sources of variation labeled "bromine" and "interaction" are small enough to reject the null hypothesis and declare these factors— B and the A × B interaction—to be statistically significant at the 0.05 significance level. The row labeled "within" in Table 11.14 calculates what is known as *within-treatment variation*—that is, the variation that occurs between replicates within the same run. The value of 0.080833 shown in the MS column of the "within" row is the estimate of the variance of these replicate values. If replication hadn't been used, this number, which indicates the size of the experimental error, would not have been available. What the ANOVA test really does is compare the between-treatment variation with the within-treatment variation. The *F*-statistic shown in the column labeled "*F*" in Table 11.14 is obtained by dividing the corresponding MS value by the within-MS value. The first *F*-ratio, about 2.6, shows that the variation due to changing the levels of factor A is about 2.6 times the within-treatment error.

Two-Level Fractional Factorial Experiments

The full-factorial experiments described in the previous section require a large number of runs, especially if several factors or several levels are involved. Recall that the formula for number of runs in a full-factorial experiment is

$$\text{Number of runs} = L^F$$

where:

L = Number of levels

F = Number of factors

For example, an experiment with eight two-level factors has $2^8 = 256$ runs, and an experiment with five three-level factors has $3^5 = 243$ runs. If runs are replicated, the number of tests will be multiples of these values. If the experiment is testing the effect of various agricultural factors on crop production, a plot of ground is divided into the required number of subplots, and all runs and replicates can be conducted simultaneously. For instance, a 243-run experiment with four replications of each run would require 972 plots of ground. If a total of an acre is available for experimentation, each plot could be approximately 45 ft^2.

If, however, the experiment is testing the effect of various factors on product quality in a manufacturing process, the tests typically must be run sequentially rather than simultaneously. A full-factorial experiment with several factors and/or levels may require the piece of production equipment to be taken out of production for a considerable amount of time. Because of the extensive resource requirements of full-factorial experiments, fractional factorial experimental designs were developed.

Robustness Concepts

Robustness means resistance to the effect of variation of some factor. For example, if brand A chocolate bar is very soft at 100°F and brittle at 40°F, and brand B maintains the same level of hardness at these temperature extremes, it could be said that brand B is more robust to temperature changes in this range. If a painting process produces the same color on moist wood as on dry wood, the color is robust to variation in moisture content. The changes in temperature and humidity are referred to as *noise*. Products and processes that are robust to noise of various kinds are clearly desirable. The Japanese engineer Genichi Taguchi is credited with developing techniques for improving robustness of products and processes. One approach to improving robustness is illustrated in Table 11.15.

As usual, the average value for each run is calculated and is labeled $\bar{y}$. In addition, the standard deviation of the values in the run is calculated and shown in the column labeled "S." Now the experimenter can complete the usual main effects calculations to determine the levels of each of the factors that will optimize the response value y. In addition, the main effects calculations can be run using the values in the S column to find the levels of each of the factors that will minimize the S value. If these two combinations of levels do not agree, then a compromise between optimizing the response and minimizing the variation must be made. One way to approach the compromising process is through what Taguchi called the *signal-to-noise (S/N) ratio*.

If it is desirable to maximize y, the signal-to-noise ratio may be calculated for each run, using

$$S/N = \frac{\bar{y}}{S}$$

The main effects may then be calculated using the S/N ratios to find the best levels for each factor. If, instead, it is desirable to make y as small as possible, the S/N ratio can be defined as

$$S/N = \frac{1}{\bar{y}S}$$

If it is desirable to make y as close to some nominal value N as possible, the S/N ratio can be defined as

$$S/N = \frac{1}{|\bar{y} - N|S}$$

Note that the S/N ratio is an attempt to find a useful compromise between two competing goals, optimizing y and minimizing S. It does not necessarily accomplish either of these goals, so it should be used with a bit of judgment.

Table 11.15 Robustness example using signal-to-noise ratio.

A	B	C	Replications				$\bar{y}$	S
−	−	−	34	29	38	25	31.5	5.7
−	−	+	42	47	39	38	41.5	4.0
−	+	−	54	41	48	43	46.5	5.8
−	+	+	35	31	32	34	33.0	1.8
+	−	−	62	68	63	69	65.5	3.5
+	−	+	25	33	36	21	28.8	6.9
+	+	−	58	54	58	60	57.5	2.5
+	+	+	39	35	42	45	40.3	4.3

Another technique Taguchi used for improving robustness is called the *inner/outer array design*. In this procedure, the uncontrolled factors—those factors that the experimenter either cannot control or chooses not to control—are placed in separate columns next to the controllable factors, as shown in Table 11.16. In this example, hardness of the steel and the ambient temperature are the uncontrolled factors. These factors could conceivably be controlled by putting the machine in an environmental enclosure and putting a tighter specification on the steel, but the experimenter chooses not to do either of these. Instead, anticipated extremes of hardness and ambient temperature are used for the experiment to determine settings of the controllable variables that will minimize variation in the output quality characteristic.

When the first run of the design in Table 11.16 is executed, the feed, speed, and coolant temperature are all set at their low levels. One part is made with low-hardness steel and low ambient temperature, and the value of the quality characteristic is entered in the spot labeled "a." When all 32 values have been entered, the averages and standard deviations are calculated. In this inner/outer array approach, the design intentionally causes perturbations in the uncontrollable factors to find level combinations for the controllable factors that will minimize the variation in the quality characteristics under the anticipated hardness and ambient temperature variation. One might ask why hardness and ambient temperature are not merely added to the factor list, making five factors at two levels, which would require $2^5 = 32$ tests, exactly the number required in this example. That approach would establish the best settings for hardness and ambient temperature. But it would also require a tighter spec on hardness and ambient temperature. Instead, the inner/outer array design determines optimum levels for the control factors in the presence of variation in the outer array factors.

Table 11.16 Illustration of inner and outer arrays.

Inner array			Outer array							
			Hardness	−	−	+	+		
Feed	**Speed**	**Coolant temp.**	**Ambient temp.**	−	+	−	+	$\bar{y}$	S
−	−	−		a					
−	−	+							
−	+	−							
−	+	+							
+	−	−							
+	−	+							
+	+	−							
+	+	+							

4. RELIABILITY OPTIMIZATION

> Use various approaches to optimize reliability within the constraints of cost, schedule, weight, and other design requirements. (Apply)
>
> Body of Knowledge V.A.4

The reliability engineer involved in the design process will frequently be doing some sort of balancing act. The standard ways to improve reliability, redundancy, derating, and environmental robustness tend to increase cost and weight, and delay the design process. The prioritization matrix discussed in Example 11.2 can aid in this balancing act.

EXAMPLE 11.2

A design team is charged with optimization of the motor/drive train for a commercial air handler. The reliability engineer is considering several options, which are listed in the left column of the matrix in Figure 11.5. The other columns are self-explanatory, and additional columns may be necessary to cover additional constraints. Once the matrix has been constructed, the decisions become a little more quantitative. In this case the team might decide that the hardened motor can be sold as an alternative but not be included in the standard product. The additional motor might be eliminated from the product line.

Option	Advantage	Cost ($)	Weight (kg)	Schedule delay (days)
Derate motor	Increase motor life Handle excess load	900	25	0
Derate drive belt	Extend maintenance schedule	100	2	0
Add 2nd drive belt	Allow operation with failed belt	400	10	5
Harden motor	Allow use in caustic environment	2000	95	10
Add 2nd motor	Allow use after motor failure	2000	300	15

Figure 11.5 Prioritization matrix.

Reliability Optimization Process

The reliability optimization process is a reliability tool that analyzes a system to help determine which components will meet the performance goals at the lowest cost. The reliability optimization process is comprised of three steps including;

1. Develop a model that represents the entire system, by constructing a system reliability block diagram that represents the reliability relationships of the components in the system

2. Using this model estimate the reliability and costs that would be incurred in the process of making modifications

3. Then perform an optimization analysis to find the best combination of component reliability improvements that meet or exceed the performance goals at the lowest cost

---

EXAMPLE 11.3

Suppose we have the reliability block diagram representing a three-step process, required reliability = 0.90.

What should we do to meet the reliability goal? What is the impact on cost? Required reliability = 0.90, one solution:

EXAMPLE 11.4

The assembly line of a "widget" is defined in Table 11.17. The processes are numbered 1–9. Each process has a probability of human error (per million operations).

Table 11.17   Example probability of human error (per million operations).

Process	Operation	Error rate/millions operations
1	Read gauge	4500
2	Close valve	2000
3	Solder connectors	6500
4	Actuate switch	1128
5	Install nut & bolt	600
6	Tighten nut & bolt	4800
7	Adjust mechanical linkage	6700
8	Connect hose	4700
9	Route part	1000

Continued

Part V.A.4

Objective:

Design a system with all of these operations using redundancy in any of them to decrease the probability of error that will give at least 9800 good assemblies in 10,000 parts.

Operation	Error rate/ millions operations				
Read gauge	4500				
Close valve	2000				
Solder connectors	6500	→	Dual redundant=42/1000000		0.000004225
Actuate switch	1128				
Install nut & bolt	600				
Tighten nut & bolt	4800				
Adjust mechanical linkage	6700	→	Dual redundant=279/1000000		0.000004489
Connect hose	4700				
Route part	1000				
	0.031501045	Before redundant	Prob of at least 1 error =		0.031501045
	0.01867468	After redundant	Prob of at least 1 error =		0.018904183
			with mech linkage redundant		

5. HUMAN FACTORS

Describe the relationship between human factors and reliability engineering, including user safety, user and usage profiles, failure modes and mechanisms. (Understand)

Body of Knowledge V.A.5

Human Factors

Humans play an important role in the overall reliability of engineering systems (recognized in the 1950s). Reliability of the human aspect can be improved by:

- Following human-factor principles in system design
- Careful selection and training of personnel

Stress affects human performance and human reliability, but is not necessarily an entirely negative state. Stress at a moderate level is useful in increasing human effectiveness to its optimal level. At very low stress, the task will be unchallenging and dull and human performance will not be at its peak (Figure 11.6).

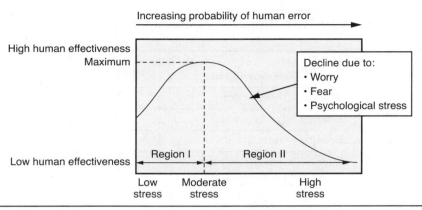

Figure 11.6 The effect of stress on the probability of human failure.

Four types of occupational stressors are:

1. Work overload or work underload

   – Job overload occurs when requirements exceed individual ability

   – Job underload occurs when the work performed fails to provide meaningful stimulation

2. Occupational change (e.g., organizational restructuring, promotion, relocation)

3. Occupational frustration (e.g., job inhibits the meeting of goals because of lack of communication, role ambiguity, bureaucracy difficulties)

4. Other sources (e.g., noise, too little or too much lighting, poor interpersonal relationships)

Human Performance Reliability Modeling

The *human performance reliability* follows analogously from our work on hazard functions:

$$R_e(t) = \exp\left[-\int_0^t h_e(t)dt\right]$$

where $R_e(t)$ is the human performance reliability at time t and $h_e(t)$ is the time-dependent human error rate.

This holds for constant or nonconstant human error rate. In fact, when data has been collected experimentally from time-continuous tasks (observing clock-type displays of lights, where the subjects were asked to press a handheld switch when a failed light occurred) the Weibull distribution fits the data quite well (Table 11.18; Figure 11.7).

Part V.A.5

Table 11.18   Human error probability estimates for selected tasks.

Task description	Human error probability
Reading a chart recorder	0.006
Reading an analog meter	0.003
Reading graphs	0.01
Interpreting incorrectly the indication on the indicator lamps	0.001
Turning a control in the incorrect direction under high stress	0.5
Using the checklist correctly	0.5
Mating a connector	0.01
Choosing an incorrect panel control out of a number of similar controls	0.003

Figure 11.7   Human error prevention: man–machine systems analysis.

EXAMPLE 11.5

Suppose we have a parallel system of two independent and identical active units. Each unit may fail due to a hardware failure or a noncritical human error. The system may fail due to the occurrence of a critical human error. The probabilities of failure are illustrated: F is hardware probability of failure, f is human probability of failure.

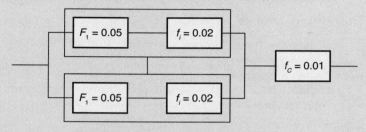

So, calculating the system reliability with these human error probabilities:

$$R_s = [1 - (1 - (1 - 0.05)(1 - 0.02)2](1 - 0.01) = 0.9853$$

Therefore the system reliability is 0.9853.

Human Reliability Data Sources

Human reliability analysis (HRA) is the utilization of systems engineering and behavioral science methods to identify ways to reduce risk.

1. Past experience

2. Customer's failure-reporting system

3. Product development data

4. Repair reports

5. Field installation testing

6. Manufacturing and quality control

7. Acceptance tests in the factory

8. Field demonstration and environmental qualification tests

Human Factors Considerations in Various Stages of a System Development

There are several human factors to consider when developing a system, including:

1. Preliminary design phase

   - Who will be the users of the system under design?

   - What are the environments in which the system is expected to operate?

- What is the function that the system under consideration is expected to accomplish?
- Who will operate and maintain the system?
- What are the important technological options?
- What are the mission execution stages?

2. Advanced design phase

- What information is needed by operators or maintainers?
- What kind of indicators are needed to eliminate operator errors?
- What type of special skill is expected from operators for effective performance?
- What is the size of the manpower required during normal operation?
- What means are available for quick recovery when operator error occurs?
- What are the conditions that will be detrimental to operator performance?
- What functions are to be assigned to operating personnel?
- In what form should the information be presented to the operator?

3. Mock-up or prototype fabrication phase

- What effect will any proposed changes in configuration have on safety, human performance, reliability, etc.?
- What quality control methods and procedures will fulfill the task of ensuring the validity of human-factor considerations in the resulting system?
- Are there any options for simplifying any of the instrumentation used in the product?

4. Test and evaluation phase

- How can the testing and evaluation be made more realistic as possible with respect to operating personnel?
- What criteria of equipment and operating personnel performance are logical with respect to functions and assigned mission?

System Safety

A typical system safety program has three key elements:

1. *Identification of safety hazards.* The reliability engineer working with the safety organization to achieve a safe product must be innovative and diligent in the discovery of all possible ways that any failure,

combination of failures, or other combination of circumstances would present a safety hazard to personnel. Warranty data and other forms of customer feedback should be analyzed. Product testing reports should include safety issues that may have emerged. All available product data should be searched for occurrence of safety hazards. In addition, if databases for similar products are available, they should also be studied.

2. *Risk analysis.* The standard analysis techniques are failure modes and effects analysis (FMEA); failure modes, effects, and criticality analysis (FMECA); production reliability acceptance test (PRAT); fault tree analysis (FTA); success tree analysis (STA); failure reporting, analysis, and corrective action system (FRACAS).

   Monte Carlo simulation can be used for those instances where detailed failure times (by mode) are available, or where there are competing modes of failure that will affect the component or system. The risk matrix is another approach to quantifying risk. These techniques can be used to estimate the risk associated with various events. It then becomes possible to establish a prioritized list that will provide guidance as the root causes are attacked and resolved.

3. *Correction and prevention.* In the case of safety hazards, there is the additional urgency to avoid harm to personnel. In cases in which flaws in products or processes permit hazardous conditions to occur, an engineering change request (ECR) should be initiated. It is always necessary to consider human error. From one perspective, human error occurs because no system is in place to prevent it. In other words, the onus is on the product/process design community to reduce or eliminate errors. Procedures for preventing/mitigating human error are variously called *idiotproofing, mistake-proofing, poka-yoke,* and *zero quality control* (ZQC). Human error tends to fall into the following categories: misunderstanding, misidentification, inexperience, inattention, and lack of standards. The ideal way to deal with human mistakes is to incorporate design elements that will prevent them from occurring or prevent their occurrence from causing defects. Principal types of mistake-proofing techniques include:

   – *Physical barriers to errors.* (The round shaft won't fit through the square hole.)

   – *Visual reminders.* (A photograph of correct and incorrect results is better than a note written on a print or a paragraph of text.)

   – *Use of automated equipment.* (The conveyor will stop if the microswitch detects an error.)

   – *Standardizing.* (The operator takes the same action on a family of parts.)

Often, the best way to prevent reoccurrence of human error is to approach a person who has made the error with the question, "How can we design a system that will make that error impossible to occur?"

Activity must be continuous in the three elements of the system safety program. As the higher-priority hazards are corrected/prevented, action can focus on the lower-priority items.

Reliability Testing

Reliability testing must consider variation introduced by differences between people. These differences can be categorized as *usage factors*, *installation factors*, and *process management factors*.

Use Factors

When conducting tests on a home laundry appliance, consideration must be given to the differences in the way people slam doors, choose washing detergent, maintain cleanliness, load the washer, and so on. Automotive components also experience a wide variety of operator habits. If the testing protocol calls for 100,000 door slams using a particular force, it has not accommodated all the variations that customers may employ.

Installation Factors

Products may be installed in a wide variety of environments. For building materials, automotive spare parts, stationary equipment, and many other products, the useful lifetime is impacted by the quality of the installation and the location parameters. For instance, if a window is installed slightly out of plumb, it may not be as reliable as a properly installed unit. This has implications for design and testing procedures because the window should be robust to minor out-of-plumbness. Knowledge in this area also will impact installation instructions.

Process Management Factors

If reliability testing is conducted on products that are produced by an ideal process, the variation introduced by people in the production process may not be taken into consideration. Operators or process managers can influence product characteristics by the way they hold the paint gun or welding stick, the promptness with which a tank is evacuated, or the delay between molding cycles, and so on.

Recommendations

From the testing viewpoint, it would be easier if all this human variation could be removed by specifying usage, installation, and processing parameters, and in fact that is typically done. A balance must be struck, of course, between the narrowness of the specifications and the attendant loss in flexibility. If, for instance, an installation specification states that the ambient air must be between 65°F and 75°F, the testing will be simplified, but some customers will be lost and others will ignore the specification and be disappointed with product performance. Therefore, the product design team should strive for robustness to the variation introduced by these human factors, keeping the specifications as broad as possible. This means that the reliability testing procedures must include tests throughout the specification spectrum.

6. DESIGN FOR X (DFX)

> Apply DFX techniques such as design for manufacturability, testability, and maintainability. (Apply)
>
> Body of Knowledge V.A.6

Every design team has constraints within which they must function. The items listed in this Body of Knowledge excerpt constitute design constraints. The relative importance of each of these characteristics has an impact on the resulting design:

- *Design for assembly* refers to the conscious thought given to the assembly process by the product design team. Decisions by the team affect the simplicity and ease of the assembly process by giving consideration to visual and mechanical access to fasteners, special tooling or fixturing that may be required, safeguards against incorrect assembly, and so forth.

- *Design for manufacturability* is similar to design for assembly but tends to put more emphasis on the fabrication or primary functions that precede assembly. Here, consideration is given to narrowness of tolerances and difficult configurations such as deep dead-end holes, thin walls, and so on.

- *Design for testability* looks at testing procedures and tries to develop a design for which important characteristics are easily and accurately measured.

- *Design for cost* puts emphasis on final cost of the product and makes this a strong constraint on product or process design.

- *Design for serviceability* considers the ease and simplicity of installing replacement parts, as well as standard servicing requirements.

- *Design for reliability* emphasizes the long-term usefulness of the product to the customer.

- *Design for environment* considers the activity beyond the useful life of the product. While considering the various tradeoffs in the design process, it is becoming increasingly important to study issues of recycling, reclamation, and disposal. Issues to take into account include contractual obligations/warranties and regulatory and certification requirements.

Many of these constraints are applied to typical designs, and often the extent of the constraint is a matter of emphasis.

The maintainability of a system is influenced by the ability to detect and repair a system fault. Therefore, the testing requirements for a system should provide for a method to detect a system fault and isolate the failed component. In some cases, such as for a complex system, the requirement could be met with a built-in test system. This could add additional complexity to the system, and care must be taken to assure the reliability of the test system.

The testability requirements of systems can also be met by providing easily accessible test points for critical measurements taken using external test equipment. It is important that a maintainability engineering effort is included in the design stage to ensure testability of the system. The testability of a system must be developed as part of the system design. At the system or subsystem level, the testability requirements should reflect the need to be able to detect failure quickly and isolate the failure so that replacement or repair can be accomplished in an acceptable amount of time.

When designing for testability it is important to consider the various conditions when testing is required, such as during new product development, conducting safety analysis or fatigue analysis, and other times, depending on the product. *Fault detection capability* is a measure of the faults detected by the fault detection system (usually built-in test) compared to the total number of system faults. *Fault isolation capability* is a measure of the percentage of time the failure can be isolated to a given number of replaceable (repairable) components. Fault isolation can be accomplished by a diagnostic analysis, built-in test, or using external test equipment. *False-alarm rate* is a measure of the rate at which the system declares the detection of a failure when no failure has occurred. A *fault recording and analysis system* that identifies specific components will aid in improving reliability. Particular attention should be paid to the possibility of dependence among fault types. The discovery of a cascading pattern among faults permits work on the root cause rather than on symptoms.

7. DESIGN FOR RELIABILITY (DfR)

> Apply DfR in order to meet reliability requirements throughout the product or system lifecycle. Understand how built-in reliability and fault tolerance/avoidance are key goals for design for reliability. (Evaluate)
>
> Body of Knowledge V.A.7

Reliability design is an iterative process that begins with the specification of reliability goals consistent with customer requirements. It considers lifecycle costs of the system and system effectiveness. The flow of designing for reliability is shown in Figure 11.8.

Design for reliability (DfR) is a concurrent engineering program where the reliability engineer is part of the product development team working with the design

Figure 11.8 Flow of designing for reliability.

engineers to design reliable products with overall low lifecycle costs. A DfR program encompasses the following steps:

- Reliability program planning
- Reliability predictions
- Parts derating
- Thermal analysis
- Component wear-out

- FMEA and fault tree analysis
- Availability and system modeling
- HALT, HASS, and HASA
- Design verification testing (DVT)
- Product return rate analysis
- FRACAS and root cause failure analysis
- Internal process sharing and benchmarking

Reliability Specification and System Measurements

Reliability specification and system measurements are usually designated by mean time to failure (MTTF) or mean time between failures (MTBF).

- MTTF or MTBF has been the primary and often only measure of reliability.
- This parameter is not sufficient except in the case of exponential failure distribution.
- A better measure would be to specify the reliability at specific points in time.

  For example, to state that 99% reliability is required after two years of operation and 95% reliability is required after five years of operation is much more precise than stating an MTTF of 10 years is required.

- If the MTTF is to be the only reliability specification to be used, a constant failure rate should be assumed as part of the specification and subsequently demonstrated. Otherwise, a wide range of distributions must be tried.

Considerations in Designing in Reliability

Fault tolerance refers to the ability of a system to perform according to specifications even when undesired changes occur in its internal or external environment. The reliability engineer's task here is to use knowledge of system design to prevent a fault from causing a failure. Single-fault tolerance can be affected by a system design that will permit a component (hardware or software) to be removed and replaced without causing system failure. Multiple-fault tolerant systems are designed to continue operating in the presence of more than one concurrent failure. Various techniques have been employed to produce fault-tolerant systems.

Redundancy is a standard technique for mitigation of system failure. The theory is that if two or more parallel channels are available for the system, the likelihood of failure is reduced. Redundancy alone is often insufficient because the common cause variation may overwhelm all branches of the system.

Examples:

- The catastrophic failure that caused United Airlines Flight 232 to attempt a landing at Sioux City in 1989. The DC-10 was designed with three independent hydraulic systems so that if one or two failed, the surviving system could manage flight control surfaces. Unfortunately, all three lines were at one point in close proximity. Shrapnel from a damaged engine passed through that point and severed all three lines, causing loss of control.

- The use of parallel CPUs in computers performing critical tasks. Some systems are set up to process every command by two different processors and compare the results. If the results do not match, an error flag is set and the system is put in a safe mode and maintenance is performed. A problem here is that if the software is defective, the two results may agree but be erroneous. The common cause in this case is the software bug. It caused errors in both branches of the parallel design. A variant on this approach is to have simultaneous calculations performed by several processors. When the results are compared, a *voter* module compares the results and goes with the one produced by the majority of the processors.

- Improper maintenance of all branches of a parallel system.

- Use of a process material that corrodes all redundant branches.

- Computer backup systems using identical disk drives in an identical environment (which often results in identical failures).

Diversity and separation are two techniques that have been used to make redundancy more effective.

Diversity is employed to construct parallel channels different in ways that will make them immune to failure by the same cause. This implies an understanding of the common causes—an understanding that will only come from considerable study. In the case of the parallel CPUs mentioned previously, a different piece of software could be employed to make the calculation for one of the CPUs.

Separation can apply to branches that have separate physical environments, electronic isolation, or other means of preventing a common cause from causing multiple-branch failure. In the case of the DC-10 accident mentioned earlier, the hydraulic lines were not adequately separated.

Reducing variation in design is essential to success and applies not only to physical tolerances, but all portions of the product and process (i.e., using robust design principles throughout the design process to ensure all portions operate as closely as possible to nominal). Taguchi design of experiments methods and Monte Carlo simulation are powerful tools used in parameter design to reduce design variation.

Chapter 12
B. Parts and Systems Development

1. MATERIALS AND COMPONENTS SELECTION TECHNIQUES

> Apply techniques (e.g., derating and commercial off-the-shelf [COTS]) for selecting materials and components to meet reliability goals and requirements. (Analyze)
>
> Body of Knowledge V.B.1

In some fields, especially electronics, standard ratings are available for components. These include stress limits, environmental conditions, and other characteristics. The *rating* is the maximum level for stresses such as temperature, voltage, pressure, and so on. Manufacturers will generally provide safe operating area (SOA) information defining the conditions (voltage and current) in which the component or device is rated to operate without self-damage. Figure 12.1 provides the SOA, which is labeled as the "Recommended Safe Area." Operating beyond the rated value may reduce reliability and increase the risks associated with damage or failure. Derating can also impart the margin of safety. Derating techniques are especially useful for commercial off-the-shelf (COTS) components. Many COTS components will provide derating information (see Figure 12.1).

Some common standards are MIL-HDBK-217, Bellcore (SR-22), Naval Surface Warfare Center 98 (LEI), China 299B, and Reliability Data Handbook 2000. *Derating* is the practice of operating components at lower stress levels than those specified by the standards. It usually refers to limiting electrical, thermal, or mechanical stresses. In general, the more a part is derated, the lower its failure rate. The extent to which derating impacts failure rate is technology dependent. Paradoxically, derating is also used to permit operating at a higher stress level. For instance, rather than install a more powerful, noisier fan, an electronics designer may choose to use a component with higher thermal rating. To avoid excessive costs, derating should be done selectively rather than using a mass indiscriminate derating scheme.

Underclocking of synchronous electronic devices can be thought of as another form of derating. This refers to running the device, such as a CPU, at a slower-than-designed speed. This may decrease the rate of heat generation, therefore prolonging life and/or decreasing the ventilation or heat sinking requirements.

Figure 12.1 Example electrical derating graph.

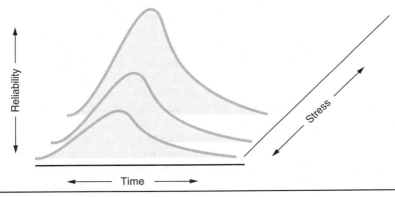

Figure 12.2 Stress–life distributions.

Stress-Life Relationships

The analysis of reliability data can be used to generate a *life distribution*. This distribution is typically defined for a given stress level. In situations where the stress may change, another dimension is added to the life distribution, as depicted in Figure 12.2, which illustrates the fact that there may be a different life distribution for different stress levels.

2. PARTS STANDARDIZATION AND SYSTEM SIMPLIFICATION

Describe the importance of standardization, simplification, and parts re-use to meet reliability goals and requirements. (Apply)

Body of Knowledge V.B.2

Part V.B.2

Parts standardization refers to the use of the same components in several products. An example in the automotive industry is the use of the same chassis or engine for several automobile models. In some families of electronic products the same circuit board may be used, with different functions activated depending on the application. A parts reduction initiative makes an effort to reduce the number of parts required to perform a function. If, for instance, a two-bar linkage can be used to replace a three-bar linkage, there will be an associated simplification in parts, assembly, and maintenance. When product families are essentially the same except for size, they are sometimes referred to as *parallel models*. A valve producer, for instance, may offer essentially the same geometry in valves for pipes ranging from one inch to ten inches. During the fabrication process, if parts are maintained in a state where they may be used in several models and then customized as they are needed, the *raw as possible* (RAP) principle is being used. For example, a dome-shaped sheet metal part requires two, three, or four triangular holes depending on the product. Rather than producing an inventory of each type, it might be useful to use one die to cut and form the dome shape and put a small press on the assembly line to punch the triangular holes as needed.

If a module of software can be structured so that it is usable in more than one application, the costs of generating and testing the module are reduced. There are obvious cost advantages associated with these techniques in terms of inventory, purchasing efficiencies, storage, accounting, and auditing. Reducing the costs of reliability testing is an often overlooked advantage. If the function of three very similar items can be handled by a single item, the costs for reliability testing may be reduced by 67%. And if that item is one that has already been tested, further savings are realized.

These testing cost savings can be very substantial, so design teams are well advised to look to families of parts and consider potential standardization.

During product design it is important to consider the variation in materials. Probabilistic methods permit the design team to produce products that are robust to this variation. This is accomplished by constructing distribution models that describe the variability in materials.

EXAMPLE 12.1

A design team is selecting building materials for a set of livestock shelters and is considering the use of a clip that slips over two two-by-fours.

The failure mode of concern occurs if the gap is so narrow that the two-by-fours won't fit. The nominal thickness of the two-by-fours is 1.5 inches, and the gap is 3.010 ± 0.005. What percent of the clips will be too narrow?

Solution:

The team finds that the thickness of the two-by-fours to be used has $\mu_{2\times4} = 1.500$ and $\sigma_{2\times4} = 0.001$ and is normally distributed. The gap in the proposed clip has $\mu_{Gap} = 3.011$ and $\sigma_{Gap} = 0.002$ and is normally distributed. The pair of two-by-fours has a total thickness that is normally distributed, with $\mu_{Pair} = 3.000$ and

$$\sigma_{Pair} = \sqrt{\sigma_{2\times4}^2 + \sigma_{2\times4}^2} \approx 0.0014$$

The clearance between the clip and the pair of two-by-fours is normally distributed, with

$$\mu_{Clear} = \mu_{Gap} - \mu_{Pair} = 3.011 - 3.000 = 0.011$$

$$\sigma_{Clear} = \sqrt{\sigma_{2\times4}^2 + \sigma_{2\times4}^2 + \sigma_{Gap}^2} \approx 0.0024$$

Then,

$$z = \frac{\mu_{Clear}}{\sigma_{Clear}} \approx 0.46$$

From a normal distribution table, about 32% of the clips will be too narrow. The design team returns to the drawing board.

Chapter 13
C. Maintainability

1. MAINTENANCE STRATEGIES

Maintenance strategies should be chosen to ensure a high level of availability while controlling costs. Preventive maintenance does not improve the inherent reliability of the system. Preventive maintenance will maintain the reliability level of useful life, keeping the failure rate low. It will also delay the onset of wear, thus increasing the length of useful life. Preventive maintenance actions can also introduce a fault into the system, causing the system to fail and the need for corrective maintenance. A study should be done to determine the most cost-effective scheduling of maintenance actions necessary to keep the system operational. Maintenance actions that are unnecessary should be eliminated.

A single unit, such as a pump, could be considered a system. Or, the pump could be considered a component of a larger system. In either case, system reliability is at the highest level if all units are in their useful life phase. Preventive maintenance strategies such as *reliability-centered maintenance* and *predictive maintenance* are proactive and require the replacement or refurbishment of the components of the system that are nearing the end of their useful life or entering wear-out. Replacement is made before failure occurs. *Condition-based maintenance* is reactive and is a corrective maintenance strategy. Replacement is made after failure occurs.

The appropriate strategy for replacement needs to be chosen. The information needed in order to choose the most appropriate replacement strategy includes:

- The failure distribution of the unit
- The cost associated with the failure of the unit
- Any safety issues associated with the failure

- The cost of the replacement unit

- The cost associated with scheduled replacements

- The cost of inspection or test

Predictive and Reliability-Centered Maintenance

Predictive maintenance assumes that the operator can detect the imminent failure of a unit. This detection can be by observation, analysis, or using test equipment. The analysis of an oil sample or the measurement of increased vibration might indicate wear and an increasing failure probability. If the increasing failure probability cannot be detected by the operator, a reliability-centered maintenance strategy could be adopted. This strategy uses the predicted failure distributions to determine the optimum replacement time for units about to enter the wear-out phase. Replacement of units that are entering the wear-out portion of the bathtub curve will maintain the system reliability at the useful life level.

It is possible that any maintenance action can negatively impact reliability by inducing failure modes due to the maintenance action. These maintenance-induced failures are similar to the early-life failures due to the manufacturing or installation of a system. An effort should be made during design to ensure that standard preventive maintenance actions can be performed quickly and with a low risk of introducing problems due to the maintenance actions.

Maintainability/Apportionment/Allocation

Reliability deals with reducing failures of the system and thus reducing the frequency of unscheduled maintenance actions. Maintainability deals with reducing the duration of the downtime that is a result of both scheduled and unscheduled maintenance actions. Maintainability is often thought of as a technique for making repairs easy. It is, however, the engineering involved in minimizing the total downtime.

MIL-HDBK-472 gives the following definition of maintainability:

Maintainability is the ability of an item to be retained in or restored to specified conditions when maintenance action is performed by personnel having specified skill levels and using prescribed procedures and resources at each prescribed level of maintenance and repair.

The maintenance actions are to be performed by skilled personnel, using proper procedures, with the proper tools, and having access to standard replacement parts. The objective is best accomplished if an effort is made to eliminate unscheduled downtime and reduce the duration of scheduled downtime.

A system-level maintainability requirement may need to be allocated to lower levels of the system. *Maintainability allocation* is a continuing process of apportioning requirements at the system level to subsystem levels. This will give values the designer can work toward. This is similar to a system reliability requirement being allocated to the various subsystems. To allocate the maintainability requirements, the failure rate and the *mean time to repair* (MTTR) are used.

MTTR Allocation

- A series system has three subsystems
- The failure rate for subsystem i is λ_i, and the MTTR for subsystem i is t_i
- The system failure rate is $\lambda = \lambda_1 + \lambda_2 + \lambda_3$
- The system-level MTTR requirement is t^*

$$\text{MTTR}_{(System)} = t = \frac{\left(\lambda_1 t_1 + \lambda_2 t_2 + \lambda_3 t_3\right)}{\left(\lambda_1 + \lambda_2 + \lambda_3\right)} = \frac{\lambda_1 t_1}{\lambda} + \frac{\lambda_2 t_2}{\lambda} + \frac{\lambda_3 t_3}{\lambda}$$

EXAMPLE 13.1

A series system has three subsystems. The failure rates of the subsystems are:

$\lambda_1 = 10 \times 10^{-6}$ failures/hr

$\lambda_2 = 30 \times 10^{-6}$ failures/hr

$\lambda_3 = 60 \times 10^{-6}$ failures/hr

The subsystem MTTR values are:

$t_1 = 150$ min

$t_2 = 100$ min

$t_3 = 50$ min

The system MTTR requirement is one hour ($t^* = 60$ min).

$$\text{MTTR}_{(System)} = (10/100)(150) + (30/100)(100) + (60/100)(50) = 75 \text{ min}$$

The attained value of the system MTTR is greater than the requirement.
In order to meet the system requirement, the maintainability allocation to each subsystem will be:

$t_1^* = (150/75) \times 60 \text{ min} = 120 \text{ min}$

$t_2^* = (100/75) \times 60 \text{ min} = 80 \text{ min}$

$t_3^* = (50/75) \times 60 \text{ min} = 40 \text{ min}$

In order to meet the maintainability goal, an MTTR allocation to each subsystem must be made if the $\text{MTTR}_{(System)} > t^*$. The MTTR allocation to subsystem i is

$$t_i^* = [t_i/t] \times t^*$$

The designer can work to subsystem MTTR requirements better than to system-level MTTR requirements.

Spare Parts Analysis

The required number of spares necessary for a given period of time is a function of the expected number of failures and the number of spares required for preventive maintenance. The number of failures is a function of the unit operating time and the failure rate. If any spares are required for preventive maintenance, the number is a function of operating time and the preventive maintenance cycle.

The MTTR calculation assumes that spare parts are readily available. This means that spares must be in inventory when they are needed. If there is waiting time to obtain a spare, the unit downtime will increase and availability will suffer. If the unit has a constant failure rate, the probability of requiring no more than r replacement units can be found using the cumulative Poisson distribution.

The probability of having r or fewer failures in operating time t if the unit is operating with a constant failure rate of λ is:

$$P(r) = \sum_{n=0}^{r} \frac{(\lambda t)^n e^{-\lambda t}}{n!}$$

where:

r = Number of failures

λ = Failure rate

t = Operating time

n = Number of spares required for preventative maintenance

Tables are available to evaluate the cumulative Poisson distribution; see Appendix N.

EXAMPLE 13.2

A unit that operates an average of 2000 hours per year has a constant failure rate:

$$\lambda = 100 \times 10^{-6} \text{ failures/hour}$$

The maintenance strategy is to replace the unit every 5000 operating hours. In a five-year period:

a. How many spares will be necessary for preventive maintenance?

b. With a 0.90 probability, how many spares will be necessary for corrective maintenance?

Solution:

a. The operating time in a five-year period is $t = 5 \times 2000 = 10{,}000$ hours.

The preventive maintenance cycle is 1/5000 hours.

The number of spares required for preventive maintenance is

$$n = (1/5000) \times (10{,}000) = 2$$

b. We want $P(r) \geq 0.90$.

$$\lambda t = (100 \times 10^{-6})(10{,}000) = 1.0$$

From the cumulative Poisson tables in Appendix N, use the row with λ value of 1 in the left column and find the first element in this row that is greater than 0.90.

$$P(r \leq 2) = 0.92$$
$$\lambda t = 1.0$$

With a probability of 0.92, the number of spares needed for corrective maintenance is no more than two.

If preventive maintenance requires spare parts, the number of spares necessary is a function of the operating time and the maintenance cycle. The number of spares required for preventive maintenance is the product of the maintenance cycle and the total operating time. The total number of spares that must be kept in inventory is a function of the delivery time, the cost of maintaining the inventory, and the availability requirement.

Several methods are in use for forecasting spare parts requirements. Four methods are presented here. Experience will help determine which is best for a given part.

Moving Average

The forecasted value of the spare parts requirement is the average of the previous n requirements. The value of n is determined by experience. The formula is

$$R_t = \frac{X_{t-1} + X_{t-2} + \ldots + X_{t-n}}{n}$$

where:

R_t = Forecasted spare parts requirement at time t

X_t = Actual spare parts requirement at time t

n = Determined by experience

EXAMPLE 13.3

If the best value of n has been found to be 5, and the last eight weeks' requirements were given as 23 25 22 26 21 20 23 24, then the predicted spare parts requirement for this part for the ninth week is:

$$R_9 = \frac{26 + 21 + 20 + 23 + 24}{5} \approx 23$$

Weighted Moving Average

This method weights the most recent values higher than the previous values. The n-period weighted moving average uses the formula

$$R_t = \frac{nX_{t-1} + (n-1)X_{t-2} + \ldots + X_{t-n}}{n + n - 1 + \ldots + 1}$$

where:

R_t = Forecasted spare parts requirement at time t

X_t = Actual spare parts requirement at time t

n = Determined by experience

> ## EXAMPLE 13.4
>
> If the best value of n has been found to be 5, and the last eight weeks have seen spare part requirements for a particular part of 23 25 22 26 21 20 23 24, then the predicted spare parts requirement for this part for the ninth week is:
>
> $$R_9 = \frac{(5)24 + 4(23) + (3)20 + (2)21 + 26}{5 + 4 + 3 + 2 + 1} \approx 23$$

Single Exponential Smoothing

The formula for predicting the spare parts requirement is

$$R_t = \alpha X_{t-1} + (1 - \alpha)R_{t-1}$$

where:

R_t = Forecasted spare parts requirement at time t.

X_t = Actual spare parts requirement at time t.

α = Smoothing factor, usually between 0.1 and 0.4 with unstable demand situations using higher α-values. Experience dictates the best values for α.

(To get the time series started, it is common practice to use the forecast for time $t = 2$ to be the actual requirement for time $t = 1$.)

> ## EXAMPLE 13.5
>
> Assume time periods of one week are used, and the spare parts requirement for the first week was 23 items. Assume further that an α-value of 0.2 is used, and that the actual requirement for the second week was 16 parts. The forecasted spare parts requirement for the third week would be
>
> $$R_3 = 0.2(16) + 0.8(23) = 21.6 \text{ or } 22 \text{ items}$$
>
> If the actual requirement for week three was 18 items, the forecasted requirement for week four would be
>
> $$R_4 = 0.2(18) + 0.8(21.6) = 20.9 \text{ or } 21 \text{ items}$$

Croston Method

The Croston method applies exponential smoothing to both the magnitude of the spare parts requirement, Z, and the time period, P, between demands for the spare part. If no spare part is needed at the end of the review period, the values of Z and P are unchanged. If, however, X_t spare parts are needed at time t, the revised estimates for Z and P are given by the smoothing formulas

$$Z_{t+1} = \alpha X_{t+1} + (1 - \alpha)Z_t$$
$$P_{t+1} = \beta G_{t+1} + (1 - \beta)P_t$$

where:

X_t = Actual value of demand at time t

Z_t = Forecasted value of demand at time t

G_t = Actual time between previous demand and this demand

P_t = Forecasted value of time between previous demand and this demand

α, β = Smoothing factors between 0 and 1

Then, the forecast value for number of parts required per period for the next period would be:

$$R_{t+2} = \frac{Z_{t+1}}{P_{t+1}}$$

EXAMPLE 13.6

Assume time periods of one week are used, and the spare parts requirement for the first week was 23 items. Assume further that $\alpha = 0.2$ and $\beta = 0.3$, and that the actual requirement for the second week was 0 parts, and the actual requirement for the third week was 16 parts. The forecasted spare parts requirement for the fourth week would be calculated as follows:

$$Z_3 = 0.2(16) + 0.8(23) = 21.6$$

$$P_3 = 0.3(2) + 0.7(1) = 1.3$$

$$R_4 = \frac{21.6}{1.3} = 16.6$$

Planning

Repairable systems are systems that can be restored to service following a failure. The actions to restore a system to service following a failure are *corrective maintenance* actions. Most repairable systems can also have prescribed maintenance actions to keep the system in operating condition as well as reduce the probability of a failure due to wear-out. These actions are *preventive maintenance* actions.

Preventive maintenance (PM) includes all the actions performed to keep the system in an operating state by preventing wear-out failures. Preventive maintenance does not reduce the constant failure rate that is inherent to the system but tends to maintain the system at that level of failure probability. Preventive maintenance actions can be planned and, if possible, be performed when there is no demand to use the system.

Corrective maintenance (CM) includes all the actions required to return the system to an operating state once failure has occurred. Corrective maintenance actions cannot be planned and must be performed when the system fails. Corrective maintenance actions may be deferred in some cases; however, the system is not operable until the corrective maintenance is completed.

Availability is a measure of the likelihood that a system will be ready to operate (system is up) when it is called on to operate. Reasons the system would not be ready to operate (system is down) include the possibility that a failure has occurred and the corrective action has not been completed. Also, a system may not be operable because preventive maintenance actions are necessary. There could also be other logistic reasons that the system is not operable. Availability is a function of the number of corrective maintenance actions necessary and the time required to complete these actions, as well as the amount of maintenance required and the time necessary to restore the unit to service.

Availability is a function of reliability and maintainability. *Reliability* deals with reducing the frequency of unscheduled downtime. *Maintainability* is the ability of an item to be retained in or restored to specified conditions when maintenance actions are necessary. Maintainability deals with reducing the duration of downtime. This downtime includes both scheduled and unscheduled actions. If the preventive maintenance actions can be planned and performed when there will be no demand to use the system, the time to perform these actions will not affect the availability. Availability can be perceived as uptime (the time the system is operable) divided by total time (the time during which there could be a demand to use the system).

The mean time required to bring a system back to an operable state after a failure is expressed as the mean time to repair (MTTR). This value is the mean of all corrective maintenance actions and includes the probability that the action is necessary and the time required to complete the action:

$$MTTR = \frac{\Sigma(\lambda_i t_i)}{\Sigma \lambda_i}$$

where:

λ_i = Failure rate (probability of occurrence) for the *i*th failure mode

t_i = Time to repair the system after the failure has occurred

The distribution usually used to model times to repair is the lognormal. Most repairs can be made in a time less than the mean.

A mean for preventive maintenance actions can be found by replacing the failure rate for each failure mode with the frequency of occurrence of each preventive maintenance action and the time to perform that maintenance action. The steady state or inherent availability of a system with a constant failure rate is

$$A = \frac{MTBF}{MTBF + MTTR}$$

In order to increase the availability of a system, the system reliability could be increased (increase *mean time between failures* [MTBF]), or the time to restore the system to service could be reduced (decrease MTTR).

The MTTR is the mean time to repair the system to service after a failure. In other forms of the availability relationship, MTBF is replaced with a term that expresses the mean time between system downtimes for any reason, and MTTR is replaced with a term that includes corrective maintenance, preventive maintenance, and logistic and administrative downtimes.

2. PREVENTIVE MAINTENANCE (PM) ANALYSIS

> Define and use PM tasks, optimum PM intervals, and other elements of this analysis. Identify situations when PM is not effective. (Apply)
>
> Body of Knowledge V.C.2

The goal of preventive maintenance is to optimize system reliability. Procedures must be established for preventive maintenance taking into consideration the failure rate pattern of the system or its various subsystems. Cost savings can be realized if preventive maintenance (replacement) is performed on systems with increasing failure rates. A preventive maintenance action can also be advantageous for a unit with a constant failure rate if that failure rate will begin to increase if the maintenance is not performed. For example, if a unit in its useful life phase is not lubricated periodically, the failure rate could increase due to excessive wear. If the preventive maintenance action is to replace a working unit, this would only be advantageous if the unit is nearing the end of its useful life or entering wear-out.

It is possible that the maintenance action could induce a failure, causing a negative impact on the reliability of the system. An optimum maintenance interval can be determined by considering the cost of performing the maintenance, the cost of a failure if the maintenance is not performed, and the cost associated with system downtime. If the interval is too short, the maintenance costs increase. If the interval is too long, the costs due to failure increase.

The cost due to system downtime can be minimized if preventive maintenance can be scheduled when there will be no demand to use the system. Downtime can also be reduced if scheduling will allow multiple maintenance actions to be performed once the system is taken off-line.

It is possible that the preventive maintenance action will consist of replacing a unit before failure can occur. O'Connor (2002) lists the following as necessary to determining the optimum replacement time:

1. The time-to-failure distribution and the parameters of that distribution.

2. The effect on the system of the failure.

3. The cost of the failure. This includes the cost of downtime because of the failure and any cost incurred due to safety considerations because of the failure.

4. The cost of the scheduled maintenance, including the cost of the replaced unit.

5. The effect that scheduled maintenance has on reliability. Will the maintenance activity introduce failures into the system?

6. Is the potential failure detectable by an operator? Can the operator take corrective action before the failure propagates throughout the system, causing other failures?

7. The cost of inspection and testing.

3. CORRECTIVE MAINTENANCE ANALYSIS

> Describe and apply the elements of corrective
> maintenance analysis (e.g., fault-isolation time,
> repair/replace time, skill level, and crew hours).
> (Apply)
>
> Body of Knowledge V.C.3

Corrective maintenance is performed in the event of a failure or malfunction of the system. The corrective maintenance actions cannot be planned, as the time the system will fail is not known. The goal is to return the system to an operable state while incurring a minimum amount of downtime. The total downtime includes both active maintenance time and inactive or delay time. The active corrective maintenance time can be analyzed as seven steps (MIL-HDBK-472). This active corrective maintenance time can be quantified as time to repair. A value referred to as the mean time to repair (MTTR) can be determined using the probability that the repair will be necessary and the average time required to perform that repair.

The seven steps are:

1. *Localization.* Determining the system fault without using test equipment.

2. *Isolation.* Verification of the system fault using test equipment.

3. *Disassembly.* Accessing the fault.

4. *Interchange.* Replacing or repairing the fault.

5. *Reassembly.* Rebuilding the item.

6. *Alignment.* Adjusting the item per specifications.

7. *Checkout.* Performing standard quality assurance (QA) checks to verify correct operation.

In order to minimize the repair time, it is necessary to minimize the time required for each step. The time to work on reducing maintenance time is during the design phase of product development. The MTTR for each failure could be found.

A designer would not intentionally design an automotive system in such a way that it was necessary to remove the engine in order to replace a broken fan belt. However, unless there is active maintainability engineering input at the design stage, such absurdities can be sent to the customer. Good design practice would dictate that repairs with long MTTR values will rarely be necessary.

The task of isolating faults in complex systems, especially systems that are computer controlled, can be difficult and time-consuming. Computer-controlled automotive engines, flight control systems, electronic-controlled weapons systems, and many other complex systems can be designed to include *built-in testing* (BIT). The design could include test ports to connect diagnostic testing equipment to the system, or have indicators to display the probable fault. Built-in testing can increase the availability of the system by reducing the time to locate and isolate the fault so that the process of restoring the system to service can begin earlier.

Failure of the built-in test system can negatively impact reliability. The BIT system in many cases consists of additional hardware. The probability of failure can increase as additional complexity is designed and built into the system.

Improvement in reliability can be achieved if it is possible to use software to monitor the system and report faults instead of using mechanical or electrical sensors. In order to minimize the total downtime, it is also necessary to minimize the inactive maintenance time. Inactive maintenance time includes the time waiting to obtain spare parts, tools, or test equipment; any delay in delivering the failed system to the repair facility; and administrative delay time.

Part VI
Appendices

Appendix A
ASQ Certified Reliability Engineer Body of Knowledge

The topics in this Body of Knowledge include additional detail in the form of sub-text explanations and the cognitive level at which the questions will be written. This information will provide useful guidance for both the Examination Development Committee and the candidates preparing to take the exam. The subtext is not intended to limit the subject matter or be all-inclusive of what might be covered in an exam. It is intended to clarify the type of content to be included in the exam. The descriptor in parentheses at the end of each entry refers to the highest cognitive level at which the topic will be tested. A more comprehensive description of cognitive levels is provided at the end of this document.

I. Reliability Fundamentals (25 questions)

A. Leadership Foundations

1. Benefits of reliability engineering

   Describe the value that reliability has on achieving company goals and objectives, and how reliability engineering techniques and methods improve programs, processes, products, systems, and services. (Understand)

2. Interrelationship of safety, quality, and reliability

   Describe the relationship of and distinguish between reliability and quality, and describe the importance of safety in reliability engineering and how reliability impacts safety. (Understand)

3. Reliability engineer leadership responsibilities

   Describe how to be a reliability champion by influencing program decisions and facilitating cross functional communication. (Understand)

4. Reliability engineer role and responsibilities in the product lifecycle

   Describe how the reliability engineer influences the product lifecycle, and describe a reliability engineer's role in the design review process in order to anticipate how reliability can impact risk and costs, and ensure performance over time. (Understand)

5. Function of reliability in engineering

   Describe how reliability techniques can be used to apply best practices in engineering (e.g., measuring reliability early), how industry standards can impact reliability, and how reliability can inform the decision analysis process. (Analyze)

6. Ethics in reliability engineering

   Identify appropriate ethical behaviors for a reliability engineer in various situations. (Evaluate)

7. Supplier reliability assessments

   Explain how supplier reliability impacts the overall reliability program and describe key reliability concepts that should be included in supplier reliability assessments. (Analyze)

8. Performance monitoring

   Describe the importance of performance monitoring to ensure that product reliability or safety requirements continue to be met, and identify lifecycle points in which process and product reliability data are collected and evaluated. (Understand)

B. Reliability Foundations

1. Basic reliability terminology

   Explain basic terms related to reliability and the associated metrics (e.g., MTTF, MTBF, MTTR, service interval, maintainability, availability, failure rate, reliability, and bathtub curve). (Apply)

2. Drivers of reliability requirements and targets

   Describe how customer expectations and industry standards, safety, liability, and regulatory concerns drive reliability requirements. (Understand)

3. Corrective and preventive action (CAPA)

   Identify corrective and preventive actions to take in specific situations and evaluate their measures of effectiveness. (Evaluate)

4. Root cause analysis

   Describe root cause analysis, and use a root cause and failure analysis tool to determine the causes of degradation or failure. (Evaluate)

5. Product lifecycle engineering stages

   Describe the impact various lifecycle stages (concept/design, development/test, introduction, growth, maturity, decline) have on reliability, and the cost issues (product maintenance, life expectation, software defect phase containment, etc.) associated with those stages. (Understand)

6. Economics of product maintainability and availability

   Describe the cost tradeoffs associated with product maintainability strategies and availability. (Understand)

7. Cost of poor reliability

   Describe how poor reliability affects costs over the lifecycle. (Understand)

8. Quality triangle

   Describe the relationship between cost, time and quality with respect to reliability. (Understand)

9. Six sigma methodologies

   Describe how six sigma principles support reliability engineering. (Understand)

10. Systems engineering and integration

    Describe the role of reliability engineering within systems engineering, including the integration of components and their interfaces/interactions within the system. (Understand)

II. Risk Management (25 questions)

A. Identification

1. Risk management techniques

   Use risk management tools and processes to identify, document and track concerns. Identify and prioritize safety, economic, performance, and customer satisfaction concerns utilizing an appropriate risk management framework. (Analyze)

2. Types of risk

   Identify the various types of risks, including technical, scheduling, safety, and financial, and describe their relationship to reliability. (Analyze)

B. Analysis

1. Fault tree analysis (FTA)

   Use fault tree analysis (FTA) techniques to evaluate product or process failure. (Analyze)

2. Failure mode and effects analysis (FMEA)

   Define and distinguish between failure mode and effects analysis (FMEA) and failure mode, effects, and criticality analysis (FMECA) and apply these techniques to systems, products, processes, and designs. (Evaluate)

3. Common mode failure analysis

   Describe common mode failure (also known as common cause failure) and how it affects risk. (Understand)

4. Hazard analysis

   Describe how hazard analysis informs the development process, and how information obtained as a result of the hazard analysis is used by the reliability engineer. (Understand)

5. Risk matrix

   Describe how risk matrices are used in the assessment of risk in regard to likelihood and severity. (Understand)

6. System safety

Identify safety-related issues by analyzing customer feedback, design data, field data, and other information. Prioritize safety concerns, and identify steps that will minimize the improper use of equipment, products or processes. (Evaluate)

C. **Mitigation**

Identify appropriate risk mitigation (treatment) plans to include controls that will minimize risk and subsequent impact in terms of safety, liability, and regulatory compliance. (Evaluate)

III. **Probability and Statistics for Reliability (35 questions)**

A. **Basic Concepts**

1. Basic statistics

Define various basic statistical terms (e.g., population, parameter, statistic, sample, the central limit theorem, parametric and non-parametric), and compute and interpret their values. (Analyze)

2. Basic probability concepts

Use basic probability concepts (e.g., independence, mutually exclusive, conditional probability), and compute and interpret the expected values. (Analyze)

3. Probability distributions

Compare and contrast various distributions (e.g., binomial, Poisson, exponential, Weibull, normal, and log-normal), and recognize their associated probability plots. (Analyze)

4. Probability functions

Compare and contrast various probability functions (e.g., cumulative distribution functions (CDFs), probability density functions (PDFs), and hazard functions), and recognize their application in various situations. (Apply)

5. Sampling plans for statistics and reliability testing

Use various theories, tables, and formulas to determine appropriate sample sizes or testing time for statistical and reliability testing. (Apply)

6. Statistical process control (SPC) and process capability studies (C_p, C_{pk})

Define and describe SPC and process capability studies (C_p, C_{pk}, etc.), control charts, and how each is related to reliability. (Understand)

7. Confidence and tolerance intervals

Compute confidence intervals and tolerance intervals, draw conclusions from the results, and describe how point estimates are used to determine the interval. (Evaluate)

B. Data Management

1. Sources and uses of reliability data

   Describe sources of reliability data (prototype, development, test, field, warranty, published, etc.), their advantages and limitations, and how the data can be used to measure and enhance product reliability. (Analyze)

2. Types of data

   Identify and distinguish between various types of data (e.g., attributes vs. variable, discrete vs. continuous, censored vs. complete, and univariate vs. multivariate). Select appropriate analysis tools based on the data type. (Evaluate)

3. Data collection methods

   Identify and select appropriate data collection methods (e.g., surveys, automated tests, automated monitoring and reporting tools) in order to meet various data analysis objectives and data quality needs. (Evaluate)

4. Data summary and reporting

   Examine collected data for accuracy and usefulness. Analyze, interpret, and summarize data for presentation using various techniques, based on data types, sources, and required output. (Create)

5. Failure analysis methods

   Describe failure analysis tools and methods (e.g., mechanical, materials, physical analysis, and scanning electron microscopy (SEM)) that are used to identify failure mechanisms. (Understand)

6. Failure reporting, analysis, and corrective action system (FRACAS)

   Identify elements necessary for FRACAS, and demonstrate the importance of a closed-loop process. (Evaluate)

III. Reliability Planning, Testing, and Modeling (35 questions)

A. Planning

1. Reliability test strategies

   Develop and apply the appropriate test strategies (e.g., truncation, test-to-failure, degradation, growth plan, and test, analyze and fix (TAAF)) for various product development phases. (Evaluate)

2. Environmental and conditions of use factors

   Identify environmental and use factors (e.g., temperature, humidity, and vibration) and stresses (e.g., severity of service, electrostatic discharge (ESD), throughput, and duty cycle) to which a product may be subjected. (Analyze)

3. Failure consequence

   Describe the importance of identifying the consequences of failure modes when establishing reliability acceptance criteria. (Understand)

4. Failure criteria

Define and describe failure criteria based on system requirements and warranty terms and conditions. (Understand)

5. Test environment

Appraise the environment in terms of system location and operational conditions, and designate the environment in the test plan to ensure an appropriate test strategy is implemented. (Evaluate)

B. **Testing**

Describe the purpose, advantages, and limitations of each of the following types of tests, and use common models to develop test plans, evaluate risks, and interpret test results. (Evaluate)

1. Accelerated life tests (single-stress, multiple-stress, sequential stress, step-stress, HALT, margin tests)

2. Stress screening (ESS, HASS, burn-in tests)

3. Qualification/demonstration testing (sequential tests, fixed-length tests)

4. Degradation (wear-to-failure) testing

5. Software Testing (white-box, black-box, operational profile, and fault-injection)

C. **Modeling**

1. Reliability block diagrams and models

Generate and analyze various types of block diagrams and models, including series, parallel, partial redundancy, and time-dependent. (Evaluate)

2. Physics of failure and failure mechanisms

Identify various potential failure mechanisms (e.g., fracture, corrosion, memory corruption) and describe the physical process of these failures. (Apply)

3. Failure models

Select appropriate theoretical models (e.g., Arrhenius, S-N curve) to assess or predict failure rates. (Analyze)

4. Reliability prediction methods

Use various reliability prediction methods (e.g., Monte Carlo Simulation, part stress analysis, and parts count prediction) for both repairable and non-repairable components and systems, and describe the inputs into the model. (Apply)

5. Design prototyping

Describe the advantages and limitations of prototyping to enhance product reliability. (Understand)

IV. **Lifecycle Reliability (30 questions)**

A. **Reliability design techniques**

1. Design evaluation techniques (validation and verification)

   Explain how validation, verification, and other review techniques are used to assess the reliability of a product's design at various lifecycle stages. (Apply)

2. Stress-strength analysis

   Apply the stress-strength analysis method of calculating probability of failure, and interpret the results. (Analyze)

3. Design of experiments (DOE)

   Develop and interpret the results of a standard design of experiments (DOE) (e.g., full-factorial and fractional factorial). (Analyze)

4. Reliability optimization

   Use various approaches to optimize reliability within the constraints of cost, schedule, weight, and other design requirements. (Apply)

5. Human factors

   Describe the relationship between human factors and reliability engineering, including user safety, user and usage profiles, failure modes and mechanisms. (Understand)

6. Design for X (DFX)

   Apply DFX techniques such as design for manufacturability, testability, and maintainability. (Apply)

7. Design for Reliability

   Apply DfR in order to meet reliability requirements throughout the product or system lifecycle. Understand how built-in reliability and fault tolerance/avoidance are key goals for design for reliability. (Evaluate)

B. **Parts and systems development**

1. Materials and components selection techniques

   Apply techniques (e.g., derating and Commercial off-the-shelf (COTS)) for selecting materials and components to meet reliability goals and requirements. (Analyze)

2. Parts standardization and system simplification

   Describe the importance of standardization, simplification, and parts re-use to meet reliability goals and requirements. (Apply)

C. **Maintainability**

1. Maintenance strategies

   Develop a maintenance plan incorporating various strategies (e.g., predictive maintenance, repair or replace decision making, spare parts analysis/forecasting, and equipment warranties). (Apply)

2. Preventive maintenance (PM) analysis

   Define and use PM tasks, optimum PM intervals, and other elements of this analysis. Identify situations when PM is not effective. (Apply)

3. Corrective maintenance analysis

   Describe and apply the elements of corrective maintenance analysis (e.g., fault-isolation time, repair/replace time, skill level, and crew hours). (Apply)

LEVELS OF COGNITION BASED ON BLOOM'S TAXONOMY— REVISED (2001)

In addition to *content* specifics, the subtext for each topic in this BOK also indicates the intended *complexity level* of the test questions for that topic. These levels are based on "Levels of Cognition" (from Bloom's Taxonomy—Revised, 2001) and are presented below in rank order, from least complex to most complex.

Understand

Read and understand descriptions, communications, reports, tables, diagrams, directions, regulations, etc.

Apply

Know when and how to use ideas, procedures, methods, formulas, principles, theories, etc.

Analyze

Break down information into its constituent parts and recognize their relationship to one another and how they are organized; identify sublevel factors or salient data from a complex scenario.

Evaluate

Make judgments about the value of proposed ideas, solutions, etc., by comparing the proposal to specific criteria or standards.

Create

Put parts or elements together in such a way as to reveal a pattern or structure not clearly there before; identify which data or information from a complex set is appropriate to examine further or from which supported conclusions can be drawn.

Appendix A

Appendix B
ASQ Code of Ethics

FUNDAMENTAL PRINCIPLES

ASQ requires its members and certification holders to conduct themselves ethically by:

1. Being honest and impartial in serving the public, their employers, customers, and clients.

2. Striving to increase the competence and prestige of the quality profession, and

3. Using their knowledge and skill for the enhancement of human welfare.

Members and certification holders are required to observe the tenets set forth below.

RELATIONS WITH THE PUBLIC

Article 1—Hold paramount the safety, health, and welfare of the public in the performance of their professional duties.

RELATIONS WITH EMPLOYERS, CUSTOMERS, AND CLIENTS

Article 2—Perform services only in their areas of competence.

Article 3—Continue their professional development throughout their careers and provide opportunities for the professional and ethical development of others.

Article 4—Act in a professional manner in dealings with ASQ staff and each employer, customer or client.

Article 5—Act as faithful agents or trustees and avoid conflict of interest and the appearance of conflicts of interest.

RELATIONS WITH PEERS

Article 6—Build their professional reputation on the merit of their services and not compete unfairly with others.

Article 7—Assure that credit for the work of others is given to those to whom it is due.

Appendix C
Control Limit Formulas

VARIABLES CHARTS

$\bar{x}$ and R chart:

  Averages chart : $\bar{\bar{x}} \pm A_2 \bar{R}$ *Range chart* : $\text{LCL} = D_3 \bar{R}$ $\text{UCL} = D_4 \bar{R}$

$\bar{x}$ and s chart:

  Averages chart : $\bar{\bar{x}} \pm A_3 \bar{s}$ *Standard deviation chart* : $\text{LCL} = B_3 \bar{s}$ $\text{UCL} = B_4 \bar{s}$

Individuals and moving range chart (two-value moving window):

  Individuals chart : $\bar{x} \pm 2.66 \bar{R}$ *Moving range* : $\text{UCL} = 3.267 \bar{R}$

Moving average and moving range (two-value moving window):

  Moving average : $\bar{\bar{x}} \pm 1.88 \bar{R}$ *Moving range* : $\text{UCL} = 3.267 \bar{R}$

Median chart:

  Median chart : $\bar{x}' \pm A_2' \bar{R}$ *Range chart* : $\text{LCL} = D_3 \bar{R}$ $\text{UCL} = D_4 \bar{R}$

ATTRIBUTE CHARTS

p-chart: $\bar{p} \pm 3 \sqrt{\dfrac{\bar{p}(1-\bar{p})}{n}}$ c-chart: $\bar{c} \pm 3 \sqrt{\bar{c}}$

np-chart: $n\bar{p} \pm 3 \sqrt{n\bar{p}(1-\bar{p})}$ u-chart: $\bar{u} \pm 3 \sqrt{\dfrac{\bar{u}}{n}}$

Appendix D
Constants for Control Charts

Subgroup size										A_2 for median			
N	A_2	d_2	D_3	D_4	A_3	c_4	B_3	B_4	E_2	charts	A_4	D_5	D_6
2	1.880	1.128	–	3.267	2.659	0.798	–	3.267	2.660	1.880	2.224	–	3.865
3	1.023	1.693	–	2.574	1.954	0.886	–	2.568	1.772	1.187	1.091	–	2.745
4	0.729	2.059	–	2.282	1.628	0.921	–	2.266	1.457	0.796	0.758	–	2.375
5	0.577	2.326	–	2.114	1.427	0.940	–	2.089	1.290	0.691	0.594	–	2.179
6	0.483	2.534	–	2.004	1.287	0.952	0.030	1.970	1.184	0.548	0.495	–	2.055
7	0.419	2.704	0.076	1.924	1.182	0.959	0.118	1.882	1.109	0.508	0.429	0.078	1.967
8	0.373	2.847	0.136	1.864	1.099	0.965	0.185	1.815	1.054	0.433	0.380	0.139	1.901
9	0.337	2.970	0.184	1.816	1.032	0.969	0.239	1.761	1.010	0.412	0.343	0.187	1.850
10	0.308	3.078	0.223	1.777	0.975	0.973	0.284	1.716	0.975	0.362	0.314	0.227	1.809

Appendix E
Areas under Standard Normal Curve

z	0.00	0.01	0.02	0.03	0.04	0.05	0.06	0.07	0.08	0.09
0.0	0.5000	0.4960	0.4920	0.4880	0.4840	0.4801	0.4761	0.4721	0.4681	0.4641
0.1	0.4602	0.4562	0.4522	0.448	0.4443	0.4404	0.4364	0.4325	0.4286	0.4247
0.2	0.4207	0.4168	0.4129	0.4090	0.4051	0.4013	0.3974	0.3936	0.3897	0.3859
0.3	0.3821	0.3783	0.3745	0.3707	0.3669	0.3632	0.3594	0.3557	0.3520	0.3483
0.4	0.3446	0.3409	0.3372	0.3336	0.3300	0.3264	0.3228	0.3192	0.3156	0.3121
0.5	0.3085	0.3050	0.3015	0.2981	0.2946	0.2912	0.2877	0.2843	0.2810	0.2776
0.6	0.2743	0.2709	0.2676	0.2643	0.2611	0.2578	0.2546	0.2514	0.2483	0.2451
0.7	0.2420	0.2389	0.2358	0.2327	0.2296	0.2266	0.2236	0.2206	0.2177	0.2148
0.8	0.2119	0.2090	0.2061	0.2033	0.2005	0.1977	0.1949	0.1922	0.1894	0.1867
0.9	0.1841	0.1814	0.1788	0.1762	0.1736	0.1711	0.1685	0.1660	0.1635	0.1611
1.0	0.1587	0.1562	0.1539	0.1515	0.1492	0.1469	0.1446	0.1423	0.1401	0.1379
1.1	0.1357	0.1335	0.1314	0.1292	0.1271	0.1251	0.1230	0.1210	0.1190	0.1170
1.2	0.1151	0.1131	0.1112	0.1093	0.1075	0.1056	0.1038	0.1020	0.1003	0.0985
1.3	0.0968	0.0951	0.0934	0.0918	0.0901	0.0885	0.0869	0.0853	0.0838	0.0823
1.4	0.0808	0.0793	0.0778	0.0764	0.0749	0.0735	0.0721	0.0708	0.0694	0.0681
1.5	0.0668	0.0655	0.0643	0.0630	0.0618	0.0606	0.0594	0.0582	0.0571	0.0559
1.6	0.0548	0.0537	0.0526	0.0516	0.0505	0.0495	0.0485	0.0475	0.0465	0.0455
1.7	0.0446	0.0436	0.0427	0.0418	0.0409	0.0401	0.0392	0.0384	0.0375	0.0367
1.8	0.0359	0.0351	0.0344	0.0336	0.0329	0.0322	0.0314	0.0307	0.0300	0.0294
1.9	0.0287	0.0281	0.0274	0.0268	0.0262	0.0256	0.0250	0.0244	0.0239	0.0233
2.0	0.0228	0.0222	0.0217	0.0212	0.0207	0.0202	0.0197	0.0192	0.0188	0.0183
2.1	0.0179	0.0174	0.0170	0.0166	0.0162	0.0158	0.0152	0.0150	0.0146	0.0143
2.2	0.0139	0.0136	0.0132	0.0129	0.0125	0.0122	0.0119	0.0116	0.0113	0.0110
2.3	0.0107	0.0104	0.0102	0.0099	0.0096	0.0094	0.0091	0.0089	0.0087	0.0084
2.4	0.0082	0.0080	0.0078	0.0075	0.0073	0.0071	0.0069	0.0068	0.0066	0.0064
2.5	0.0062	0.0060	0.0059	0.0057	0.0055	0.0054	0.0052	0.0051	0.0049	0.0048
2.6	0.0047	0.0045	0.0044	0.0043	0.0041	0.0040	0.0039	0.0038	0.0037	0.0036
2.7	0.0035	0.0034	0.0033	0.0032	0.0031	0.0030	0.0029	0.0028	0.0027	0.0026
2.8	0.0026	0.0025	0.0024	0.0023	0.0023	0.0022	0.0021	0.0021	0.0020	0.0019
2.9	0.0019	0.0018	0.0018	0.0017	0.0016	0.0016	0.0015	0.0015	0.0014	0.0014

Continued

z	0.00	0.01	0.02	0.03	0.04	0.05	0.06	0.07	0.08	0.09
3.0	0.0013	0.0013	0.0013	0.0012	0.0012	0.0011	0.0011	0.0011	0.0010	0.0010
3.1	0.0010	0.0009	0.0009	0.0009	0.0008	0.0008	0.0008	0.0008	0.0007	0.0007
3.2	0.0007	0.0007	0.0006	0.0006	0.0006	0.0006	0.0006	0.0005	0.0005	0.0005
3.3	0.0005	0.0005	0.0005	0.0004	0.0004	0.0004	0.0004	0.0004	0.0004	0.0003
3.4	0.0003	0.0003	0.0003	0.0003	0.0003	0.0003	0.0003	0.0003	0.0003	0.0002
3.5	0.0002	0.0002	0.0002	0.0002	0.0002	0.0002	0.0002	0.0002	0.0002	0.0002
3.6	0.0002	0.0002	0.0001	0.0001	0.0001	0.0001	0.0001	0.0001	0.0001	0.0001
3.7	0.0001	0.0001	0.0001	0.0001	0.0001	0.0001	0.0001	0.0001	0.0001	0.0001
3.8	0.0001	0.0001	0.0001	0.0001	0.0001	0.0001	0.0001	0.0001	0.0001	0.0001

For $z \geq 3.90$, areas are 0.0000 correct to four places.

Appendix F
F Distribution $F_{0.1}$

F distribution $F_{0.1}$

	Numerator degrees of freedom										
	1	**2**	**3**	**4**	**5**	**6**	**7**	**8**	**9**	**10**	**11**
1	39.86	49.50	53.59	55.83	57.24	58.20	58.91	59.44	59.86	60.19	60.47
2	8.53	9.00	9.16	9.24	9.29	9.33	9.35	9.37	9.38	9.39	9.40
3	5.54	5.46	5.39	5.34	5.31	5.28	5.27	5.25	5.24	5.23	5.22
4	4.54	4.32	4.19	4.11	4.05	4.01	3.98	3.95	3.94	3.92	3.91
5	4.06	3.78	3.62	3.52	3.45	3.40	3.37	3.34	3.32	3.30	3.28
6	3.78	3.46	3.29	3.18	3.11	3.05	3.01	2.98	2.96	2.94	2.92
7	3.59	3.26	3.07	2.96	2.88	2.83	2.78	2.75	2.72	2.70	2.68
8	3.46	3.11	2.92	2.81	2.73	2.67	2.62	2.59	2.56	2.54	2.52
9	3.36	3.01	2.81	2.69	2.61	2.55	2.51	2.47	2.44	2.42	2.40
10	3.29	2.92	2.73	2.61	2.52	2.46	2.41	2.38	2.35	2.32	2.30
11	3.23	2.86	2.66	2.54	2.45	2.39	2.34	2.30	2.27	2.25	2.23
12	3.18	2.81	2.61	2.48	2.39	2.33	2.28	2.24	2.21	2.19	2.17
13	3.14	2.76	2.56	2.43	2.35	2.28	2.23	2.20	2.16	2.14	2.12
14	3.10	2.73	2.52	2.39	2.31	2.24	2.19	2.15	2.12	2.10	2.07
15	3.07	2.70	2.49	2.36	2.27	2.21	2.16	2.12	2.09	2.06	2.04
16	3.05	2.67	2.46	2.33	2.24	2.18	2.13	2.09	2.06	2.03	2.01
17	3.03	2.64	2.44	2.31	2.22	2.15	2.10	2.06	2.03	2.00	1.98
18	3.01	2.62	2.42	2.29	2.20	2.13	2.08	2.04	2.00	1.98	1.95
19	2.99	2.61	2.40	2.27	2.18	2.11	2.06	2.02	1.98	1.96	1.93
20	2.97	2.59	2.38	2.25	2.16	2.09	2.04	2.00	1.96	1.94	1.91
21	2.96	2.57	2.36	2.23	2.14	2.08	2.02	1.98	1.95	1.92	1.90
22	2.95	2.56	2.35	2.22	2.13	2.06	2.01	1.97	1.93	1.90	1.88
23	2.94	2.55	2.34	2.21	2.11	2.05	1.99	1.95	1.92	1.89	1.87
24	2.93	2.54	2.33	2.19	2.10	2.04	1.98	1.94	1.91	1.88	1.85
25	2.92	2.53	2.32	2.18	2.09	2.02	1.97	1.93	1.89	1.87	1.84
26	2.91	2.52	2.31	2.17	2.08	2.01	1.96	1.92	1.88	1.86	1.83
27	2.90	2.51	2.30	2.17	2.07	2.00	1.95	1.91	1.87	1.85	1.82
28	2.89	2.50	2.29	2.16	2.06	2.00	1.94	1.90	1.87	1.84	1.81
29	2.89	2.50	2.28	2.15	2.06	1.99	1.93	1.89	1.86	1.83	1.80
30	2.88	2.49	2.28	2.14	2.05	1.98	1.93	1.88	1.85	1.82	1.79
40	2.84	2.44	2.23	2.09	2.00	1.93	1.87	1.83	1.79	1.76	1.74
60	2.79	2.39	2.18	2.04	1.95	1.87	1.82	1.77	1.74	1.71	1.68
100	2.76	2.36	2.14	2.00	1.91	1.83	1.78	1.73	1.69	1.66	1.64
150	2.74	2.34	2.12	1.98	1.89	1.81	1.76	1.71	1.67	1.64	1.61
200	2.73	2.33	2.11	1.97	1.88	1.80	1.75	1.70	1.66	1.63	1.60

Denominator degrees of freedom

Continued

Appendix F

F distribution *$F_{0.1}$* *(continued)*

		Numerator degrees of freedom										
		12	13	14	15	16	17	18	19	20	21	22
Denominator degrees of freedom	1	60.71	60.90	61.07	61.22	61.35	61.46	61.57	61.66	61.74	61.81	61.88
	2	9.41	9.41	9.42	9.42	9.43	9.43	9.44	9.44	9.44	9.44	9.45
	3	5.22	5.21	5.20	5.20	5.20	5.19	5.19	5.19	5.18	5.18	5.18
	4	3.90	3.89	3.88	3.87	3.86	3.86	3.85	3.85	3.84	3.84	3.84
	5	3.27	3.26	3.25	3.24	3.23	3.22	3.22	3.21	3.21	3.20	3.20
	6	2.90	2.89	2.88	2.87	2.86	2.85	2.85	2.84	2.84	2.83	2.83
	7	2.67	2.65	2.64	2.63	2.62	2.61	2.61	2.60	2.59	2.59	2.58
	8	2.50	2.49	2.48	2.46	2.45	2.45	2.44	2.43	2.42	2.42	2.41
	9	2.38	2.36	2.35	2.34	2.33	2.32	2.31	2.30	2.30	2.29	2.29
	10	2.28	2.27	2.26	2.24	2.23	2.22	2.22	2.21	2.20	2.19	2.19
	11	2.21	2.19	2.18	2.17	2.16	2.15	2.14	2.13	2.12	2.12	2.11
	12	2.15	2.13	2.12	2.10	2.09	2.08	2.08	2.07	2.06	2.05	2.05
	13	2.10	2.08	2.07	2.05	2.04	2.03	2.02	2.01	2.01	2.00	1.99
	14	2.05	2.04	2.02	2.01	2.00	1.99	1.98	1.97	1.96	1.96	1.95
	15	2.02	2.00	1.99	1.97	1.96	1.95	1.94	1.93	1.92	1.92	1.91
	16	1.99	1.97	1.95	1.94	1.93	1.92	1.91	1.90	1.89	1.88	1.88
	17	1.96	1.94	1.93	1.91	1.90	1.89	1.88	1.87	1.86	1.86	1.85
	18	1.93	1.92	1.90	1.89	1.87	1.86	1.85	1.84	1.84	1.83	1.82
	19	1.91	1.89	1.88	1.86	1.85	1.84	1.83	1.82	1.81	1.81	1.80
	20	1.89	1.87	1.86	1.84	1.83	1.82	1.81	1.80	1.79	1.79	1.78
	21	1.87	1.86	1.84	1.83	1.81	1.80	1.79	1.78	1.78	1.77	1.76
	22	1.86	1.84	1.83	1.81	1.80	1.79	1.78	1.77	1.76	1.75	1.74
	23	1.84	1.83	1.81	1.80	1.78	1.77	1.76	1.75	1.74	1.74	1.73
	24	1.83	1.81	1.80	1.78	1.77	1.76	1.75	1.74	1.73	1.72	1.71
	25	1.82	1.80	1.79	1.77	1.76	1.75	1.74	1.73	1.72	1.71	1.70
	26	1.81	1.79	1.77	1.76	1.75	1.73	1.72	1.71	1.71	1.70	1.69
	27	1.80	1.78	1.76	1.75	1.74	1.72	1.71	1.70	1.70	1.69	1.68
	28	1.79	1.77	1.75	1.74	1.73	1.71	1.70	1.69	1.69	1.68	1.67
	29	1.78	1.76	1.75	1.73	1.72	1.71	1.69	1.68	1.68	1.67	1.66
	30	1.77	1.75	1.74	1.72	1.71	1.70	1.69	1.68	1.67	1.66	1.65
	40	1.71	1.70	1.68	1.66	1.65	1.64	1.62	1.61	1.61	1.60	1.59
	60	1.66	1.64	1.62	1.60	1.59	1.58	1.56	1.55	1.54	1.53	1.53
	100	1.61	1.59	1.57	1.56	1.54	1.53	1.52	1.50	1.49	1.48	1.48
	150	1.59	1.57	1.55	1.53	1.52	1.50	1.49	1.48	1.47	1.46	1.45
	200	1.58	1.56	1.54	1.52	1.51	1.49	1.48	1.47	1.46	1.45	1.44

Continued

F distribution $F_{0.1}$ *(continued)*

	23	24	25	26	27	28	29	30	40	60	100
1	61.94	62.00	62.05	62.10	62.15	62.19	62.23	62.26	62.53	62.79	63.01
2	9.45	9.45	9.45	9.45	9.45	9.46	9.46	9.46	9.47	9.47	9.48
3	5.18	5.18	5.17	5.17	5.17	5.17	5.17	5.17	5.16	5.15	5.14
4	3.83	3.83	3.83	3.83	3.82	3.82	3.82	3.82	3.80	3.79	3.78
5	3.19	3.19	3.19	3.18	3.18	3.18	3.18	3.17	3.16	3.14	3.13
6	2.82	2.82	2.81	2.81	2.81	2.81	2.80	2.80	2.78	2.76	2.75
7	2.58	2.58	2.57	2.57	2.56	2.56	2.56	2.56	2.54	2.51	2.50
8	2.41	2.40	2.40	2.40	2.39	2.39	2.39	2.38	2.36	2.34	2.32
9	2.28	2.28	2.27	2.27	2.26	2.26	2.26	2.25	2.23	2.21	2.19
10	2.18	2.18	2.17	2.17	2.17	2.16	2.16	2.16	2.13	2.11	2.09
11	2.11	2.10	2.10	2.09	2.09	2.08	2.08	2.08	2.05	2.03	2.01
12	2.04	2.04	2.03	2.03	2.02	2.02	2.01	2.01	1.99	1.96	1.94
13	1.99	1.98	1.98	1.97	1.97	1.96	1.96	1.96	1.93	1.90	1.88
14	1.94	1.94	1.93	1.93	1.92	1.92	1.92	1.91	1.89	1.86	1.83
15	1.90	1.90	1.89	1.89	1.88	1.88	1.88	1.87	1.85	1.82	1.79
16	1.87	1.87	1.86	1.86	1.85	1.85	1.84	1.84	1.81	1.78	1.76
17	1.84	1.84	1.83	1.83	1.82	1.82	1.81	1.81	1.78	1.75	1.73
18	1.82	1.81	1.80	1.80	1.80	1.79	1.79	1.78	1.75	1.72	1.70
19	1.79	1.79	1.78	1.78	1.77	1.77	1.76	1.76	1.73	1.70	1.67
20	1.77	1.77	1.76	1.76	1.75	1.75	1.74	1.74	1.71	1.68	1.65
21	1.75	1.75	1.74	1.74	1.73	1.73	1.72	1.72	1.69	1.66	1.63
22	1.74	1.73	1.73	1.72	1.72	1.71	1.71	1.70	1.67	1.64	1.61
23	1.72	1.72	1.71	1.70	1.70	1.69	1.69	1.69	1.66	1.62	1.59
24	1.71	1.70	1.70	1.69	1.69	1.68	1.68	1.67	1.64	1.61	1.58
25	1.70	1.69	1.68	1.68	1.67	1.67	1.66	1.66	1.63	1.59	1.56
26	1.68	1.68	1.67	1.67	1.66	1.66	1.65	1.65	1.61	1.58	1.55
27	1.67	1.67	1.66	1.65	1.65	1.64	1.64	1.64	1.60	1.57	1.54
28	1.66	1.66	1.65	1.64	1.64	1.63	1.63	1.63	1.59	1.56	1.53
29	1.65	1.65	1.64	1.63	1.63	1.62	1.62	1.62	1.58	1.55	1.52
30	1.64	1.64	1.63	1.63	1.62	1.62	1.61	1.61	1.57	1.54	1.51
40	1.58	1.57	1.57	1.56	1.56	1.55	1.55	1.54	1.51	1.47	1.43
60	1.52	1.51	1.50	1.50	1.49	1.49	1.48	1.48	1.44	1.40	1.36
100	1.47	1.46	1.45	1.45	1.44	1.43	1.43	1.42	1.38	1.34	1.29
150	1.44	1.43	1.43	1.42	1.41	1.41	1.40	1.40	1.35	1.30	1.26
200	1.43	1.42	1.41	1.41	1.40	1.39	1.39	1.38	1.34	1.29	1.24

Numerator degrees of freedom

Denominator degrees of freedom

Appendix F

Appendix G
F Distribution $F_{0.05}$

Appendix G

F distribution $F_{0.05}$

	Numerator degrees of freedom										
	1	**2**	**3**	**4**	**5**	**6**	**7**	**8**	**9**	**10**	**11**
1	161.4	199.5	215.7	224.6	230.2	234.0	236.8	238.9	240.5	241.9	243.0
2	18.51	19.00	19.16	19.25	19.30	19.33	19.35	19.37	19.38	19.40	19.40
3	10.13	9.55	9.28	9.12	9.01	8.94	8.89	8.85	8.81	8.79	8.76
4	7.71	6.94	6.59	6.39	6.26	6.16	6.09	6.04	6.00	5.96	5.94
5	6.61	5.79	5.41	5.19	5.05	4.95	4.88	4.82	4.77	4.74	4.70
6	5.99	5.14	4.76	4.53	4.39	4.28	4.21	4.15	4.10	4.06	4.03
7	5.59	4.74	4.35	4.12	3.97	3.87	3.79	3.73	3.68	3.64	3.60
8	5.32	4.46	4.07	3.84	3.69	3.58	3.50	3.44	3.39	3.35	3.31
9	5.12	4.26	3.86	3.63	3.48	3.37	3.29	3.23	3.18	3.14	3.10
10	4.96	4.10	3.71	3.48	3.33	3.22	3.14	3.07	3.02	2.98	2.94
11	4.84	3.98	3.59	3.36	3.20	3.09	3.01	2.95	2.90	2.85	2.82
12	4.75	3.89	3.49	3.26	3.11	3.00	2.91	2.85	2.80	2.75	2.72
13	4.67	3.81	3.41	3.18	3.03	2.92	2.83	2.77	2.71	2.67	2.63
14	4.60	3.74	3.34	3.11	2.96	2.85	2.76	2.70	2.65	2.60	2.57
15	4.54	3.68	3.29	3.06	2.90	2.79	2.71	2.64	2.59	2.54	2.51
16	4.49	3.63	3.24	3.01	2.85	2.74	2.66	2.59	2.54	2.49	2.46
17	4.45	3.59	3.20	2.96	2.81	2.70	2.61	2.55	2.49	2.45	2.41
18	4.41	3.55	3.16	2.93	2.77	2.66	2.58	2.51	2.46	2.41	2.37
19	4.38	3.52	3.13	2.90	2.74	2.63	2.54	2.48	2.42	2.38	2.34
20	4.35	3.49	3.10	2.87	2.71	2.60	2.51	2.45	2.39	2.35	2.31
21	4.32	3.47	3.07	2.84	2.68	2.57	2.49	2.42	2.37	2.32	2.28
22	4.30	3.44	3.05	2.82	2.66	2.55	2.46	2.40	2.34	2.30	2.26
23	4.28	3.42	3.03	2.80	2.64	2.53	2.44	2.37	2.32	2.27	2.24
24	4.26	3.40	3.01	2.78	2.62	2.51	2.42	2.36	2.30	2.25	2.22
25	4.24	3.39	2.99	2.76	2.60	2.49	2.40	2.34	2.28	2.24	2.20
26	4.23	3.37	2.98	2.74	2.59	2.47	2.39	2.32	2.27	2.22	2.18
27	4.21	3.35	2.96	2.73	2.57	2.46	2.37	2.31	2.25	2.20	2.17
28	4.20	3.34	2.95	2.71	2.56	2.45	2.36	2.29	2.24	2.19	2.15
29	4.18	3.33	2.93	2.70	2.55	2.43	2.35	2.28	2.22	2.18	2.14
30	4.17	3.32	2.92	2.69	2.53	2.42	2.33	2.27	2.21	2.16	2.13
40	4.08	3.23	2.84	2.61	2.45	2.34	2.25	2.18	2.12	2.08	2.04
60	4.00	3.15	2.76	2.53	2.37	2.25	2.17	2.10	2.04	1.99	1.95
100	3.94	3.09	2.70	2.46	2.31	2.19	2.10	2.03	1.97	1.93	1.89

Continued

F distribution $F_{0.05}$ *(continued)*

		Numerator degrees of freedom										
		12	13	14	15	16	17	18	19	20	21	22
	1	243.9	244.7	245.4	245.9	246.5	246.9	247.3	247.7	248.0	248.3	248.6
	2	19.41	19.42	19.42	19.43	19.43	19.44	19.44	19.44	19.45	19.45	19.45
	3	8.74	8.73	8.71	8.70	8.69	8.68	8.67	8.67	8.66	8.65	8.65
	4	5.91	5.89	5.87	5.86	5.84	5.83	5.82	5.81	5.80	5.79	5.79
	5	4.68	4.66	4.64	4.62	4.60	4.59	4.58	4.57	4.56	4.55	4.54
	6	4.00	3.98	3.96	3.94	3.92	3.91	3.90	3.88	3.87	3.86	3.86
	7	3.57	3.55	3.53	3.51	3.49	3.48	3.47	3.46	3.44	3.43	3.43
	8	3.28	3.26	3.24	3.22	3.20	3.19	3.17	3.16	3.15	3.14	3.13
	9	3.07	3.05	3.03	3.01	2.99	2.97	2.96	2.95	2.94	2.93	2.92
	10	2.91	2.89	2.86	2.85	2.83	2.81	2.80	2.79	2.77	2.76	2.75
	11	2.79	2.76	2.74	2.72	2.70	2.69	2.67	2.66	2.65	2.64	2.63
Denominator degrees of freedom	12	2.69	2.66	2.64	2.62	2.60	2.58	2.57	2.56	2.54	2.53	2.52
	13	2.60	2.58	2.55	2.53	2.51	2.50	2.48	2.47	2.46	2.45	2.44
	14	2.53	2.51	2.48	2.46	2.44	2.43	2.41	2.40	2.39	2.38	2.37
	15	2.48	2.45	2.42	2.40	2.38	2.37	2.35	2.34	2.33	2.32	2.31
	16	2.42	2.40	2.37	2.35	2.33	2.32	2.30	2.29	2.28	2.26	2.25
	17	2.38	2.35	2.33	2.31	2.29	2.27	2.26	2.24	2.23	2.22	2.21
	18	2.34	2.31	2.29	2.27	2.25	2.23	2.22	2.20	2.19	2.18	2.17
	19	2.31	2.28	2.26	2.23	2.21	2.20	2.18	2.17	2.16	2.14	2.13
	20	2.28	2.25	2.22	2.20	2.18	2.17	2.15	2.14	2.12	2.11	2.10
	21	2.25	2.22	2.20	2.18	2.16	2.14	2.12	2.11	2.10	2.08	2.07
	22	2.23	2.20	2.17	2.15	2.13	2.11	2.10	2.08	2.07	2.06	2.05
	23	2.20	2.18	2.15	2.13	2.11	2.09	2.08	2.06	2.05	2.04	2.02
	24	2.18	2.15	2.13	2.11	2.09	2.07	2.05	2.04	2.03	2.01	2.00
	25	2.16	2.14	2.11	2.09	2.07	2.05	2.04	2.02	2.01	2.00	1.98
	26	2.15	2.12	2.09	2.07	2.05	2.03	2.02	2.00	1.99	1.98	1.97
	27	2.13	2.10	2.08	2.06	2.04	2.02	2.00	1.99	1.97	1.96	1.95
	28	2.12	2.09	2.06	2.04	2.02	2.00	1.99	1.97	1.96	1.95	1.93
	29	2.10	2.08	2.05	2.03	2.01	1.99	1.97	1.96	1.94	1.93	1.92
	30	2.09	2.06	2.04	2.01	1.99	1.98	1.96	1.95	1.93	1.92	1.91
	40	2.00	1.97	1.95	1.92	1.90	1.89	1.87	1.85	1.84	1.83	1.81
	60	1.92	1.89	1.86	1.84	1.82	1.80	1.78	1.76	1.75	1.73	1.72
	100	1.85	1.82	1.79	1.77	1.75	1.73	1.71	1.69	1.68	1.66	1.65

Continued

F distribution $F_{0.05}$ *(continued)*

					Numerator degrees of freedom						
	23	**24**	**25**	**26**	**27**	**28**	**29**	**30**	**40**	**60**	**100**
1	248.8	249.1	249.3	249.5	249.6	249.8	250.0	250.1	251.1	252.2	253.0
2	19.45	19.45	19.46	19.46	19.46	19.46	19.46	19.46	19.47	19.48	19.49
3	8.64	8.64	8.63	8.63	8.63	8.62	8.62	8.62	8.59	8.57	8.55
4	5.78	5.77	5.77	5.76	5.76	5.75	5.75	5.75	5.72	5.69	5.66
5	4.53	4.53	4.52	4.52	4.51	4.50	4.50	4.50	4.46	4.43	4.41
6	3.85	3.84	3.83	3.83	3.82	3.82	3.81	3.81	3.77	3.74	3.71
7	3.42	3.41	3.40	3.40	3.39	3.39	3.38	3.38	3.34	3.30	3.27
8	3.12	3.12	3.11	3.10	3.10	3.09	3.08	3.08	3.04	3.01	2.97
9	2.91	2.90	2.89	2.89	2.88	2.87	2.87	2.86	2.83	2.79	2.76
10	2.75	2.74	2.73	2.72	2.72	2.71	2.70	2.70	2.66	2.62	2.59
11	2.62	2.61	2.60	2.59	2.59	2.58	2.58	2.57	2.53	2.49	2.46
12	2.51	2.51	2.50	2.49	2.48	2.48	2.47	2.47	2.43	2.38	2.35
13	2.43	2.42	2.41	2.41	2.40	2.39	2.39	2.38	2.34	2.30	2.26
14	2.36	2.35	2.34	2.33	2.33	2.32	2.31	2.31	2.27	2.22	2.19
15	2.30	2.29	2.28	2.27	2.27	2.26	2.25	2.25	2.20	2.16	2.12
16	2.24	2.24	2.23	2.22	2.21	2.21	2.20	2.19	2.15	2.11	2.07
17	2.20	2.19	2.18	2.17	2.17	2.16	2.15	2.15	2.10	2.06	2.02
18	2.16	2.15	2.14	2.13	2.13	2.12	2.11	2.11	2.06	2.02	1.98
19	2.12	2.11	2.11	2.10	2.09	2.08	2.08	2.07	2.03	1.98	1.94
20	2.09	2.08	2.07	2.07	2.06	2.05	2.05	2.04	1.99	1.95	1.91
21	2.06	2.05	2.05	2.04	2.03	2.02	2.02	2.01	1.96	1.92	1.88
22	2.04	2.03	2.02	2.01	2.00	2.00	1.99	1.98	1.94	1.89	1.85
23	2.01	2.01	2.00	1.99	1.98	1.97	1.97	1.96	1.91	1.86	1.82
24	1.99	1.98	1.97	1.97	1.96	1.95	1.95	1.94	1.89	1.84	1.80
25	1.97	1.96	1.96	1.95	1.94	1.93	1.93	1.92	1.87	1.82	1.78
26	1.96	1.95	1.94	1.93	1.92	1.91	1.91	1.90	1.85	1.80	1.76
27	1.94	1.93	1.92	1.91	1.90	1.90	1.89	1.88	1.84	1.79	1.74
28	1.92	1.91	1.91	1.90	1.89	1.88	1.88	1.87	1.82	1.77	1.73
29	1.91	1.90	1.89	1.88	1.88	1.87	1.86	1.85	1.81	1.75	1.71
30	1.90	1.89	1.88	1.87	1.86	1.85	1.85	1.84	1.79	1.74	1.70
40	1.80	1.79	1.78	1.77	1.77	1.76	1.75	1.74	1.69	1.64	1.59
60	1.71	1.70	1.69	1.68	1.67	1.66	1.66	1.65	1.59	1.53	1.48
100	1.64	1.63	1.62	1.61	1.60	1.59	1.58	1.57	1.52	1.45	1.39

Denominator degrees of freedom

Appendix G

Appendix H
F Distribution $F_{0.01}$

F distribution $F_{0.01}$

						Numerator degrees of freedom					
	1	**2**	**3**	**4**	**5**	**6**	**7**	**8**	**9**	**10**	**11**
1	4052	4999	5404	5624	5764	5859	5928	5981	6022	6056	6083
2	98.5	99	99.16	99.25	99.3	99.33	99.36	99.38	99.39	99.4	99.41
3	34.12	30.82	29.46	28.71	28.24	27.91	27.67	27.49	27.34	27.23	27.13
4	21.2	18	16.69	15.98	15.52	15.21	14.98	14.8	14.66	14.55	14.45
5	16.26	13.27	12.06	11.39	10.97	10.67	10.46	10.29	10.16	10.05	9.963
6	13.75	10.92	9.78	9.148	8.746	8.466	8.26	8.102	7.976	7.874	7.79
7	12.25	9.547	8.451	7.847	7.46	7.191	6.993	6.84	6.719	6.62	6.538
8	11.26	8.649	7.591	7.006	6.632	6.371	6.178	6.029	5.911	5.814	5.734
9	10.56	8.022	6.992	6.422	6.057	5.802	5.613	5.467	5.351	5.257	5.178
10	10.04	7.559	6.552	5.994	5.636	5.386	5.2	5.057	4.942	4.849	4.772
11	9.646	7.206	6.217	5.668	5.316	5.069	4.886	4.744	4.632	4.539	4.462
12	9.33	6.927	5.953	5.412	5.064	4.821	4.64	4.499	4.388	4.296	4.22
13	9.074	6.701	5.739	5.205	4.862	4.62	4.441	4.302	4.191	4.1	4.025
14	8.862	6.515	5.564	5.035	4.695	4.456	4.278	4.14	4.03	3.939	3.864
15	8.683	6.359	5.417	4.893	4.556	4.318	4.142	4.004	3.895	3.805	3.73
16	8.531	6.226	5.292	4.773	4.437	4.202	4.026	3.89	3.78	3.691	3.616
17	8.4	6.112	5.185	4.669	4.336	4.101	3.927	3.791	3.682	3.593	3.518
18	8.285	6.013	5.092	4.579	4.248	4.015	3.841	3.705	3.597	3.508	3.434
19	8.185	5.926	5.01	4.5	4.171	3.939	3.765	3.631	3.523	3.434	3.36
20	8.096	5.849	4.938	4.431	4.103	3.871	3.699	3.564	3.457	3.368	3.294
21	8.017	5.78	4.874	4.369	4.042	3.812	3.64	3.506	3.398	3.31	3.236
22	7.945	5.719	4.817	4.313	3.988	3.758	3.587	3.453	3.346	3.258	3.184
23	7.881	5.664	4.765	4.264	3.939	3.71	3.539	3.406	3.299	3.211	3.137
24	7.823	5.614	4.718	4.218	3.895	3.667	3.496	3.363	3.256	3.168	3.094
25	7.77	5.568	4.675	4.177	3.855	3.627	3.457	3.324	3.217	3.129	3.056
26	7.721	5.526	4.637	4.14	3.818	3.591	3.421	3.288	3.182	3.094	3.021
27	7.677	5.488	4.601	4.106	3.785	3.558	3.388	3.256	3.149	3.062	2.988
28	7.636	5.453	4.568	4.074	3.754	3.528	3.358	3.226	3.12	3.032	2.959
29	7.598	5.42	4.538	4.045	3.725	3.499	3.33	3.198	3.092	3.005	2.931
30	7.562	5.39	4.51	4.018	3.699	3.473	3.305	3.173	3.067	2.979	2.906
40	7.314	5.178	4.313	3.828	3.514	3.291	3.124	2.993	2.888	2.801	2.727
60	7.077	4.977	4.126	3.649	3.339	3.119	2.953	2.823	2.718	2.632	2.559
100	6.895	4.824	3.984	3.513	3.206	2.988	2.823	2.694	2.59	2.503	2.43

Denominator degrees of freedom

Continued

F distribution $F_{0.01}$ *(continued)*

	Numerator degrees of freedom										
	12	**13**	**14**	**15**	**16**	**17**	**18**	**19**	**20**	**21**	**22**
1	6107	6126	6143	6157	6170	6181	6191	6201	6208.7	6216.1	6223.1
2	99.42	99.42	99.43	99.43	99.44	99.44	99.44	99.45	99.448	99.451	99.455
3	27.05	26.98	26.92	26.87	26.83	26.79	26.75	26.72	26.69	26.664	26.639
4	14.37	14.31	14.25	14.2	14.15	14.11	14.08	14.05	14.019	13.994	13.97
5	9.888	9.825	9.77	9.722	9.68	9.643	9.609	9.58	9.5527	9.5281	9.5058
6	7.718	7.657	7.605	7.559	7.519	7.483	7.451	7.422	7.3958	7.3721	7.3506
7	6.469	6.41	6.359	6.314	6.275	6.24	6.209	6.181	6.1555	6.1324	6.1113
8	5.667	5.609	5.559	5.515	5.477	5.442	5.412	5.384	5.3591	5.3365	5.3157
9	5.111	5.055	5.005	4.962	4.924	4.89	4.86	4.833	4.808	4.7855	4.7651
10	4.706	4.65	4.601	4.558	4.52	4.487	4.457	4.43	4.4054	4.3831	4.3628
11	4.397	4.342	4.293	4.251	4.213	4.18	4.15	4.123	4.099	4.0769	4.0566
12	4.155	4.1	4.052	4.01	3.972	3.939	3.91	3.883	3.8584	3.8363	3.8161
13	3.96	3.905	3.857	3.815	3.778	3.745	3.716	3.689	3.6646	3.6425	3.6223
14	3.8	3.745	3.698	3.656	3.619	3.586	3.556	3.529	3.5052	3.4832	3.463
15	3.666	3.612	3.564	3.522	3.485	3.452	3.423	3.396	3.3719	3.3498	3.3297
16	3.553	3.498	3.451	3.409	3.372	3.339	3.31	3.283	3.2587	3.2367	3.2165
17	3.455	3.401	3.353	3.312	3.275	3.242	3.212	3.186	3.1615	3.1394	3.1192
18	3.371	3.316	3.269	3.227	3.19	3.158	3.128	3.101	3.0771	3.055	3.0348
19	3.297	3.242	3.195	3.153	3.116	3.084	3.054	3.027	3.0031	2.981	2.9607
20	3.231	3.177	3.13	3.088	3.051	3.018	2.989	2.962	2.9377	2.9156	2.8953
21	3.173	3.119	3.072	3.03	2.993	2.96	2.931	2.904	2.8795	2.8574	2.837
22	3.121	3.067	3.019	2.978	2.941	2.908	2.879	2.852	2.8274	2.8052	2.7849
23	3.074	3.02	2.973	2.931	2.894	2.861	2.832	2.805	2.7805	2.7582	2.7378
24	3.032	2.977	2.93	2.889	2.852	2.819	2.789	2.762	2.738	2.7157	2.6953
25	2.993	2.939	2.892	2.85	2.813	2.78	2.751	2.724	2.6993	2.677	2.6565
26	2.958	2.904	2.857	2.815	2.778	2.745	2.715	2.688	2.664	2.6416	2.6211
27	2.926	2.872	2.824	2.783	2.746	2.713	2.683	2.656	2.6316	2.609	2.5886
28	2.896	2.842	2.795	2.753	2.716	2.683	2.653	2.626	2.6018	2.5793	2.5587
29	2.868	2.814	2.767	2.726	2.689	2.656	2.626	2.599	2.5742	2.5517	2.5311
30	2.843	2.789	2.742	2.7	2.663	2.63	2.6	2.573	2.5487	2.5262	2.5055
40	2.665	2.611	2.563	2.522	2.484	2.451	2.421	2.394	2.3689	2.3461	2.3252
60	2.496	2.442	2.394	2.352	2.315	2.281	2.251	2.223	2.1978	2.1747	2.1533
10	2.368	2.313	2.265	2.223	2.185	2.151	2.12	2.092	2.0666	2.0431	2.0214

Continued

F distribution $F_{0.01}$ (continued)

						Numerator degrees of freedom					
	23	**24**	**25**	**26**	**27**	**28**	**29**	**30**	**40**	**60**	**100**
1	6228.7	6234.3	6239.9	6244.5	6249.2	6252.9	6257.1	6260.4	6286.4	6313	6333.9
2	99.455	99.455	99.459	99.462	99.462	99.462	99.462	99.466	99.477	99.484	99.491
3	26.617	26.597	26.579	26.562	26.546	26.531	26.517	26.504	26.411	26.316	26.241
4	13.949	13.929	13.911	13.894	13.878	13.864	13.85	13.838	13.745	13.652	13.577
5	9.4853	9.4665	9.4492	9.4331	9.4183	9.4044	9.3914	9.3794	9.2912	9.202	9.13
6	7.3309	7.3128	7.296	7.2805	7.2661	7.2528	7.2403	7.2286	7.1432	7.0568	6.9867
7	6.092	6.0743	6.0579	6.0428	6.0287	6.0156	6.0035	5.992	5.9084	5.8236	5.7546
8	5.2967	5.2793	5.2631	5.2482	5.2344	5.2214	5.2094	5.1981	5.1156	5.0316	4.9633
9	4.7463	4.729	4.713	4.6982	4.6845	4.6717	4.6598	4.6486	4.5667	4.4831	4.415
10	4.3441	4.3269	4.3111	4.2963	4.2827	4.27	4.2582	4.2469	4.1653	4.0819	4.0137
11	4.038	4.0209	4.0051	3.9904	3.9768	3.9641	3.9522	3.9411	3.8596	3.7761	3.7077
12	3.7976	3.7805	3.7647	3.7501	3.7364	3.7238	3.7119	3.7008	3.6192	3.5355	3.4668
13	3.6038	3.5868	3.571	3.5563	3.5427	3.53	3.5182	3.507	3.4253	3.3413	3.2723
14	3.4445	3.4274	3.4116	3.3969	3.3833	3.3706	3.3587	3.3476	3.2657	3.1813	3.1118
15	3.3111	3.294	3.2782	3.2636	3.2499	3.2372	3.2253	3.2141	3.1319	3.0471	2.9772
16	3.1979	3.1808	3.165	3.1503	3.1366	3.1238	3.1119	3.1007	3.0182	2.933	2.8627
17	3.1006	3.0835	3.0676	3.0529	3.0392	3.0264	3.0145	3.0032	2.9204	2.8348	2.7639
18	3.0161	2.999	2.9831	2.9683	2.9546	2.9418	2.9298	2.9185	2.8354	2.7493	2.6779
19	2.9421	2.9249	2.9089	2.8942	2.8804	2.8675	2.8555	2.8442	2.7608	2.6742	2.6023
20	2.8766	2.8594	2.8434	2.8286	2.8148	2.8019	2.7898	2.7785	2.6947	2.6077	2.5353
21	2.8183	2.801	2.785	2.7702	2.7563	2.7434	2.7313	2.72	2.6359	2.5484	2.4755
22	2.7661	2.7488	2.7328	2.7179	2.704	2.691	2.6789	2.6675	2.5831	2.4951	2.4218
23	2.7191	2.7017	2.6857	2.6707	2.6568	2.6438	2.6316	2.6202	2.5355	2.4471	2.3732
24	2.6764	2.6591	2.643	2.628	2.614	2.601	2.5888	2.5773	2.4923	2.4035	2.3291
25	2.6377	2.6203	2.6041	2.5891	2.5751	2.562	2.5498	2.5383	2.453	2.3637	2.2888
26	2.6022	2.5848	2.5686	2.5535	2.5395	2.5264	2.5142	2.5026	2.417	2.3273	2.2519
27	2.5697	2.5522	2.536	2.5209	2.5069	2.4937	2.4814	2.4699	2.384	2.2938	2.218
28	2.5398	2.5223	2.506	2.4909	2.4768	2.4636	2.4513	2.4397	2.3535	2.2629	2.1867
29	2.5121	2.4946	2.4783	2.4631	2.449	2.4358	2.4234	2.4118	2.3253	2.2344	2.1577
30	2.4865	2.4689	2.4526	2.4374	2.4233	2.41	2.3976	2.386	2.2992	2.2079	2.1307
40	2.3059	2.288	2.2714	2.2559	2.2415	2.228	2.2153	2.2034	2.1142	2.0194	1.9383
60	2.1336	2.1154	2.0984	2.0825	2.0677	2.0538	2.0408	2.0285	1.936	1.8363	1.7493
100	2.0012	1.9826	1.9651	1.9489	1.9337	1.9194	1.9059	1.8933	1.7972	1.6918	1.5977

Denominator degrees of freedom

Appendix H

Appendix I
Chi-Square Distribution

Chi-square distribution

df	$\chi^2_{0.995}$	$\chi^2_{0.99}$	$\chi^2_{0.975}$	$\chi^2_{0.95}$	$\chi^2_{0.90}$	$\chi^2_{0.10}$	$\chi^2_{0.05}$	$\chi^2_{0.025}$	$\chi^2_{0.01}$	$\chi^2_{0.005}$
1	0.000	0.000	0.001	0.004	0.016	2.706	3.841	5.024	6.635	7.879
2	0.010	0.020	0.051	0.103	0.211	4.605	5.991	7.378	9.210	10.597
3	0.072	0.115	0.216	0.352	0.584	6.251	7.815	9.348	11.345	12.838
4	0.207	0.297	0.484	0.711	1.064	7.779	9.488	11.143	13.277	14.860
5	0.412	0.554	0.831	1.145	1.610	9.236	11.070	12.832	15.086	16.750
6	0.676	0.872	1.237	1.635	2.204	10.645	12.592	14.449	16.812	18.548
7	0.989	1.239	1.690	2.167	2.833	12.017	14.067	16.013	18.475	20.278
8	1.344	1.647	2.180	2.733	3.490	13.362	15.507	17.535	20.090	21.955
9	1.735	2.088	2.700	3.325	4.168	14.684	16.919	19.023	21.666	23.589
10	2.156	2.558	3.247	3.940	4.865	15.987	18.307	20.483	23.209	25.188
11	2.603	3.053	3.816	4.575	5.578	17.275	19.675	21.920	24.725	26.757
12	3.074	3.571	4.404	5.226	6.304	18.549	21.026	23.337	26.217	28.300
13	3.565	4.107	5.009	5.892	7.041	19.812	22.362	24.736	27.688	29.819
14	4.075	4.660	5.629	6.571	7.790	21.064	23.685	26.119	29.141	31.319
15	4.601	5.229	6.262	7.261	8.547	22.307	24.996	27.488	30.578	32.801
16	5.142	5.812	6.908	7.962	9.312	23.542	26.296	28.845	32.000	34.267
17	5.697	6.408	7.564	8.672	10.085	24.769	27.587	30.191	33.409	35.718
18	6.265	7.015	8.231	9.390	10.865	25.989	28.869	31.526	34.805	37.156
19	6.844	7.633	8.907	10.117	11.651	27.204	30.144	32.852	36.191	38.582
20	7.434	8.260	9.591	10.851	12.443	28.412	31.410	34.170	37.566	39.997
21	8.034	8.897	10.283	11.591	13.240	29.615	32.671	35.479	38.932	41.401
22	8.643	9.542	10.982	12.338	14.041	30.813	33.924	36.781	40.289	42.796
23	9.260	10.196	11.689	13.091	14.848	32.007	35.172	38.076	41.638	44.181
24	9.886	10.856	12.401	13.848	15.659	33.196	36.415	39.364	42.980	45.558
25	10.520	11.524	13.120	14.611	16.473	34.382	37.652	40.646	44.314	46.928
26	11.160	12.198	13.844	15.379	17.292	35.563	38.885	41.923	45.642	48.290
27	11.808	12.878	14.573	16.151	18.114	36.741	40.113	43.195	46.963	49.645
28	12.461	13.565	15.308	16.928	18.939	37.916	41.337	44.461	48.278	50.994

Continued

Chi-square distribution *(continued)*

df	$\chi^2_{0.995}$	$\chi^2_{0.99}$	$\chi^2_{0.975}$	$\chi^2_{0.95}$	$\chi^2_{0.90}$	$\chi^2_{0.10}$	$\chi^2_{0.05}$	$\chi^2_{0.025}$	$\chi^2_{0.01}$	$\chi^2_{0.005}$
29	13.121	14.256	16.047	17.708	19.768	39.087	42.557	45.722	49.588	52.335
30	13.787	14.953	16.791	18.493	20.599	40.256	43.773	46.979	50.892	53.672
31	14.458	15.655	17.539	19.281	21.434	41.422	44.985	48.232	52.191	55.002
32	15.134	16.362	18.291	20.072	22.271	42.585	46.194	49.480	53.486	56.328
33	15.815	17.073	19.047	20.867	23.110	43.745	47.400	50.725	54.775	57.648
34	16.501	17.789	19.806	21.664	23.952	44.903	48.602	51.966	56.061	58.964
35	17.192	18.509	20.569	22.465	24.797	46.059	49.802	53.203	57.342	60.275
40	20.707	22.164	24.433	26.509	29.051	51.805	55.758	59.342	63.691	66.766
45	24.311	25.901	28.366	30.612	33.350	57.505	61.656	65.410	69.957	73.166
50	27.991	29.707	32.357	34.764	37.689	63.167	67.505	71.420	76.154	79.490
55	31.735	33.571	36.398	38.958	42.060	68.796	73.311	77.380	82.292	85.749
60	35.534	37.485	40.482	43.188	46.459	74.397	79.082	83.298	88.379	91.952
65	39.383	41.444	44.603	47.450	50.883	79.973	84.821	89.177	94.422	98.105
70	43.275	45.442	48.758	51.739	55.329	85.527	90.531	95.023	100.425	104.215
75	47.206	49.475	52.942	56.054	59.795	91.061	96.217	100.839	106.393	110.285
80	51.172	53.540	57.153	60.391	64.278	96.578	101.879	106.629	112.329	116.321
85	55.170	57.634	61.389	64.749	68.777	102.079	107.522	112.393	118.236	122.324
90	59.196	61.754	65.647	69.126	73.291	107.565	113.145	118.136	124.116	128.299
95	63.250	65.898	69.925	73.520	77.818	113.038	118.752	123.858	129.973	134.247
100	67.328	70.065	74.222	77.929	82.358	118.498	124.342	129.561	135.807	140.170

Appendix I

Appendix J
Values of the *t* Distribution

Values of *t* distribution

ν	$t_{0.100}$	$t_{0.050}$	$t_{0.025}$	$t_{0.010}$	$t_{0.005}$	ν
1	3.078	6.314	12.706	31.821	63.656	1
2	1.886	2.920	4.303	6.965	9.925	2
3	1.638	2.353	3.182	4.541	5.841	3
4	1.533	2.132	2.776	3.747	4.604	4
5	1.476	2.015	2.571	3.365	4.032	5
6	1.440	1.943	2.447	3.143	3.707	6
7	1.415	1.895	2.365	2.998	3.499	7
8	1.397	1.860	2.306	2.896	3.355	8
9	1.383	1.833	2.262	2.821	3.250	9
10	1.372	1.812	2.228	2.764	3.169	10
11	1.363	1.796	2.201	2.718	3.106	11
12	1.356	1.782	2.179	2.681	3.055	12
13	1.350	1.771	2.160	2.650	3.012	13
14	1.345	1.761	2.145	2.624	2.977	14
15	1.341	1.753	2.131	2.602	2.947	15
16	1.337	1.746	2.120	2.583	2.921	16
17	1.333	1.740	2.110	2.567	2.898	17
18	1.330	1.734	2.101	2.552	2.878	18
19	1.328	1.729	2.093	2.539	2.861	19
20	1.325	1.725	2.086	2.528	2.845	20
21	1.323	1.721	2.080	2.518	2.831	21
22	1.321	1.717	2.074	2.508	2.819	22
23	1.319	1.714	2.069	2.500	2.807	23
24	1.318	1.711	2.064	2.492	2.797	24
25	1.316	1.708	2.060	2.485	2.787	25
26	1.315	1.706	2.056	2.479	2.779	26
27	1.314	1.703	2.052	2.473	2.771	27
28	1.313	1.701	2.048	2.467	2.763	28

Continued

Values of *t* distribution *(continued)*

ν	$t_{0.10}$	$t_{0.05}$	$t_{0.025}$	$t_{0.01}$	$t_{0.005}$	ν
29	1.311	1.699	2.045	2.462	2.756	29
30	1.310	1.697	2.042	2.457	2.750	30
31	1.309	1.696	2.040	2.453	2.744	31
32	1.309	1.694	2.037	2.449	2.738	32
33	1.308	1.692	2.035	2.445	2.733	33
34	1.307	1.691	2.032	2.441	2.728	34
35	1.306	1.690	2.030	2.438	2.724	35
40	1.303	1.684	2.021	2.423	2.704	40
45	1.301	1.679	2.014	2.412	2.690	45
50	1.299	1.676	2.009	2.403	2.678	50
55	1.297	1.673	2.004	2.396	2.668	55
60	1.296	1.671	2.000	2.390	2.660	60
70	1.294	1.667	1.994	2.381	2.648	70
80	1.292	1.664	1.990	2.374	2.639	80
90	1.291	1.662	1.987	2.368	2.632	90
100	1.290	1.660	1.984	2.364	2.626	100
200	1.286	1.653	1.972	2.345	2.601	200
400	1.284	1.649	1.966	2.336	2.588	400
600	1.283	1.647	1.964	2.333	2.584	600
800	1.283	1.647	1.963	2.331	2.582	800
999	1.282	1.646	1.962	2.330	2.581	999

Appendix J

Appendix K

Statistical Tolerance Factors for at Least 99% of the Population

("*k*-Values")

	One-sided tolerance Confidence level				Two-sided tolerance Confidence level		
n	0.90	0.95	0.99	*n*	0.90	0.95	0.99
10	3.532	3.981	5.075	10	3.959	4.433	5.594
11	3.444	3.852	4.828	11	3.849	4.277	5.308
12	3.371	3.747	4.633	12	3.758	4.150	5.079
13	3.310	3.659	4.472	13	3.682	4.044	4.893
14	3.257	3.585	4.336	14	3.618	3.955	4.737
15	3.212	3.520	4.224	15	3.562	3.878	4.605
16	3.172	3.463	4.124	16	3.514	3.812	4.492
17	3.136	3.415	4.038	17	3.471	3.754	4.393
18	3.106	3.370	3.961	18	3.433	3.702	4.307
19	3.078	3.331	3.893	19	3.399	3.656	4.230
20	3.052	3.295	3.832	20	3.368	3.615	4.161
21	3.028	3.262	3.776	21	3.340	3.577	4.100
22	3.007	3.233	3.727	22	3.315	3.543	4.044
23	2.987	3.206	3.680	23	3.292	3.512	3.993
24	2.969	3.181	3.638	24	3.270	3.483	3.947
25	2.952	3.158	3.601	25	3.251	3.457	3.904
30	2.884	3.064	3.446	30	3.170	3.350	3.733
40	2.793	2.941	3.250	40	3.066	3.213	3.518
50	2.735	2.863	3.124	50	3.001	3.126	3.385

Appendix L
Critical Values for the Mann-Whitney Test

Critical values for a one-tailed Mann-Whitney test with $\alpha = 0.05$ or a two-tailed test with $\alpha = 0.10$.

n_2 \ n_1	3 M_L	3 M_R	4 M_L	4 M_R	5 M_L	5 M_R	6 M_L	6 M_R	7 M_L	7 M_R	8 M_L	8 M_R	9 M_L	9 M_R	10 M_L	10 M_R
3	6	15														
4	7	17	12	24												
5	7	20	13	27	19	36										
6	8	22	14	30	20	40	28	50								
7	9	24	15	33	22	43	30	54	39	66						
8	9	27	16	36	24	46	32	58	41	71	52	84				
9	10	29	17	39	25	50	33	63	43	76	54	90	66	105		
10	11	31	18	42	26	54	35	67	46	80	57	95	69	111	83	127

Critical values for a one-tailed Mann-Whitney test with $\alpha = 0.025$ or a two-tailed test with $\alpha = 0.05$.

n_2 \ n_1	3 M_L	3 M_R	4 M_L	4 M_R	5 M_L	5 M_R	6 M_L	6 M_R	7 M_L	7 M_R	8 M_L	8 M_R	9 M_L	9 M_R	10 M_L	10 M_R
3	–	–														
4	6	18	11	25												
5	6	21	12	28	18	37										
6	7	23	12	32	19	41	26	52								
7	7	26	13	35	20	45	28	56	37	68						
8	8	28	14	38	21	49	29	61	39	73	49	87				
9	8	31	15	41	22	53	31	65	41	78	51	93	63	108		
10	9	33	16	44	24	56	32	70	43	83	54	98	66	114	79	131

Appendix M
Critical Values for
Wilcoxon Signed Rank Test

n	Approx. α value 1 tail	2 tail	Critical value W_l	W_r
7	0.01	0.02	0	28
	0.025	0.05	2	26
	0.05	0.1	4	24
	0.1	0.2	6	32
8	0.005	0.01	0	36
	0.01	0.02	2	34
	0.025	0.05	4	32
	0.05	0.1	6	30
	0.1	0.2	8	28
9	0.005	0.01	2	43
	0.01	0.02	3	42
	0.025	0.05	6	39
	0.05	0.1	8	37
	0.1	0.2	11	34
10	0.005	0.01	3	52
	0.01	0.02	5	50
	0.025	0.05	8	47
	0.05	0.1	11	44
	0.1	0.2	14	41
11	0.005	0.01	5	61
	0.01	0.02	7	59
	0.025	0.05	11	55
	0.05	0.1	14	52
	0.1	0.2	18	48
12	0.005	0.01	7	71
	0.01	0.02	10	68
	0.025	0.05	14	64
	0.05	0.1	17	61
	0.1	0.2	22	56
13	0.005	0.01	10	81
	0.01	0.02	13	78
	0.025	0.05	17	74
	0.05	0.1	21	70
	0.1	0.2	26	65

n	Approx. α value 1 tail	2 tail	Critical value W_l	W_r
14	0.005	0.01	13	92
	0.01	0.02	16	89
	0.025	0.05	21	84
	0.05	0.1	26	79
	0.1	0.2	31	74
15	0.005	0.01	16	104
	0.01	0.02	20	100
	0.025	0.05	25	95
	0.05	0.1	30	90
	0.1	0.2	37	83
16	0.005	0.01	19	117
	0.01	0.02	24	112
	0.025	0.05	30	106
	0.05	0.1	36	100
	0.1	0.2	42	94
17	0.005	0.01	23	130
	0.01	0.02	28	125
	0.025	0.05	35	118
	0.05	0.1	41	112
	0.1	0.2	49	104
18	0.005	0.01	28	143
	0.01	0.02	33	138
	0.025	0.05	40	131
	0.05	0.1	47	124
	0.1	0.2	55	116
19	0.005	0.01	32	158
	0.01	0.02	38	152
	0.025	0.05	46	144
	0.05	0.1	54	136
	0.1	0.2	62	128
20	0.005	0.01	37	173
	0.01	0.02	43	167
	0.025	0.05	52	158
	0.05	0.1	60	150
	0.1	0.2	70	140

Appendix N
Poisson Distribution

Probability of x or fewer occurrences of an event

Poisson distribution

$\lambda\downarrow x\rightarrow$	0	1	2	3	4	5	6	7	8	9	10	11	12	13	14	15	16	17
0.005	0.995	1.000	1.000	1.000	1.000	1.000	1.000	1.000	1.000	1.000	1.000	1.000	1.000	1.000	1.000	1.000	1.000	1.000
0.01	0.990	1.000	1.000	1.000	1.000	1.000	1.000	1.000	1.000	1.000	1.000	1.000	1.000	1.000	1.000	1.000	1.000	1.000
0.02	0.980	1.000	1.000	1.000	1.000	1.000	1.000	1.000	1.000	1.000	1.000	1.000	1.000	1.000	1.000	1.000	1.000	1.000
0.03	0.970	1.000	1.000	1.000	1.000	1.000	1.000	1.000	1.000	1.000	1.000	1.000	1.000	1.000	1.000	1.000	1.000	1.000
0.04	0.961	0.999	1.000	1.000	1.000	1.000	1.000	1.000	1.000	1.000	1.000	1.000	1.000	1.000	1.000	1.000	1.000	1.000
0.05	0.951	0.999	1.000	1.000	1.000	1.000	1.000	1.000	1.000	1.000	1.000	1.000	1.000	1.000	1.000	1.000	1.000	1.000
0.06	0.942	0.998	1.000	1.000	1.000	1.000	1.000	1.000	1.000	1.000	1.000	1.000	1.000	1.000	1.000	1.000	1.000	1.000
0.07	0.932	0.998	1.000	1.000	1.000	1.000	1.000	1.000	1.000	1.000	1.000	1.000	1.000	1.000	1.000	1.000	1.000	1.000
0.08	0.923	0.997	1.000	1.000	1.000	1.000	1.000	1.000	1.000	1.000	1.000	1.000	1.000	1.000	1.000	1.000	1.000	1.000
0.09	0.914	0.996	1.000	1.000	1.000	1.000	1.000	1.000	1.000	1.000	1.000	1.000	1.000	1.000	1.000	1.000	1.000	1.000
0.1	0.905	0.995	1.000	1.000	1.000	1.000	1.000	1.000	1.000	1.000	1.000	1.000	1.000	1.000	1.000	1.000	1.000	1.000
0.15	0.861	0.990	0.999	1.000	1.000	1.000	1.000	1.000	1.000	1.000	1.000	1.000	1.000	1.000	1.000	1.000	1.000	1.000
0.2	0.819	0.982	0.999	1.000	1.000	1.000	1.000	1.000	1.000	1.000	1.000	1.000	1.000	1.000	1.000	1.000	1.000	1.000
0.25	0.779	0.974	0.998	1.000	1.000	1.000	1.000	1.000	1.000	1.000	1.000	1.000	1.000	1.000	1.000	1.000	1.000	1.000
0.3	0.741	0.963	0.996	1.000	1.000	1.000	1.000	1.000	1.000	1.000	1.000	1.000	1.000	1.000	1.000	1.000	1.000	1.000
0.35	0.705	0.951	0.994	1.000	1.000	1.000	1.000	1.000	1.000	1.000	1.000	1.000	1.000	1.000	1.000	1.000	1.000	1.000
0.4	0.670	0.938	0.992	0.999	1.000	1.000	1.000	1.000	1.000	1.000	1.000	1.000	1.000	1.000	1.000	1.000	1.000	1.000
0.5	0.607	0.910	0.986	0.998	1.000	1.000	1.000	1.000	1.000	1.000	1.000	1.000	1.000	1.000	1.000	1.000	1.000	1.000
0.6	0.549	0.878	0.977	0.997	1.000	1.000	1.000	1.000	1.000	1.000	1.000	1.000	1.000	1.000	1.000	1.000	1.000	1.000
0.7	0.497	0.844	0.966	0.994	0.999	1.000	1.000	1.000	1.000	1.000	1.000	1.000	1.000	1.000	1.000	1.000	1.000	1.000
0.8	0.449	0.809	0.953	0.991	0.999	1.000	1.000	1.000	1.000	1.000	1.000	1.000	1.000	1.000	1.000	1.000	1.000	1.000
0.9	0.407	0.772	0.937	0.987	0.998	1.000	1.000	1.000	1.000	1.000	1.000	1.000	1.000	1.000	1.000	1.000	1.000	1.000
1	0.368	0.736	0.920	0.981	0.996	0.999	1.000	1.000	1.000	1.000	1.000	1.000	1.000	1.000	1.000	1.000	1.000	1.000
1.2	0.301	0.663	0.879	0.966	0.992	0.998	1.000	1.000	1.000	1.000	1.000	1.000	1.000	1.000	1.000	1.000	1.000	1.000
1.4	0.247	0.592	0.833	0.946	0.986	0.997	0.999	1.000	1.000	1.000	1.000	1.000	1.000	1.000	1.000	1.000	1.000	1.000
1.6	0.202	0.525	0.783	0.921	0.976	0.994	0.999	1.000	1.000	1.000	1.000	1.000	1.000	1.000	1.000	1.000	1.000	1.000
1.8	0.165	0.463	0.731	0.891	0.964	0.990	0.997	0.999	1.000	1.000	1.000	1.000	1.000	1.000	1.000	1.000	1.000	1.000
2	0.135	0.406	0.677	0.857	0.947	0.983	0.995	0.999	1.000	1.000	1.000	1.000	1.000	1.000	1.000	1.000	1.000	1.000

Continued

Poisson distribution *(continued)*

λ↓x→	0	1	2	3	4	5	6	7	8	9	10	11	12	13	14	15	16	17
2.2	0.111	0.355	0.623	0.819	0.928	0.975	0.993	0.998	1.000	1.000	1.000	1.000	1.000	1.000	1.000	1.000	1.000	1.000
2.4	0.091	0.308	0.570	0.779	0.904	0.964	0.988	0.997	0.999	1.000	1.000	1.000	1.000	1.000	1.000	1.000	1.000	1.000
2.6	0.074	0.267	0.518	0.736	0.877	0.951	0.983	0.995	0.999	1.000	1.000	1.000	1.000	1.000	1.000	1.000	1.000	1.000
2.8	0.061	0.231	0.469	0.692	0.848	0.935	0.976	0.992	0.998	0.999	1.000	1.000	1.000	1.000	1.000	1.000	1.000	1.000
3	0.050	0.199	0.423	0.647	0.815	0.916	0.966	0.988	0.996	0.999	1.000	1.000	1.000	1.000	1.000	1.000	1.000	1.000
3.2	0.041	0.171	0.380	0.603	0.781	0.895	0.955	0.983	0.994	0.998	1.000	1.000	1.000	1.000	1.000	1.000	1.000	1.000
3.4	0.033	0.147	0.340	0.558	0.744	0.871	0.942	0.977	0.992	0.997	0.999	1.000	1.000	1.000	1.000	1.000	1.000	1.000
3.6	0.027	0.126	0.303	0.515	0.706	0.844	0.927	0.969	0.988	0.996	0.999	1.000	1.000	1.000	1.000	1.000	1.000	1.000
3.8	0.022	0.107	0.269	0.473	0.668	0.816	0.909	0.960	0.984	0.994	0.998	0.999	1.000	1.000	1.000	1.000	1.000	1.000
4	0.018	0.092	0.238	0.433	0.629	0.785	0.889	0.949	0.979	0.992	0.997	0.999	1.000	1.000	1.000	1.000	1.000	1.000
4.5	0.011	0.061	0.174	0.342	0.532	0.703	0.831	0.913	0.960	0.983	0.993	0.998	0.999	1.000	1.000	1.000	1.000	1.000
5	0.007	0.040	0.125	0.265	0.440	0.616	0.762	0.867	0.932	0.968	0.986	0.995	0.998	0.999	1.000	1.000	1.000	1.000
5.5	0.004	0.027	0.088	0.202	0.358	0.529	0.686	0.809	0.894	0.946	0.975	0.989	0.996	0.998	0.999	1.000	1.000	1.000
6	0.002	0.017	0.062	0.151	0.285	0.446	0.606	0.744	0.847	0.916	0.957	0.980	0.991	0.996	0.999	0.999	1.000	1.000
6.5	0.002	0.011	0.043	0.112	0.224	0.369	0.527	0.673	0.792	0.877	0.933	0.966	0.984	0.993	0.997	0.999	1.000	1.000
7	0.001	0.007	0.030	0.082	0.173	0.301	0.450	0.599	0.729	0.830	0.901	0.947	0.973	0.987	0.994	0.998	0.999	1.000
7.5	0.001	0.005	0.020	0.059	0.132	0.241	0.378	0.525	0.662	0.776	0.862	0.921	0.957	0.978	0.990	0.995	0.998	0.999
8	0.000	0.003	0.014	0.042	0.100	0.191	0.313	0.453	0.593	0.717	0.816	0.888	0.936	0.966	0.983	0.992	0.996	0.998
8.5	0.000	0.002	0.009	0.030	0.074	0.150	0.256	0.386	0.523	0.653	0.763	0.849	0.909	0.949	0.973	0.986	0.993	0.997
9	0.000	0.001	0.006	0.021	0.055	0.116	0.207	0.324	0.456	0.587	0.706	0.803	0.876	0.926	0.959	0.978	0.989	0.995
9.5	0.000	0.001	0.004	0.015	0.040	0.089	0.165	0.269	0.392	0.522	0.645	0.752	0.836	0.898	0.940	0.967	0.982	0.991
10	0.000	0.000	0.003	0.010	0.029	0.067	0.130	0.220	0.333	0.458	0.583	0.697	0.792	0.864	0.917	0.951	0.973	0.986
10.5	0.000	0.000	0.002	0.007	0.021	0.050	0.102	0.179	0.279	0.397	0.521	0.639	0.742	0.825	0.888	0.932	0.960	0.978

Appendix O
Binomial Distribution

Probability of *x* or fewer occurrences in a sample of size *n*

Binomial distribution

n	x	p 0.01	0.02	0.03	0.04	0.05	0.06	0.07	0.08	0.09	0.10	0.15	0.20	0.25	0.30	0.35	0.40	0.45	0.50
2	0	0.980	0.960	0.941	0.922	0.903	0.884	0.865	0.846	0.828	0.810	0.723	0.640	0.563	0.490	0.423	0.360	0.303	0.250
2	1	1.000	1.000	0.999	0.998	0.998	0.996	0.995	0.994	0.992	0.990	0.978	0.960	0.938	0.910	0.878	0.840	0.798	0.750
3	0	0.970	0.941	0.913	0.885	0.857	0.831	0.804	0.779	0.754	0.729	0.614	0.512	0.422	0.343	0.275	0.216	0.166	0.125
3	1	1.000	0.999	0.997	0.995	0.993	0.990	0.986	0.982	0.977	0.972	0.939	0.896	0.844	0.784	0.718	0.648	0.575	0.500
3	2	1.000	1.000	1.000	1.000	1.000	1.000	1.000	0.999	0.999	0.999	0.997	0.992	0.984	0.973	0.957	0.936	0.909	0.875
4	0	0.961	0.922	0.885	0.849	0.815	0.781	0.748	0.716	0.686	0.656	0.522	0.410	0.316	0.240	0.179	0.130	0.092	0.063
4	1	0.999	0.998	0.995	0.991	0.986	0.980	0.973	0.966	0.957	0.948	0.890	0.819	0.738	0.652	0.563	0.475	0.391	0.313
4	2	1.000	1.000	1.000	1.000	1.000	0.999	0.999	0.998	0.997	0.996	0.988	0.973	0.949	0.916	0.874	0.821	0.759	0.688
4	3	1.000	1.000	1.000	1.000	1.000	1.000	1.000	1.000	1.000	1.000	0.999	0.998	0.996	0.992	0.985	0.974	0.959	0.938
5	0	0.951	0.904	0.859	0.815	0.774	0.734	0.696	0.659	0.624	0.590	0.444	0.328	0.237	0.168	0.116	0.078	0.050	0.031
5	1	0.999	0.996	0.992	0.985	0.977	0.968	0.958	0.946	0.933	0.919	0.835	0.737	0.633	0.528	0.428	0.337	0.256	0.188
5	2	1.000	1.000	1.000	0.999	0.999	0.998	0.997	0.995	0.994	0.991	0.973	0.942	0.896	0.837	0.765	0.683	0.593	0.500
5	3	1.000	1.000	1.000	1.000	1.000	1.000	1.000	1.000	1.000	1.000	0.998	0.993	0.984	0.969	0.946	0.913	0.869	0.813
5	4	1.000	1.000	1.000	1.000	1.000	1.000	1.000	1.000	1.000	1.000	1.000	1.000	0.999	0.998	0.995	0.990	0.982	0.969
6	0	0.941	0.886	0.833	0.783	0.735	0.690	0.647	0.606	0.568	0.531	0.377	0.262	0.178	0.118	0.075	0.047	0.028	0.016
6	1	0.999	0.994	0.988	0.978	0.967	0.954	0.939	0.923	0.905	0.886	0.776	0.655	0.534	0.420	0.319	0.233	0.164	0.109
6	2	1.000	1.000	0.999	0.999	0.998	0.996	0.994	0.991	0.988	0.984	0.953	0.901	0.831	0.744	0.647	0.544	0.442	0.344
6	3	1.000	1.000	1.000	1.000	1.000	1.000	1.000	0.999	0.999	0.999	0.994	0.983	0.962	0.930	0.883	0.821	0.745	0.656
6	4	1.000	1.000	1.000	1.000	1.000	1.000	1.000	1.000	1.000	1.000	1.000	0.998	0.995	0.989	0.978	0.959	0.931	0.891
6	5	1.000	1.000	1.000	1.000	1.000	1.000	1.000	1.000	1.000	1.000	1.000	1.000	1.000	0.999	0.998	0.996	0.992	0.984
7	0	0.932	0.868	0.808	0.751	0.698	0.648	0.602	0.558	0.517	0.478	0.321	0.210	0.133	0.082	0.049	0.028	0.015	0.008
7	1	0.998	0.992	0.983	0.971	0.956	0.938	0.919	0.897	0.875	0.850	0.717	0.577	0.445	0.329	0.234	0.159	0.102	0.063
7	2	1.000	1.000	0.999	0.998	0.996	0.994	0.990	0.986	0.981	0.974	0.926	0.852	0.756	0.647	0.532	0.420	0.316	0.227
7	3	1.000	1.000	1.000	1.000	1.000	1.000	0.999	0.999	0.998	0.997	0.988	0.967	0.929	0.874	0.800	0.710	0.608	0.500
7	4	1.000	1.000	1.000	1.000	1.000	1.000	1.000	1.000	1.000	1.000	0.999	0.995	0.987	0.971	0.944	0.904	0.847	0.773
7	5	1.000	1.000	1.000	1.000	1.000	1.000	1.000	1.000	1.000	1.000	1.000	1.000	0.999	0.996	0.991	0.981	0.964	0.938
7	6	1.000	1.000	1.000	1.000	1.000	1.000	1.000	1.000	1.000	1.000	1.000	1.000	1.000	1.000	0.999	0.998	0.996	0.992

Continued

Binomial distribution *(continued)*

											p								
n	x	0.01	0.02	0.03	0.04	0.05	0.06	0.07	0.08	0.09	0.10	0.15	0.20	0.25	0.30	0.35	0.40	0.45	0.50
8	0	0.923	0.851	0.784	0.721	0.663	0.610	0.560	0.513	0.470	0.430	0.272	0.168	0.100	0.058	0.032	0.017	0.008	0.004
8	1	0.997	0.990	0.978	0.962	0.943	0.921	0.897	0.870	0.842	0.813	0.657	0.503	0.367	0.255	0.169	0.106	0.063	0.035
8	2	1.000	1.000	0.999	0.997	0.994	0.990	0.985	0.979	0.971	0.962	0.895	0.797	0.679	0.552	0.428	0.315	0.220	0.145
8	3	1.000	1.000	1.000	1.000	1.000	0.999	0.999	0.998	0.997	0.995	0.979	0.944	0.886	0.806	0.706	0.594	0.477	0.363
8	4	1.000	1.000	1.000	1.000	1.000	1.000	1.000	1.000	1.000	1.000	0.997	0.990	0.973	0.942	0.894	0.826	0.740	0.637
8	5	1.000	1.000	1.000	1.000	1.000	1.000	1.000	1.000	1.000	1.000	1.000	0.999	0.996	0.989	0.975	0.950	0.912	0.855
8	6	1.000	1.000	1.000	1.000	1.000	1.000	1.000	1.000	1.000	1.000	1.000	1.000	1.000	0.999	0.996	0.991	0.982	0.965
8	7	1.000	1.000	1.000	1.000	1.000	1.000	1.000	1.000	1.000	1.000	1.000	1.000	1.000	1.000	1.000	0.999	0.998	0.996
9	0	0.914	0.834	0.760	0.693	0.630	0.573	0.520	0.472	0.428	0.387	0.232	0.134	0.075	0.040	0.021	0.010	0.005	0.002
9	1	0.997	0.987	0.972	0.952	0.929	0.902	0.873	0.842	0.809	0.775	0.599	0.436	0.300	0.196	0.121	0.071	0.039	0.020
9	2	1.000	0.999	0.998	0.996	0.992	0.986	0.979	0.970	0.960	0.947	0.859	0.738	0.601	0.463	0.337	0.232	0.150	0.090
9	3	1.000	1.000	1.000	1.000	0.999	0.999	0.998	0.996	0.994	0.992	0.966	0.914	0.834	0.730	0.609	0.483	0.361	0.254
9	4	1.000	1.000	1.000	1.000	1.000	1.000	1.000	1.000	0.999	0.999	0.994	0.980	0.951	0.901	0.828	0.733	0.621	0.500
9	5	1.000	1.000	1.000	1.000	1.000	1.000	1.000	1.000	1.000	1.000	0.999	0.997	0.990	0.975	0.946	0.901	0.834	0.746
9	6	1.000	1.000	1.000	1.000	1.000	1.000	1.000	1.000	1.000	1.000	1.000	1.000	0.999	0.996	0.989	0.975	0.950	0.910
9	7	1.000	1.000	1.000	1.000	1.000	1.000	1.000	1.000	1.000	1.000	1.000	1.000	1.000	0.999	0.996	0.991	0.980
9	8	1.000	1.000	1.000	1.000	1.000	1.000	1.000	1.000	1.000	1.000	1.000	1.000	1.000	1.000	1.000	1.000	0.999	0.998
10	0	0.904	0.817	0.737	0.665	0.599	0.539	0.484	0.434	0.389	0.349	0.197	0.107	0.056	0.028	0.013	0.006	0.003	0.001
10	1	0.996	0.984	0.965	0.942	0.914	0.882	0.848	0.812	0.775	0.736	0.544	0.376	0.244	0.149	0.086	0.046	0.023	0.011
10	2	1.000	0.999	0.997	0.994	0.988	0.981	0.972	0.960	0.946	0.930	0.820	0.678	0.526	0.383	0.262	0.167	0.100	0.055
10	3	1.000	1.000	1.000	1.000	0.999	0.998	0.996	0.994	0.991	0.987	0.950	0.879	0.776	0.650	0.514	0.382	0.266	0.172
10	4	1.000	1.000	1.000	1.000	1.000	1.000	1.000	0.999	0.999	0.998	0.990	0.967	0.922	0.850	0.751	0.633	0.504	0.377
10	5	1.000	1.000	1.000	1.000	1.000	1.000	1.000	1.000	1.000	1.000	0.999	0.994	0.980	0.953	0.905	0.834	0.738	0.623

Appendix P
Exponential Distribution

Exponential distribution

X	Area to left of X	Area to right of X
0	0.00000	1.00000
0.1	0.09516	0.90484
0.2	0.18127	0.81873
0.3	0.25918	0.74082
0.4	0.32968	0.67032
0.5	0.39347	0.60653
0.6	0.45119	0.54881
0.7	0.50341	0.49659
0.8	0.55067	0.44933
0.9	0.59343	0.40657
1	0.63212	0.36788
1.1	0.66713	0.33287
1.2	0.69881	0.30119
1.3	0.72747	0.27253
1.4	0.75340	0.24660
1.5	0.77687	0.22313
1.6	0.79810	0.20190
1.7	0.81732	0.18268
1.8	0.83470	0.16530
1.9	0.85043	0.14957
2	0.86466	0.13534
2.1	0.87754	0.12246
2.2	0.88920	0.11080
2.3	0.89974	0.10026
2.4	0.90928	0.09072
2.5	0.91792	0.08208
2.6	0.92573	0.07427

Continued

Exponential distribution *(continued)*

X	Area to left of X	Area to right of X
2.7	0.93279	0.06721
2.8	0.93919	0.06081
2.9	0.94498	0.05502
3	0.95021	0.04979
3.1	0.95495	0.04505
3.2	0.95924	0.04076
3.3	0.96312	0.03688
3.4	0.96663	0.03337
3.5	0.96980	0.03020
3.6	0.97268	0.02732
3.7	0.97528	0.02472
3.8	0.97763	0.02237
3.9	0.97976	0.02024
4	0.98168	0.01832
4.1	0.98343	0.01657
4.2	0.98500	0.01500
4.3	0.98643	0.01357
4.4	0.98772	0.01228
4.5	0.98889	0.01111
4.6	0.98995	0.01005
4.7	0.99090	0.00910
4.8	0.99177	0.00823
4.9	0.99255	0.00745
5	0.99326	0.00674
5.1	0.99390	0.00610
5.2	0.99448	0.00552
5.3	0.99501	0.00499
5.4	0.99548	0.00452
5.5	0.99591	0.00409
5.6	0.99630	0.00370
5.7	0.99665	0.00335
5.8	0.99697	0.00303
5.9	0.99726	0.00274
6	0.99752	0.00248

Appendix Q
Median Ranks

Median ranks

n	1	2	3	4	5	6	7	8	9	10	11	12
1	0.500	0.292	0.206	0.159	0.130	0.109	0.095	0.083	0.074	0.067	0.061	0.056
2		0.708	0.500	0.386	0.315	0.266	0.230	0.202	0.181	0.163	0.149	0.137
3			0.794	0.614	0.500	0.422	0.365	0.321	0.287	0.260	0.237	0.218
4				0.841	0.685	0.578	0.500	0.440	0.394	0.356	0.325	0.298
5					0.870	0.734	0.635	0.560	0.500	0.452	0.412	0.379
6						0.891	0.770	0.679	0.606	0.548	0.500	0.460
7							0.905	0.798	0.713	0.644	0.588	0.540
8								0.917	0.819	0.740	0.675	0.621
9									0.926	0.837	0.763	0.702
10										0.933	0.851	0.782
11											0.939	0.863
12												0.944

n	13	14	15	16	17	18	19	20	21	22	23	24
1	0.052	0.049	0.045	0.043	0.040	0.038	0.036	0.034	0.033	0.031	0.030	0.029
2	0.127	0.118	0.110	0.104	0.098	0.092	0.088	0.083	0.079	0.076	0.073	0.070
3	0.201	0.188	0.175	0.165	0.155	0.147	0.139	0.132	0.126	0.121	0.115	0.111
4	0.276	0.257	0.240	0.226	0.213	0.201	0.191	0.181	0.173	0.165	0.158	0.152
5	0.351	0.326	0.305	0.287	0.270	0.255	0.242	0.230	0.220	0.210	0.201	0.193
6	0.425	0.396	0.370	0.348	0.328	0.310	0.294	0.279	0.266	0.254	0.244	0.234
7	0.500	0.465	0.435	0.409	0.385	0.364	0.345	0.328	0.313	0.299	0.286	0.275
8	0.575	0.535	0.500	0.470	0.443	0.418	0.397	0.377	0.360	0.344	0.329	0.316
9	0.649	0.604	0.565	0.530	0.500	0.473	0.448	0.426	0.407	0.388	0.372	0.357
10	0.724	0.674	0.630	0.591	0.557	0.527	0.500	0.475	0.453	0.433	0.415	0.398
11	0.799	0.743	0.695	0.652	0.615	0.582	0.552	0.525	0.500	0.478	0.457	0.439
12	0.873	0.813	0.760	0.713	0.672	0.636	0.603	0.574	0.547	0.522	0.500	0.480

Continued

Median ranks *(continued)*

n	13	14	15	16	17	18	19	20	21	22	23	24
13	0.948	0.882	0.825	0.774	0.730	0.690	0.655	0.623	0.593	0.567	0.543	0.520
14		0.951	0.890	0.835	0.787	0.745	0.706	0.672	0.640	0.612	0.585	0.561
15			0.955	0.896	0.845	0.799	0.758	0.721	0.687	0.656	0.628	0.602
16				0.957	0.902	0.853	0.809	0.770	0.734	0.701	0.671	0.643
17					0.960	0.908	0.861	0.819	0.780	0.746	0.714	0.684
18						0.962	0.912	0.868	0.827	0.790	0.756	0.725
19							0.964	0.917	0.874	0.835	0.799	0.766
20								0.966	0.921	0.879	0.842	0.807
21									0.967	0.924	0.885	0.848
22										0.969	0.927	0.889
23											0.970	0.930
24												0.971

Glossary

A

accelerated life testing—A technique in which units are tested at stress levels higher than they were designed for in an effort to cause failures sooner.

accuracy—The closeness of agreement between a test result or measurement result and the true value.

alias—Effect that is completely confounded with another effect due to the nature of the designed experiment. Aliases are the result of confounding, which may or may not be deliberate.

α (alpha)—1: The maximum probability, or risk, of making a type I error when dealing with the significance level of a test. 2: The probability or risk of incorrectly deciding that a shift in the process mean has occurred when the process is unchanged (when referring to α in general or as the p-value obtained in the test). 3: α is usually designated as producer's risk.

alternative hypothesis, H_a—A hypothesis that is accepted if the null hypothesis (H_0) is rejected. Example 1: Consider the null hypothesis that the statistical model for a population is a normal distribution. The alternative hypothesis to this null hypothesis is that the statistical model of the population is *not* a normal distribution. Note 1: The alternative hypothesis is a statement that contradicts the null hypothesis. The corresponding test statistic is used to decide between the null and alternative hypotheses. Note 2: The alternative hypothesis can also be denoted H_1, H_A, or H^A, with no clear preference as long as the symbolism parallels the null hypothesis notation.

analysis of covariance (ANCOVA)—A technique for estimating and testing the effects of treatments when one or more concomitant variables influence the response variable. Note: Analysis of covariance can be viewed as a combination of regression analysis and analysis of variance.

analysis of variance (ANOVA)—A technique to determine if there are statistically significant differences between group means by analyzing group variances.

Arrhenius model—A technique in accelerated life testing using relationships between temperature and failure rates.

attribute—A countable or categorized quality characteristic that is qualitative rather than quantitative in nature.

attribute data—Characteristic or property that is measured in terms of pass/fail or go/no-go.

availability—The probability that a system or equipment is operating satisfactorily at any point in time when used under stated conditions. The total time considered includes operating time, active repair time, administrative time, and logistic time.

B

balanced design—A design where all treatment combinations have the same number of observations. If replication in a design exists, it would be balanced only if the replication was consistent across all the treatment combinations. In other words, the number of replicates of each treatment combination is the same.

balanced incomplete block (BIB) design—Incomplete block design in which each block contains the same number (k) of different levels from the (l) levels of the principal factor arranged so that every pair of levels occurs in the same number (l) of blocks from the b blocks. Note: This design implies that every level of the principal factor appears the same number of times in the experiment.

batch—A definite quantity of some product accumulated under conditions considered uniform, or accumulated from a common source. This term is sometimes synonymous with *lot*.

β (beta)—The maximum probability, or risk, of making a type II error; see also *α (alpha)*. The probability or risk of incorrectly deciding that a shift in the process mean has not occurred when the process has changed. β is usually designated as consumer's risk. See *power curve*.

beta testing—The release of a preliminary version of a product to a restricted set of users.

bias—A systematic difference between the mean of a test result or measurement result and a true value.

BIB—See *balanced incomplete block design*.

bimodal—Having two distinct statistical modes.

binomial distribution—A two-parameter discrete distribution involving the mean μ and the variance σ^2, of the variable x with probability p, where p is a constant $0 \leq p \leq 1$, and sample size n. Mean = np and variance = $np(1 - p)$.

blemish—An imperfection that causes awareness but does not impair function or usage.

block—A collection of experimental units more homogeneous than the full set of experimental units. Blocks are usually selected to allow for special causes, in addition to those introduced as factors to be studied. These special causes may be avoidable within blocks, thus providing a more homogeneous experimental subspace.

block diagram (or reliability block diagram [RBD])—A diagram that displays the relationships of components of a system whether in serial, parallel, or some other configuration.

block effect—An effect resulting from a block in an experimental design. Existence of a block effect generally means that the method of blocking was appropriate and that an assignable cause has been found.

blocking—Method of including blocks in an experiment in order to broaden the applicability of the conclusions or to minimize the impact of selected assignable causes. The randomization of the experiment is restricted and occurs within blocks.

BX life—The time at which $X\%$ of the units in a population will have failed. For example, if an item has a B10 life of 100 hours, that means that 10% of the population will have failed by 100 hours of operation.

C

c **(count)**—The number of events (often nonconformities) of a given classification occurring in a sample of fixed size.

capability—Performance of a process demonstrated to be in a state of statistical control. See *process capability* and *process performance*.

capability index—See *process capability index*.

cause—An identified reason for the presence of a symptom, defect, or problem. See *effect*.

central limit theorem—Statistical principle that the distribution of sample averages is approximately normal even if the population from which the sample is drawn is not normally distributed. The approximation improves as the sample size increases.

chi-square distribution (χ^2 distribution)—A positively skewed distribution that varies with the degrees of freedom with a minimum value of zero.

chi-square statistic (χ^2 statistic)—A value obtained from the χ^2 distribution at a given percentage point and specified degrees of freedom.

chi-square test (χ^2 test)—A statistic used in testing a hypothesis concerning the discrepancy between observed and expected results.

coefficient of determination (R^2)—A measure of the part of the variance for one variable that can be explained by its linear relationship with another variable (or variables). The coefficient of determination is the square of the correlation between the observed y values and the fitted y values, and is also the fraction of the variation in y that is explained by the fitted equation.

coefficient of variation (CV)—Measures relative dispersion. It is the standard deviation divided by the mean and is commonly reported as a percentage.

complete block—Block that accommodates a complete set of treatment combinations.

completely randomized design—A design in which the treatments are assigned at random to the full set of experimental units. No blocks are involved in a completely randomized design.

completely randomized factorial design—A factorial design in which all the treatments are assigned at random to the full set of experimental units. See *completely randomized design*.

concomitant variable—A variable or factor that cannot be accounted for in the data analysis or design of the experiment but whose effect on the results should be accounted for.

confidence coefficient $(1 - \alpha)$—See *confidence level*.

confidence interval—An estimate of the interval between two statistics that includes the true value of the parameter with some probability.

confidence level (confidence coefficient) $(1 - \alpha)$—The probability that the confidence interval described by a set of confidence limits actually includes the population parameter.

confidence limits—The endpoints of the interval about the sample statistic that is believed, with a specified confidence level, to include the population parameter. See *confidence interval.*

confounding—Indistinguishably combining an effect with other effects or blocks.

consumer's risk (β)—Probability of acceptance when the quality level has a value stated by the acceptance sampling plan as unsatisfactory. Note 1: Such acceptance is a type II error. Note 2: Consumer's risk is usually designated as β (beta).

continuous distribution—Distribution where data is from a continuous scale. Examples of continuous scales are the normal, t, and F distributions.

continuous scale—A scale with a continuum of possible values. Note: A continuous scale can be transformed into a discrete scale by grouping values, but this leads to some loss of information.

control plan—A document describing the system elements to be applied to control variation of processes, products, and services in order to minimize deviation from their preferred values.

corrective maintenance (CM)—The actions required to return the system to an operating state once failure has occurred.

correlation—Measures the linear association between two variables. It is commonly measured by the correlation coefficient, r. See also *regression analysis.*

correlation coefficient (r)—A number between –1 and 1 that indicates the degree of linear relationship between two sets of numbers.

covariance—Measures the relationship between pairs of observations from two variables.

C_p (process capability index)—Index describing process capability in relation to specified tolerance of a characteristic divided by a measure of the length of the reference interval for a process in a state of statistical control.

C_{pk} (minimum process capability index)—Smaller of C_{pk_U} (upper process capability index) and C_{pk_L} (lower process capability index).

C_{pk_L} (lower process capability index; C_{p_L})—Index describing process capability in relation to the lower specification limit.

C_{pk_U} (upper process capability index; C_{p_U})—Index describing process capability in relation to the upper specification limit.

critical to quality (CTQ)—Characteristic of a product or service that is essential to ensure customer satisfaction.

critical value—The numerical values of the test statistic that determine the rejection region.

CTQ—See *critical to quality.*

cube point—In a design, experimental runs that are in the corner points of the design space. In general, a factorial design consists of cube points only. They also exist in fractional factorial designs and some central composite designs.

cumulative frequency distribution—The sum of the frequencies accumulated up to the upper boundary of a class in the distribution.

cumulative sum (CUSUM) chart—The CUSUM control chart calculates the cumulative sum of deviations from target to detect shifts in the level of the measurement.

CV—See *coefficient of variation*.

D

defect—Nonfulfillment of a requirement related to an intended or specified use.

defective (defective unit)—Unit with one or more defects.

defects per million opportunities (DPMO)—Measure of capability for discrete (attribute) data found by dividing the number of defects by the opportunities for defects times one million. It allows for comparison of different types of product.

defects per unit (DPU)—Measure of capability for discrete (attribute) data found by dividing the number of defects by the number of units.

degrees of freedom (*v, df*)—In general, the number of independent comparisons available to estimate a specific parameter, which serves as a means of entering certain statistical tables.

demerit—A weighting assigned to a classification of an event or events to provide a means of obtaining a weighted quality score.

design for X (DFX)—A methodology where X is a variable such as cost, manufacturability, producibility, testability, or maintainability, and where X becomes the focus of or constraint to the design process.

design for reliability (DfR)—An engineering program in which reliability engineering is considered during the development cycle to ensure reliability and cost goals are achieved.

dispersion—A quantifiable variation of measurements within a population.

DMAIC—A data driven quality strategy for improving processes and an integral part of a Six Sigma quality initiative. DMAIC is an acronym for define, measure, analyze, improve, and control.

E

effect (design of experiments usage)—A relationship between factor(s) and a response variable(s). Specific types include main effect, dispersion effect, or interaction effect.

element—See *unit*.

event—An occurrence of some attribute or outcome. In the quality field, events are often nonconformities.

evolutionary operation (EVOP)—A sequential form of experimentation conducted in production facilities during regular production. The range of variation of the factors is usually quite small in order to avoid extreme changes in settings, so it often requires considerable replication and time.

EVOP—See *evolutionary operation*.

experimental error—Variation in the response variable beyond that accounted for by the factors, blocks, or other assignable sources in the conduct of the experiment.

exploratory data analysis (EDA)—Technique that isolates patterns and features of the data and reveals these forcefully to the analyst.

Eyring model—A model used in accelerated life testing using temperature as the accelerant.

F

$F_{1,v2}$—F test statistic. See *F test*.

$F_{1,v2,\alpha}$—Critical value for F test. See *F test*.

factor or variable—An assignable cause that may affect the responses, and of which different levels are included in the experiment.

failure mode effects analysis (FMEA)—A systematized group of activities to recognize and evaluate the potential failure of a product or process and its effects, identify actions that could eliminate or reduce the occurrence of the potential failure, and document the process.

failure mode effects and criticality analysis (FMECA)—A procedure performed after a failure mode effects analysis to classify each potential failure effect according to its severity and probability of occurrence.

failure reporting, analysis, and corrective action system (FRACAS)—A methodology that provides a systematic process for reporting, classifying, and analyzing failures, as well as planning corrective actions.

fault tree analysis (FTA)—A "top down" approach that is used to identify the cause, causes, or combinations of causes of failures.

F **distribution**—A continuous distribution that is a useful reference for assessing the ratio of independent variances. See Appendices F, G, and H for the actual values of the distribution.

F **test**—A statistical test that uses the *F* distribution. It is most often used when dealing with a hypothesis related to the ratio of independent variances.

factor—Predictor variable that is varied with the intent of assessing its effect on the response variable.

factor level—See *level*.

factorial design—Experimental design consisting of all possible treatments formed from two or more factors, each being studied at two or more levels. When all combinations are run, the interaction effects as well as main effects can be estimated.

failure—The inability, because of defect(s), of an item, product, or service to perform its required functions as needed.

failure mechanism—The physical, chemical, or mechanical process that caused the defect or failure.

failure mode—The type of defect contributing to a failure.

failure rate—The number of failures per unit time (for equal time intervals).

first quartile (Q$_1$ or lower quartile)—One quarter of the data lies below. See *quartiles*.

fixed factor—A factor that only has a limited number of levels that are of interest.

fixed model—A model that contains only fixed factors.

flowchart—A basic quality tool that uses graphical representation for the steps in a process. Effective flowcharts include decisions, inputs, outputs, as well as process steps.

fractional factorial design—Experimental design consisting of a subset (fraction) of the factorial design.

frequency—Number of occurrences or observed values in a specified class, sample, or population.

frequency distribution—A set of all the various values that individual observations may have and the frequency of their occurrence in the sample or population.

G

gage R&R study—A type of measurement system analysis done to evaluate the performance of a test method or measurement system. Such a study quantifies the capabilities and limitations of a measurement instrument, often estimating its repeatability and reproducibility.

Gaussian distribution—See *normal distribution.*

generator—In experimental design, a generator is used to determine the level of confounding and the pattern of aliases in a fractional factorial design.

geometric distribution—Case of the negative binomial distribution where $c = 1$ (c is integer parameter). The geometric distribution is a discrete distribution.

Gopertz model—Use in calculating reliability growth.

H

H_0—See *null hypothesis.*

H_1—See *alternative hypothesis.*

H_A—See *alternative hypothesis.*

Hawthorne effect—The effect in an experiment that occurs when humans perform better than they normally would because they are being measured or observed.

hazard rate—Instantaneous failure rate at some specified time t.

highly accelerated life test (HALT)—A process for uncovering design defects and weaknesses in electronic and mechanical assemblies using a vibration system combined with rapid high and low temperature changes. The purpose of HALT is to optimize product reliability by identifying the functional and destructive limits of a product at an early stage in product development.

highly accelerated stress audit (HASA)—A technique in which a sample of parts (as opposed to 100% of the production as in HASS [see below]) is subjected to stresses similar to the levels and duration for HALT. In monitoring the production process, the intent of HASA is to detect slight shifts in the attributes of the product so corrective actions can be taken and implemented before the performance of outgoing product approaches the specifications.

highly accelerated stress screening (HASS)—A technique for production screening that rapidly exposes process or production flaws in products. Its purpose is to expose a product to optimized production screens without affecting product reliability. Unlike HALT, HASS uses nondestructive stresses of extreme temperatures and temperature change rates with vibration.

histogram—A plot of a frequency distribution in the form of rectangles (cells) whose bases are equal to the class interval and whose areas are proportional to the frequencies.

hypothesis—Statement about a population to be tested. See *null hypothesis, alternative hypothesis,* and *hypothesis testing.*

hypothesis testing—A statistical hypothesis that is a conjecture about a population parameter. There are two statistical hypotheses for each situation—the null hypothesis (H_0) and the alternative hypothesis (H_a). The null hypothesis proposes that there is no difference between the population of the sample and the specified population; the alternative hypothesis proposes that there is a difference between the sample and the specified population.

L

λ **(lambda)**—Failure rate.

Latin square design—A design involving three factors in which the combination of the levels of any one of them with the levels of the other two appears once and only once.

Lean—A systematic approach to identifying and eliminating waste (non-value-added activities) through continuous improvement by flowing the product at the pull of the customer in pursuit of perfection.

least squares, method of—A technique of estimating a parameter that minimizes the sum of the difference squared, where the difference is between the observed value and the predicted value (residual) derived from the model.

level—Potential setting, value, or assignment of a factor or the value of the predictor variable.

level of significance—See *significance level.*

lifecycle cost—The cost to purchase, operate, and maintain the product during its useful lifetime.

linear regression coefficients—The numbers associated with each predictor variable in a linear regression equation that tells how the response variable changes with each unit increase in the predictor variable. See *regression analysis.*

linear regression equation—A function that indicates the linear relationship between a set of predictor variables and a response variable. See *regression analysis.*

linearity (general sense)—The degree to which a pair of variables follows a straight-line relationship. Linearity can be measured by the correlation coefficient.

linearity (measurement system sense)—The difference in bias through the range of measurement. A measurement system that has good linearity will have a constant bias no matter the magnitude of measurement. If one views the relation between the observed measurement result on the y-axis and the true value on the x-axis, an ideal measurement system would have a line of slope = 1.

Lloyd-Lipow model—Used in reliability growth when fatigue is the major cause of failure.

lognormal distribution—If log x is normally distributed, it is a lognormal distribution. See *normal distribution*.

M

main effect—Influence of a single factor on the mean of the response variable.

main effects plot—Plot giving the average responses at the various levels of individual factors.

maintainability—Measure of the ability of an item to be retained or restored to specified condition when maintenance is performed by personnel having specified skill levels, using prescribed procedures and resources at each prescribed level of maintenance and repair.

mean life—The arithmetic average of the lifetimes of all items considered. A lifetime may consist of time between malfunctions, time between repairs, time to remove or replace parts, or any other desired interval of observation.

mean time between failures (MTBF)—Average time between failure events. The mean number of life units during which all parts of the item perform within their specified limits, during a particular measurement interval under stated conditions.

mean time to failure (MTTF)—Measure of system reliability for nonrepairable items. The total number of life units of an item divided by the total number of failures within that population, during a particular measurement interval under stated conditions. Expectation of the time to failure.

mean time to repair (MTTR)—Measure of maintainability. The sum of corrective maintenance times at any specific level of repair, divided by the total number of failures within an item repaired at that level, during a particular interval under stated conditions.

means, tests for—Testing for means includes computing a confidence interval and hypothesis testing by comparing means to a population mean (known or unknown) or to other sample means.

median—The value for which half the data is larger and half is smaller. The median provides an estimator that is insensitive to very extreme values in a data set, whereas the average is affected by extreme values. Note: For an odd number of units, the median is the middle measurement; for an even number of units, the median is the average of the two middle units.

meta-analysis—Use of statistical methods to combine the results of multiple studies into a single conclusion.

midrange—(Highest value + Lowest value)/2.

mistake-proofing—The use of process or design features to prevent manufacture of nonconforming product.

mixture design—A design constructed to handle the situation in which the predictor variables are constrained to sum to a fixed quantity, such as proportions of ingredients that make up a formulation or blend.

model—Description relating the response variable to predictor variable(s) and including attendant assumptions.

moving average—Let $x_1, x_2, \ldots$ denote individual observations. The moving average of span w at time i.

MTBF—See *mean time between failures.*

MTTF—See *mean time to failure.*

MTTR—See *mean time to repair.*

μ (mu)—See *population mean.*

multimodal—More than one mode.

multiple linear regression—See *regression analysis.*

multivariate control chart—A variables control chart that allows plotting of more than one variable. These charts make use of the T_2 statistic to combine information from the dispersion and mean of several variables.

N

negative binomial distribution—A two-parameter, discrete distribution.

noise factor—In robust parameter design, a predictor variable that is hard to control or is not desirable to control as part of the standard experimental conditions.

nominal scale—Scale with unordered, labeled categories, or a scale ordered by convention.

non-value-added—A term that describes a process step or function that is not required for the direct achievement of process output. This step or function is identified and examined for potential elimination.

normal distribution (Gaussian distribution)—A continuous, symmetrical, bell-shaped frequency distribution for variables that is the basis for the control charts for variables.

null hypothesis, H_0—The hypothesis that there is no difference (null) between the population of the sample and the specified population (or between the populations associated with each sample). The null hypothesis can never be proved true, but it can be shown (with specified risks of error) to be untrue; that is, that a difference exists between the populations. Example: In a random sample of independent random variables with the same normal distribution with unknown mean and unknown standard deviation, a typical null hypothesis for the mean μ is that the mean is less than or equal to a given value μ_0. The hypothesis is written as: $H_0 = \mu \le \mu_0$.

O

OC curve—See *operating characteristic curve.*

ogive—A type of graph that represents the cumulative frequencies for the classes in a frequency distribution.

1 – α—See *confidence level*.

1 – β—The power of testing a hypothesis is $1 - \beta$. It is the probability of correctly rejecting the null hypothesis, H_0.

one-tailed test—A hypothesis test that involves only one of the tails of a distribution. Example: We wish to reject the null hypothesis H_0 only if the true mean is *larger* than μ_0.

$$H_0: \mu = \mu_0$$
$$H_a: \mu < \mu_0$$

A one-tailed test is either right-tailed or left-tailed, depending on the direction of the inequality of the alternative hypothesis.

operating characteristic curve (OC curve)—A curve showing the relationship between the probability of acceptance of product and the incoming quality level for a given acceptance sampling plan.

ordinal scale—Scale with ordered labeled categories.

orthogonal design—A design in which all pairs of factors at particular levels appear together an equal number of times.

outlier—An extremely high or an extremely low data value compared to the rest of the data values. Great caution must be used when trying to identify an outlier.

output variable—Variable representing the outcome of the process.

P

parameter—A constant or coefficient describing some characteristic of a population (for example, standard deviation, mean).

Pareto chart—A graphical tool based on the Pareto principle for ranking causes from most significant to least significant.

Pareto principle—The principle, named after 19th century economist Vilfredo Pareto, that suggests that most effects come from relatively few causes; that is, about 80% of the effects come from about 20% of the possible causes.

parts per million (PPM or ppm)—One part per million (or one part per 10^6).

Pearson's correlation coefficient—See *correlation coefficient*.

percentile—Division of the data set into 100 equal groups.

physics of failure—A technique used for design and problem solving (root cause analysis) that uses the knowledge, science, and understanding of mechanisms that induce failure.

Poisson distribution—Describes occurrences of isolated events in a continuum of time or space. It is a one-parameter, discrete distribution depending only on the mean.

pooled standard deviation—A standard deviation value resulting from some combination of individual standard deviation values.

population—Entire set (totality) of units, quantity of material, or observations under consideration. A population may be real and finite, real and infinite, or completely hypothetical. See *sample*.

population mean (μ)—The true mean of the population, represented by μ (mu). The *sample mean, $\bar{x}$,* is a common estimator of the population mean.

population standard deviation—See *standard deviation*.

population variance—See *variance*.

power—Equivalent to one minus the probability of a type II error ($1 - \beta$). A higher power is associated with a higher probability of finding a statistically significant difference. Lack of power usually occurs with smaller sample sizes.

power curve—The curve showing the relationship between the probability ($1 - \beta$) of rejecting the hypothesis that a sample belongs to a given population with a given characteristic(s) and the actual population value of that characteristic(s).

P_p (process performance index)—Index describing process performance in relation to specified tolerance. s is used for standard deviation instead of σ since both random and special causes may be present. Note: A state of statistical control is not required.

P_{pk} (minimum process performance index)—Smaller of upper process performance index and lower process performance index.

P_{pk_L} (lower process performance index or P_{p_L})—Index describing process performance in relation to the lower specification limit. For a symmetrical normal distribution.

PPM (or ppm)—See *parts per million*.

predicted value—The prediction of future observations based on the formulated model.

prediction interval—Similar to a confidence interval. It is an interval based on the predicted value that is likely to contain the values of future observations. It will be wider than the confidence interval because it contains bounds on individual observations rather than a bound on the mean of a group of observations.

predictor variable—Variable that can contribute to the explanation of the outcome of an experiment.

preventive maintenance (PM)—Actions performed to keep the system in an operating state by preventing wear-out failures.

probability distribution—A function that completely describes the probabilities with which specific values occur. The values may be from a discrete scale or a continuous scale.

probability plot—Plot of ranked data versus the sample cumulative frequency on a special vertical scale. The special scale is chosen (that is, normal, lognormal, and so on) so that the cumulative distribution is a straight line.

process—A series of steps that work together to a common end. It consists of interrelated resources and activities to transform inputs into outputs. A process can be graphically represented using a flowchart.

process capability—Calculated inherent variability of a characteristic of a product. It represents the best performance of the process over a period of stable operations.

process capability index—A single-number assessment of ability to meet specification limits on the quality characteristic(s) of interest. The indices compare the variability of the characteristic to the specification limits. Three basic process capability indices are C_p, C_{pk}, and C_{pm}.

process control—Process management focused on fulfilling process requirements. Process control is also the methodology for keeping a process within boundaries and minimizing the variation of a process.

process performance—Statistical measure of the outcome of a characteristic from a process that may *not* have been demonstrated to be in a state of statistical control.

process performance index—A single-number assessment of ability to meet specification limits on the quality characteristic(s) of interest. The indices compare the variability of the characteristic to the specification limits. Three basic process capability indices are P_p, P_{pk}, and P_{pm}.

process quality—A statistical measure of the quality of product from a given process. The measure may be an attribute (qualitative) or a variable (quantitative). A common measure of process quality is the fraction or proportion of nonconforming units in the process.

producer's risk (α)—The probability of nonacceptance when the quality level has a value stated by the acceptance sampling plan as acceptable.

proportions, tests for—Tests for proportions include the binomial distribution.

p-value—Probability of observing the test statistic value or any other value at least as unfavorable to the null hypothesis.

Q

Q_1—See *first quartile*.

qualitative data—See *attribute data*.

quality—Degree to which a set of inherent characteristics fulfills requirements.

quality function deployment (QFD)—Process for planning new or redesigned products and services. The input to the process is the voice of the customer.

quality management—Coordinated activities to direct and control an organization with regard to quality. Such activities generally include establishment of the quality policy, quality objectives, quality planning, quality control, quality assurance, and quality improvement.

quartiles—Division of the distribution into four groups, denoted by Q_1 (first quartile), Q_2 (second quartile), and Q_3 (third quartile). Note that Q_1 is the same as the 25th percentile, Q_2 is the same as the 50th percentile and the median, and Q_3 corresponds to the 75th percentile.

R

r—See *correlation coefficient*.

R—See *range*.

$\bar{R}$ (pronounced r-bar)—The average range calculated from the set of subgroup ranges under consideration. See *range*.

R^2—See *coefficient of determination*.

R chart—See *range chart*.

random cause—Source of process variation that is inherent in a process over time. Also called *common cause* or *chance cause*.

random sampling—Sampling where a sample of n sampling units is taken from a population in such a way that each of the possible combinations of n sampling units has a particular probability of being taken.

random variation—Variation from random causes.

randomization—Process used to assign treatments to experimental units so that each experimental unit has an equal chance of being assigned a particular treatment.

randomized block design—Experimental design consisting of b blocks with t treatments assigned via randomization to the experimental units within each block.

range (R)—A measure of dispersion that is the absolute difference between the highest and lowest value in a given subgroup: R = highest observed value – lowest observed value.

range chart (R chart)—A variables control chart that plots the range of a subgroup to detect shifts in the subgroup range. See *range (R)*.

rapid prototyping—Refers to a sample that can be produced in a much shorter time than the standard production process.

rational subgroup—Subgroup wherein the variation is presumed to be only from random causes.

redundancy—The existence of more than one means for accomplishing a given function. Each means of accomplishing the function need not necessarily be identical.

regression—See *regression analysis*.

regression analysis—A technique that uses predictor variable(s) to predict the variation in a response variable. Regression analysis uses the method of least squares to determine the values of the linear regression coefficients and the corresponding model.

rejection region—The numerical values of the test statistic for which the null hypothesis will be rejected.

relative frequency—Number of occurrences or observed values in a specified class divided by the total number of occurrences or observed values.

reliability—The probability that an item can perform its intended function for a specified interval under stated conditions.

repairability—The probability that a failed system will be restored to operable condition in a specified active repair time.

replicate—A single repetition of the experiment. See also *replication*.

replication—Performance of an experiment more than once for a given set of predictor variables. Each of the repetitions of the experiment is called a replicate. Replication differs from repeated measures in that it is a repeat of the entire experiment for a given set of predictor variables, not just a repeat of measurements on the same experiment.

representative sample—Sample that by itself or as part of a sampling system or protocol exhibits characteristics and properties of the population sampled.

reproducibility—Precision under conditions where independent measurement results are obtained with the same method on identical measurement items with different operators using different equipment.

residual analysis—Method of using residuals to determine appropriateness of assumptions made by a statistical method.

residual plot—A plot used in residual analysis to determine appropriateness of assumptions made by a statistical method.

residuals—The difference between the observed result and the predicted value (estimated treatment response) based on an empirically determined model.

resolution—1: The smallest measurement increment that can be detected by the measurement system. 2: In the context of experimental design, resolution refers to the level of confounding in a fractional factorial design. For example, in a resolution III design, the main effects are confounded with the two-way interaction effects.

response surface design—A design intended to investigate the functional relationship between the response variable and a set of predictor variables. It is generally most useful when the predictor variables are continuous.

response surface methodology (RSM)—A methodology that uses design of experiments, regression analysis, and optimization techniques to determine the best relationship between the response variable and a set of predictor variables.

response variable—Variable representing the outcome of an experiment.

resubmitted lot—A lot that previously has been designated as not acceptable and that is submitted again for acceptance inspection after having been further tested, sorted, reprocessed, and so on.

risk, consumer's (β)—See *consumer's risk (β)*.

risk, producer's (α)—See *producer's risk (α)*.

robust—A characteristic of a statistic or statistical method. A robust statistical method still gives reasonable results even though the standard assumptions are not met. A robust statistic is unchanged by the presence of unusual data points or outliers.

robust parameter design—A design that aims at reducing the performance variation of a product or process by choosing the setting of its control factors to make it less sensitive to the variability from noise factors.

root cause analysis—The process of identifying causes. Many systems are available for analyzing data to ultimately determine the root cause.

RSM—See *response surface methodology*.

S

s—See *standard deviation*.

s^2—See *variance*.

safe operating area (SOA)—The conditions (voltage and current) in which the component or device is rated to operate without self-damage.

sample—A group of units, portions or material, or observations taken from a larger collection of units, quantity of material, or observations, that serves to provide information that may be used for making a decision concerning the larger quantity (the population).

sample mean—The sample mean (or average) is the sum of random variables in a random sample divided by the number in the sum.

sample size (*n*)—Number of sampling units in a sample.

sample standard deviation—See *standard deviation*.

sample variance—See *variance*.

sampling interval—In systematic sampling, the fixed interval of time, output, running hours, and so on, between samples.

sampling plan (acceptance sampling usage)—A specific plan that states the sample size(s) to be used and the associated criteria for accepting the lot. Note: The sampling plan does not contain the rules on how to take the sample.

scatter plot (or **diagram**)—A plot of two variables, one on the *y*-axis and the other on the *x*-axis. The resulting graph allows visual examination for patterns to determine if the variables show any relationship or if there is just random "scatter." This pattern or lack thereof aids in choosing the appropriate type of model for estimation.

serviceability—The ease or difficulty with which equipment can be repaired.

σ (sigma)—See *standard deviation*.

σ^2 (sigma square)—See *variance*.

$\sigma_{\bar{x}}$ (sigma x-bar)—The standard deviation (or standard error) of $\bar{x}$.

$\hat{\sigma}$ (sigma-hat)—In general, any estimate of the population standard deviation. There are various ways to get this estimate depending on the particular application.

signal—An indication on a control chart that a process is not stable or that a shift has occurred. Typical indicators are points outside control limits, runs, trends, cycles, patterns, and so on.

significance level—Maximum probability of rejecting the null hypothesis when in fact it is true. Note: The significance level is usually designated by α and should be set before beginning the test.

Six Sigma—A methodology that provides businesses with the tools to improve the capability of their business processes.

skewness—A measure of symmetry about the mean. For the normal distribution, skewness is zero since it is symmetric.

slope—See *regression analysis*.

special cause—Source of process variation other than inherent process variation.

specification limit(s)—Limiting value(s) stated for a characteristic. See *tolerance*.

spread—A term sometimes synonymous with variation or dispersion.

stable process—A process that is predictable within limits; a process that is subject only to random causes. (This is also known as a state of statistical control.)

standard deviation—A measure of the spread of the process output or the spread of a sampling statistic from the process. When working with the population, the standard deviation is usually denoted by σ (sigma). When working with a sample, the standard deviation is usually denoted by s.

standard error—The standard deviation of a sample statistic or estimator. When dealing with sample statistics, we either refer to the standard deviation of the sample statistic or to its standard error.

standard error of predicted values—A measure of the variation of individual predicted values of the dependent variable about the population value for a given value of the predictor variable. This includes the variability of individuals about the sample line about the population line. It measures the variability of individual observations and can be used to calculate a prediction interval.

statistic—A value calculated from or based on sample data (for example, a subgroup average or range), used to make inferences about the process that produced the output from which the sample came. A quantity calculated from a sample of observations, most often to form an estimate of some population parameter.

statistical measure—A statistic or mathematical function of a statistic.

statistical thinking—A philosophy of learning and action based on the fundamental principles:

- All work occurs in a system of interconnected processes
- Variation exists in all processes
- Understanding and reducing variation are keys to success

statistical tolerance interval—Interval estimator determined from a random sample so as to provide a specified level of confidence that the interval covers at least a specified proportion of the sampled population.

success tree analysis (STA)—Approaches and analyzes a system more positively, asking "What must occur for the system to function successfully?"

T

t **distribution**—A theoretical distribution widely used in practice to evaluate the sample mean when the population standard deviation is estimated from the data. Also known as *Student's* t *distribution.*

Taguchi design—See *robust parameter design.*

target value—Preferred reference value of a characteristic stated in a specification.

temperature–humidity model—Used in accelerated life testing when temperature and humidity are the major accelerants.

temperature–nonthermal models—Used in accelerated life testing when temperature and another factor are the major accelerants.

test statistic—A statistic calculated using data from a sample. It is used to determine whether the null hypothesis will be rejected.

testing—A means of determining the ability of an item to meet specified requirements by subjecting the item to a set of physical, chemical, environmental, or operating actions and conditions.

time series—Sequence of successive time intervals.

tolerance—Difference between upper and lower specification limits.

tolerance limits—See *specification limit(s)*.

transformation—A reexpression of the data aimed toward achieving normality.

treatment—The specific setting of factor levels for an experimental unit.

true value—A value for a quantitative characteristic that does not contain any sampling or measurement variability. (The true value is never exactly known; it is a hypothetical concept.)

t-test—A test of significance that uses the *t* distribution to compare a sample statistic to a hypothesized population mean or to compare two means.

2n factorial design—Factorial design in which *n* factors are studied, each of them at exactly two levels.

two-tailed test—A hypothesis test that involves two tails of a distribution. Example: We wish to reject the null hypothesis H_0 if the true mean is within minimum and maximum (two tails) limits.

$$H_0: \mu = \mu_0$$
$$H_a: \mu \neq \mu_0$$

type I error—The probability or risk of rejecting a hypothesis that is true. This probability is represented by α (alpha). See *operating characteristic curve* and *producer's risk*.

type II error—The probability or risk of accepting a hypothesis that is false. This probability is represented by β (beta). See *power curve* and *consumer's risk*.

U

uncertainty—A parameter that characterizes the dispersion of the values that could reasonably be attributed to the particular quantity subject to measurement or characteristic. Uncertainty indicates the variability of the measured value or characteristic that considers two major components of error: 1) bias and 2) the random error from the imprecision of the measurement process.

unique lot—Lot formed under conditions peculiar to that lot and not part of a routine sequence.

unit—A quantity of product, material, or service forming a cohesive entity on which a measurement or observation can be made.

universe—A group of populations, often reflecting different characteristics of the items or material under consideration.

V

variance—A measure of the variation in the data. When working with the entire population, the population variance is used; when working with a sample, the sample variance is used.

variances, tests for—Formal statistical tests based on the null hypothesis that the variances of different groups are equal. Many times in regression analysis a formal test of variances is not done. Instead, residual analysis checks the assumption of equal variance across the values of the response variable in the model.

variation—Difference between values of a characteristic. Variation can be measured and calculated in different ways, such as range, standard deviation, or variance. Also known as *dispersion* or *spread*.

W

warning limits—There is a high probability that the statistic under consideration is in a state of statistical control when it is within the warning limits (generally 2σ) of a control chart.

Weibull distribution—Widely used in reliability engineering. Depending on the shape parameter, it is a distribution that can take on the characteristics of other types of distributions.

References

AIAG. 2008. *Potential Failure Mode and Effects Analysis*. 4th ed.

Collins, J. A., H. Busby, and G. Staab. 2003. *Mechanical Design of Machine Elements and Machines: A Failure Prevention Perspective*. New York: John Wiley & Sons.

Dieter, G., and L. Schmidt. 2009. *Engineering Design*. 4th ed. Boston: McGraw-Hill Higher Education.

Handbook for Reliability Prediction for Mechanical Systems (NSWC-07). Bethesda, MD: Naval Surface Warfare Center, Caderock Division. http://everyspec.com/USN/NSWC/NSWC-10_RELIABILITY_HDBK_JAN2010_45818.

IEC 60812 Analysis Techniques for System Reliability—Procedure for Failure Mode and Effects Analysis (FMEA). 2006. International Electrotechnical Commission.

IEC 61025 Fault Tree Analysis. 2012. International Electrotechnical Commission.

IEC 61508 Functional Safety of Electrical/Electronic/Programmable Electronic Safety-related Systems. 2010. International Electrotechnical Commission.

IEC 61511 Functional Safety—Safety Instrumented Systems for the Process Industry Sector. 2016. International Electrotechnical Commission.

Ireson, W. G., C. F. Combs, Jr., and R. Y. Moss. 1995. *The Handbook of Reliability Engineering and Management*. 2nd ed. New York: McGraw Hill.

ISO 13849-1:2015(en) Safety of Machinery—Safety-related Parts of Control Systems—Part 1: General Principles for Design. https://www.iso.org/obp/ui/#!iso:std:69883:en.

Kececioglu, D. 1993. *Reliability and Life Testing Handbook*. Volume I. Englewood Cliffs, NJ: Prentice Hall.

———. 2001. *Reliability and Life Testing Handbook*. Volume II. Tucson, AZ: University of Arizona.

Klayman, B. 2014. "BMW Says Its Takata Inflator Work Moving from Mexico to Germany." *Automotive News*, November 19.

Manuele, J. 2003. *On the Practice of Safety*. Hoboken, NJ: John Wiley & Sons.

McLean, H. W. 2002. *HALT, HASS, and HASA Explained: Accelerated Reliability Techniques*. Milwaukee, WI: ASQ Quality Press.

Meeker, W. G., and G. J. Hahn. 1985. *How to Plan an Accelerated Life Test—Some Practical Guidelines*. Volume 10. Milwaukee, WI: ASQC Quality Press.

MIL-STD-882 Standard Practice System Safety. 2012. Department of Defense. http://www.system-safety.org/Documents/MIL-STD-882E.pdf.

Non-electronic Parts Reliability Data (NPRD-2011). Utica, NY: Reliability Information Analysis Center. https://roads.quanterion.com/text/NPRD-2011-1.pdf.

NUREG/CR-5485 Guidelines on Modeling Common-Cause Failures in Probabilistic Risk Assessment. 1998. https://nrcoe.inel.gov/resultsdb/publicdocs/CCF/NUREGCR-5485_Guidelines%20on%20Modeling%20Common-Cause%20Failures%20in%20PRA.pdf.

O'Connor, P. 2002. *Practical Reliability Engineering.* 4th ed. West Sussex, England: John Wiley & Sons.

Pecht, M., and J. Gu. 2009. "Physics-of-Failure-Based Prognostics for Electronic Product." *Transactions of the Institute for Measurement and Control* 31 (3/4): 309–22.

Peck, D. S. 1986. "Comprehensive Model for Humidity Testing Correlation." https://pdfs.semanticscholar.org/4ef0/b09d570ee5e4be0759a14d669ddb127c31f4.pdf.

Ploe, R. J., and W. H. Skewis. 1990. *Handbook of Reliability Prediction Procedures for Mechanical Equipment.* DTRC-90/010. Bethesda, MD: United States Navy-David Taylor Research Center.

Reuters. 2017. "Takata to Plead Guilty, Pay $1 Billion U.S. Penalty over Air Bag Defect." January 14.

Tabuchi, H., and C. Jensen. 2014. "Now the Air Bags Are Faulty, Too." *New York Times,* June 23.

Tseng, S-T., and Z-C. Wen. 2000. "Step-Stress Accelerated Degradation Analysis for Highly Reliable Products." *Journal of Quality Technology* 32 (3): 209–16.

Index

Note: Page numbers followed by *f* or *t* refer to figures or tables, respectively.